ORIGO

STEPPING STONES

CORE MATHEMATICS

SENIOR AUTHORS

James Burnett
Calvin Irons

CONTRIBUTING AUTHORS

Peter Stowasser
Allan Turton

PROGRAM CONSULTANTS

Diana Lambdin
Frank Lester, Jr.
Kit Norris

PROGRAM EDITORS

James Burnett
Beth Lewis
Donna Richards
Kevin Young

STUDENT JOURNAL

CONTENTS

CONTENTS

STEPPING STONES RESOURCES – PRINT

The *ORIGO Stepping Stones* program has been created to provide a smarter way to teach and learn mathematics. It has been developed by a team of experts to provide a world-class math program.

STUDENT JOURNAL

Engaging student pages accompany each lesson within *ORIGO Stepping Stones*. In the Student Journals for Grades 1–5, there are two pages for each lesson. Following are the features of the Grade 1 Student Journal as a part of the whole program.

STEP 1
Step 1 provides guided discussion of enquiry. This often sets the scene for the lesson. Teachers can project this piece of the lesson and step through each question or point one at a time.

STEP 2
Step 2 provides individual work based on the discussion above.

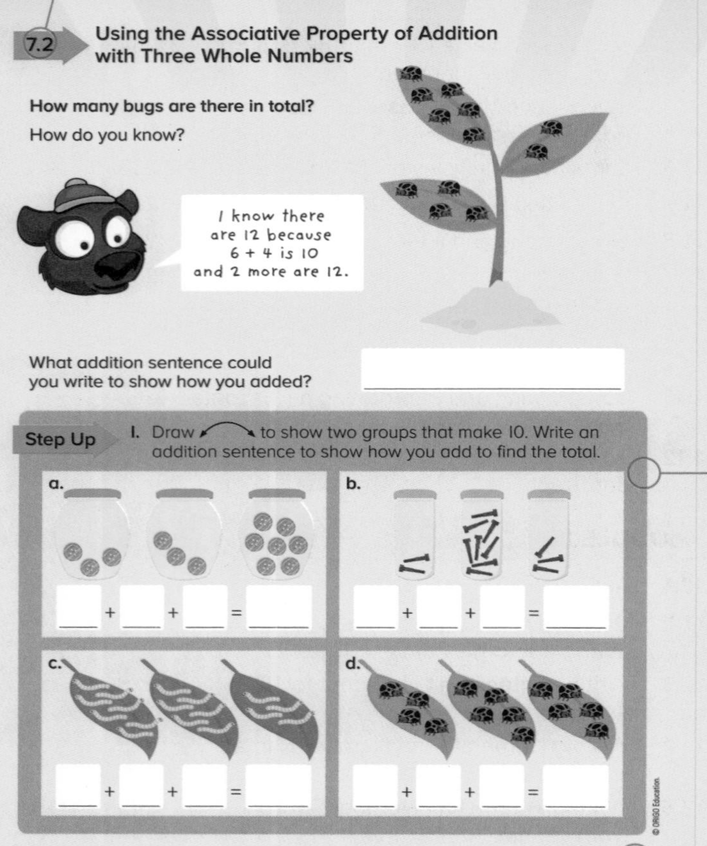

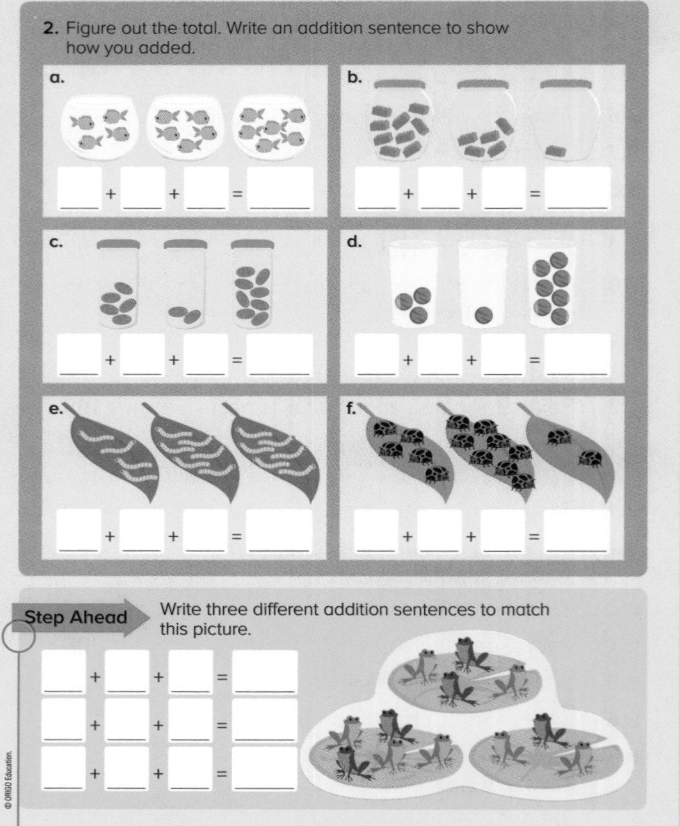

ORIGO Stepping Stones 1 · 7.2

Grade Module Lesson

STEP 3
Step 3 puts a little twist on each lesson to develop higher-order thinking skills.

PRACTICE BOOK

Regular and meaningful practice is a hallmark of *ORIGO Stepping Stones*. Each module in this book has perforated pages that practice content previously learned to maintain concepts and skills, and pages that practice computation to promote fluency.

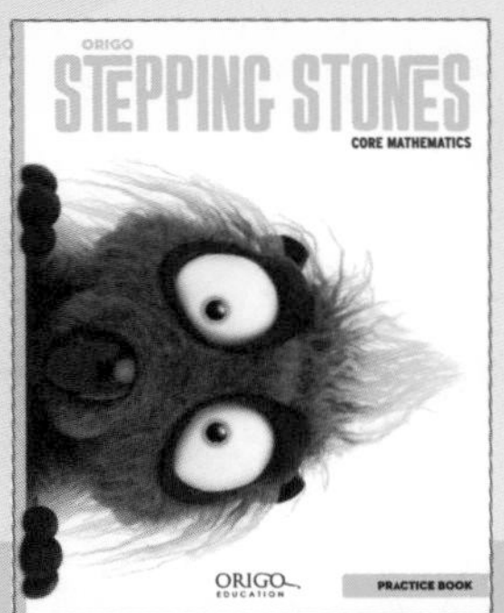

NOTES FOR HOME

Each book is one component of a comprehensive teaching program. Together they are a collection of consolidation and practice pages from lessons in the *ORIGO Stepping Stones* program.

Class teachers will decide which pages suit individual needs. So students might not complete every page in these books. For more information about the program, visit **www.origoeducation.com/steppingstones**.

ADDITIONAL RESOURCES – PRINT

ORIGO Big Books build on young students' natural love for stories to help introduce key mathematical concepts. There are 12 Big Books at this grade.

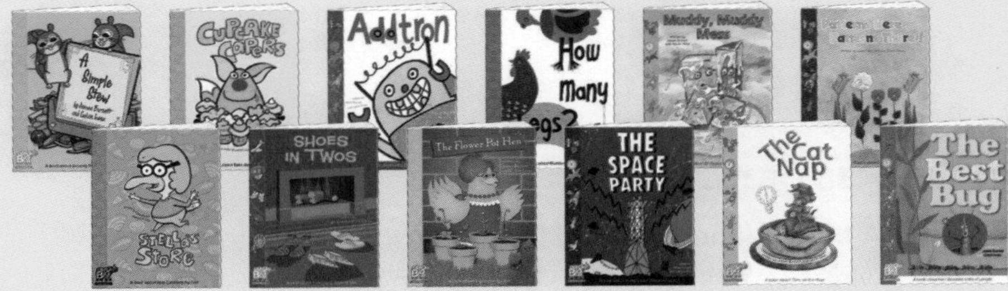

The Number Case provides teachers with ready-made resources that are designed to develop students' understanding of number.

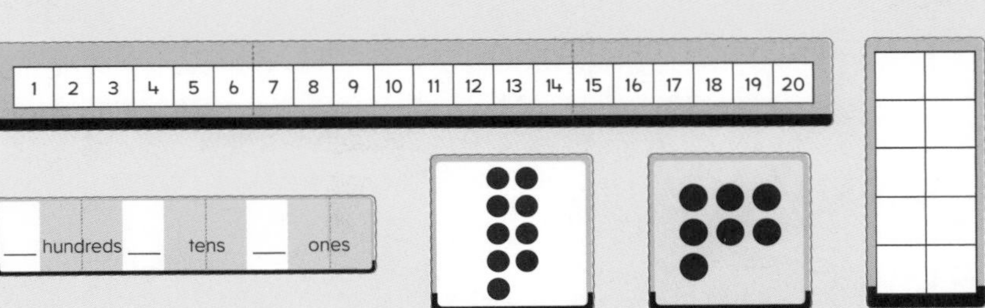

ADDITIONAL RESOURCES (ONLINE CHANNELS)

These are some of the innovative teaching channels integrated into the teacher's online program.

ORIGO MathEd

Professional learning sessions

Flare

Interactive whiteboard tools

Fundamentals Game Boards

Interactive games

GLOSSARY

2D SHAPE

A **two-dimensional (2D) shape** shows length and width. A 2D shape can be made with only straight sides, only one curved side, or straight and curved sides. For example:

A triangle is a 2D shape with three straight sides.

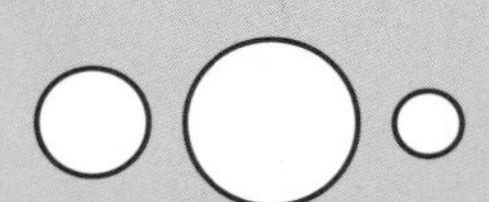

A circle is a 2D shape made with one curve.

A square rectangle is a 2D shape with four straight sides that are all the same length. Sides across from each other are the same distance apart.

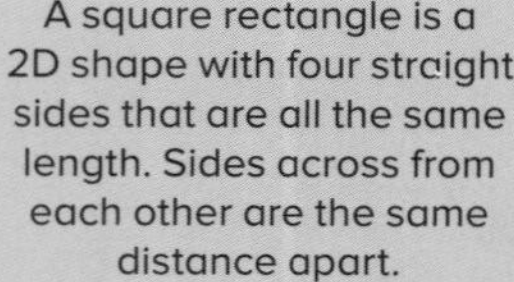

A non-square rectangle is a 2D shape with four straight sides. Pairs of sides across from each other are the same length and the same distance apart.

3D OBJECT

A **three-dimensional (3D) object** shows length, width, and height. A 3D object can be solid like a brick, hollow like a football, or skeletal like a house frame. For example:

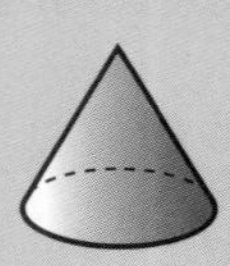

A cone is a 3D object made with one flat surface and one curved surface.

A cylinder is a 3D object made with two flat surfaces and one curved surface.

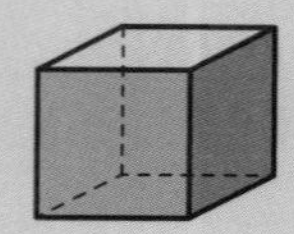

A cube is a box-shaped 3D object made with six flat surfaces that are the same size.

A sphere is a ball-shaped 3D object made with one curved surface.

ADDITION

Addition is used to find the total or sum of two or more numbers of objects. This is recorded in an addition sentence that uses words or symbols. Addition is shown by the + symbol.

For example:

two bears **plus three** bears **is five** bears
or
2 + 3 = 5

CAPACITY

Capacity is the amount something can hold.

COMPARING

The symbol > means **is greater than**.
The symbol $<$ means **is less than**.

For example: $2 < 6$ **means** 2 is less than 6

EQUALS

When something **equals** something else it means "is the same as" or "balances". Equality is shown by the = symbol. For example, 2 + 3 = 5 means 2 + 3 balances 5 or 2 + 3 is the same as 5.

FACT FAMILY

An addition **fact family** includes an addition fact, its turnaround fact and the two related subtraction facts. For example:

4 + 2 = 6 2 + 4 = 6	addition fact with its turnaround fact
6 – 4 = 2 6 – 2 = 4	the two related subtraction facts

MENTAL COMPUTATION STRATEGIES

These are strategies you can use to figure out a mathematical problem in your head.

Addition

- Count on
  See 3 + 8 *think* 8 + 1 + 1 + 1
  See 58 + 24 *think* 58 + 10 + 10 + 4
- Make ten
  See 9 + 4 *think* 9 + 1 + 3
  See 38 + 14 *think* 38 + 2 + 12
- Use a known sum (use doubles)
  See 7 + 7 *think* double 7
  See 25 + 26 *think* double 25 plus 1 more
  See 35 + 37 *think* double 35 plus 2 more

Subtraction

- Think addition
  See 17 – 9 *think* 9 + 8 = 17 *so* 17 – 9 = 8
- Count back
  See 9 – 2 *think* 9 – 1 – 1
  See 26 – 20 *think* 26 – 10 – 10

NUMBER

Number tells "how many". There are nine blocks in this group.

NUMBER FACTS

Addition facts are all the addition sentences that show two one-digit numbers being added. Addition facts can be written with the total or sum at the start or at the end.

For example: 2 + 3 = 5 or 3 = 1 + 2

Subtraction facts are all the subtraction sentences that are related to the addition facts.

For example: 5 – 2 = 3 or 3 – 2 = 1

NUMERAL

A **numeral** is the symbol used when recording a number.

ONE-FOURTH (ONE-QUARTER)

When one whole is split into four equal groups or four parts of equal size, **one-fourth** describes one of those groups or parts. One-quarter is another name for one-fourth.

ONE-HALF

When one whole is split into two equal groups or two parts of equal size, **one-half** describes one of those groups or parts.

RELATED SUBTRACTION FACTS

Each subtraction fact has a **related** fact.

For example: 7 – 4 = 3 and 7 – 3 = 4

SUBTRACTION

Subtraction involves taking one number away from another. Subtraction may be used to find an unknown addend or to find the difference between two numbers. This is recorded in a subtraction sentence that uses words or symbols. Subtraction is shown by the – symbol.

For example:

five bears **take away two** bears **is three** bears
or
5 – 2 = 3

TALLY

A **tally** is a single mark used to record the number of times something occurs. A gate tally is a mark used to group every five tallies.

For example:

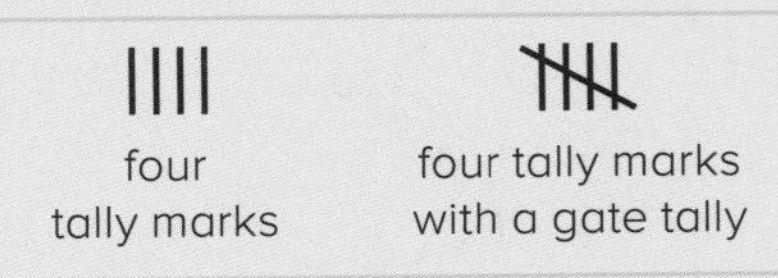

TURNAROUND FACT

Each addition fact has a related **turnaround fact**.

For example: 2 + 3 = 5 and 3 + 2 = 5

GLOSSARY

1.1 Identifying Quantities 1 to 6

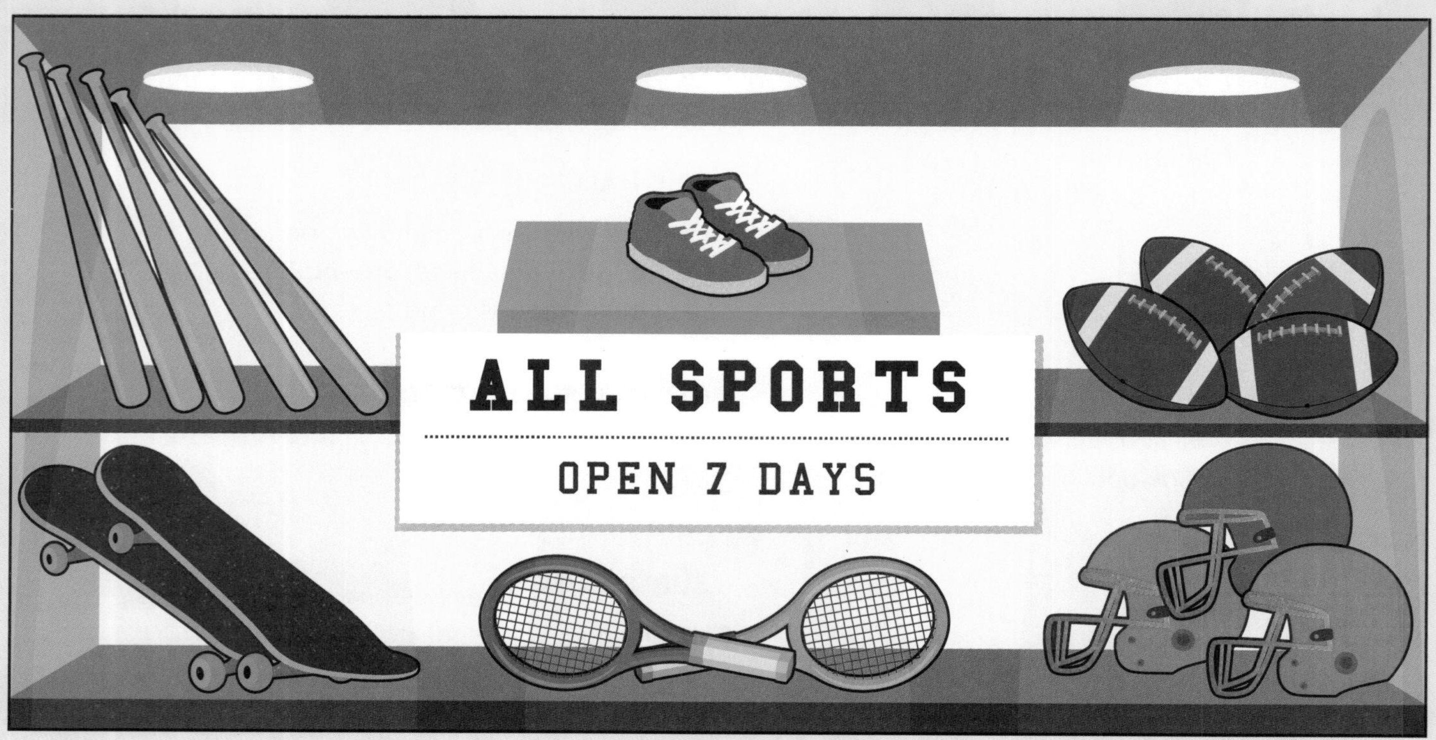

What do you know about the groups you see?

How many  do you see?

How many  do you see?

How many 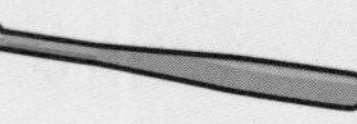 do you see?

Step Up Color objects blue.

a. Color **3** footballs.

b. Color **4** shoes.

c. Color **2** tennis rackets.

d. Color **6** baseballs.

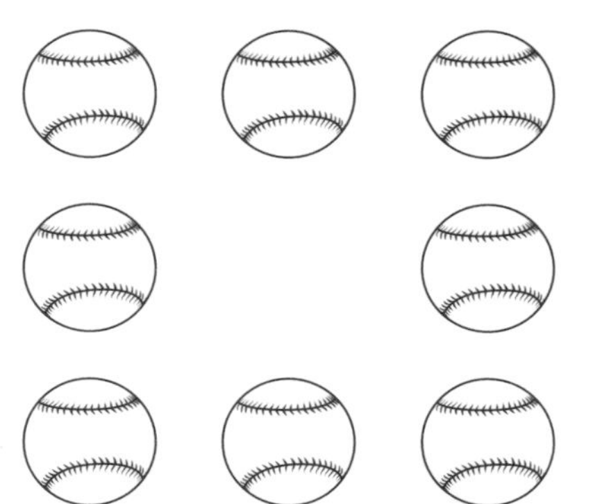

e. Color **I** helmet.

f. Color **5** skateboards.

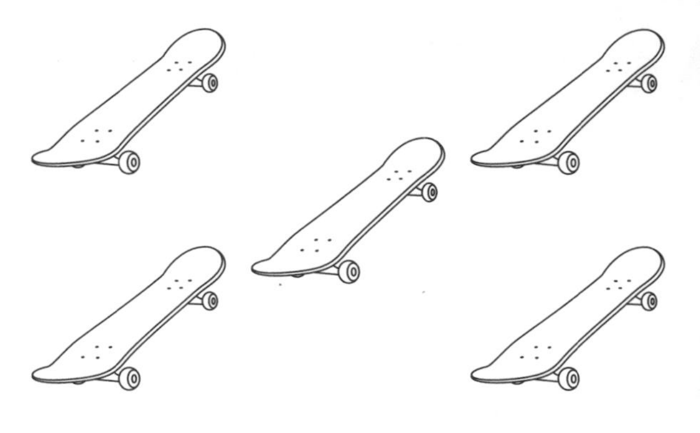

Step Ahead

Read the total. Then loop the number of pennies covered by the hand.

a. There are 6 pennies in total.

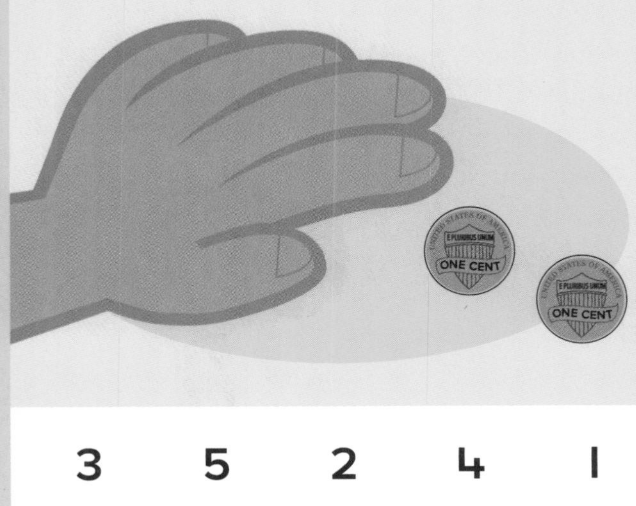

3 5 2 4 1

b. There are 5 pennies in total.

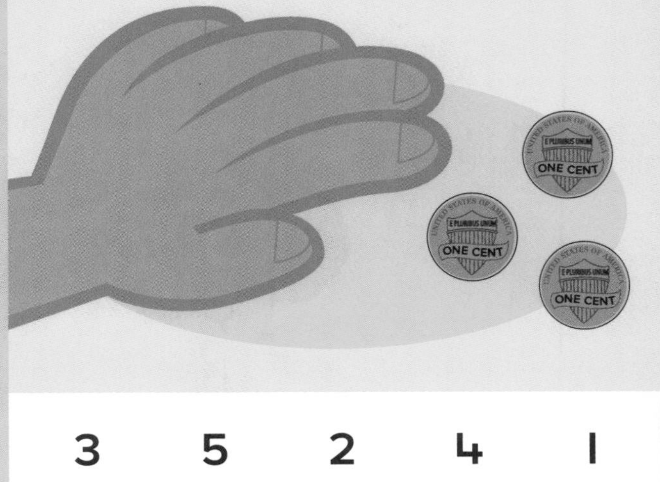

3 5 2 4 1

1.2 Identifying Quantities 1 to 10

These clowns are juggling pieces of fruit.

Count the pieces of fruit for each clown. How many is each clown juggling?

Trace each numeral in the air.

Step Up 1. Draw ○ to match the numeral.

a.

8

b.

6

2. Draw lines to match.

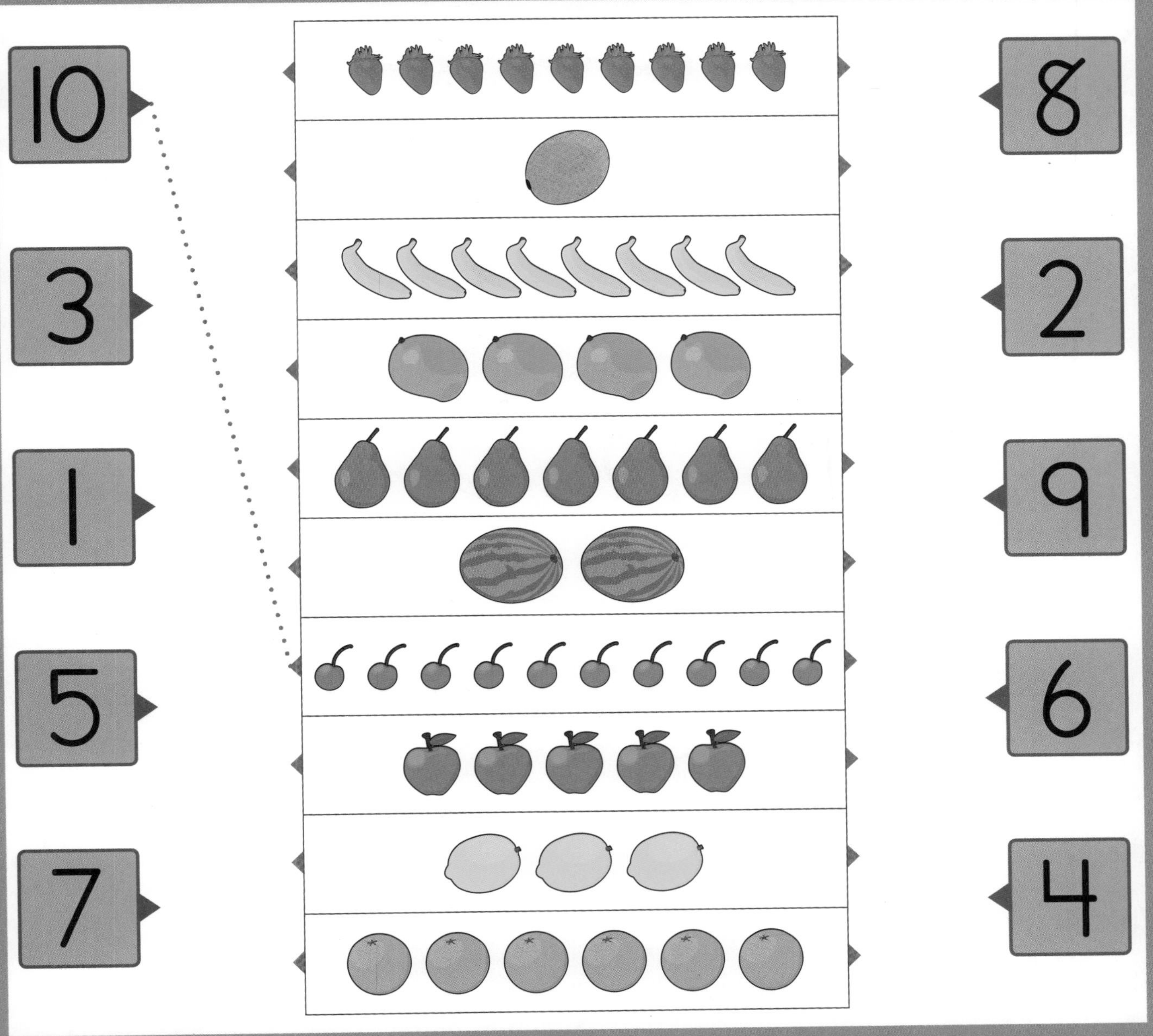

10	9 strawberries	8
3	1 melon	2
1	8 bananas	9
5	4 mangoes	6
7	7 pears	4
	2 watermelons	
	10 cherries	
	5 apples	
	3 lemons	
	6 oranges	

Step Ahead Draw ▢ on each train car to match the numeral on the side.

1.3 Writing Numerals 0 to 9

Trace the numerals.

1 1	2 2	3 3
4 4	5 5	6 6
7 7	8 8	9 9

Which numerals start down ↓?

Which numerals start left ↙?

Which numerals start right ↘?

Which numerals start up ↑?

Show how you would write the numeral for zero.

Which way did you start?

Step Up Count the fruit. Write the numeral.

a.

4 apples

b.
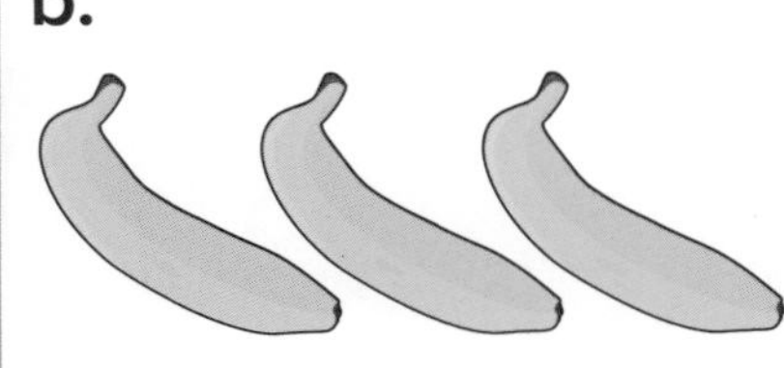
Ɛ bananas

c.
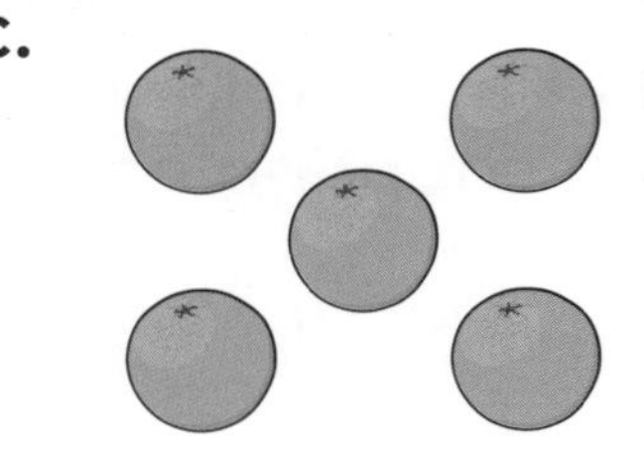
5 oranges

d.

2 pineapples

e.
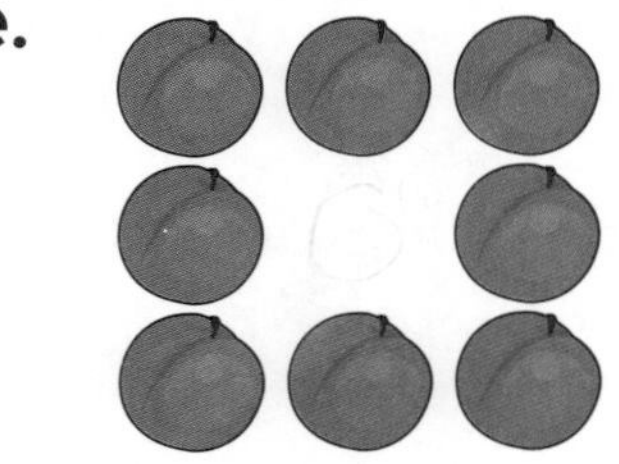
8 plums

f.

1 pear

g.
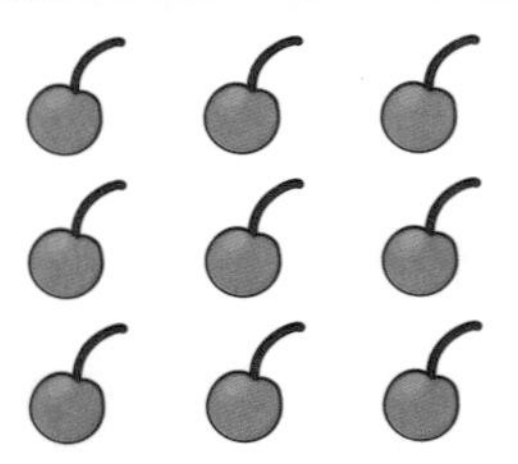
9 cherries

h.
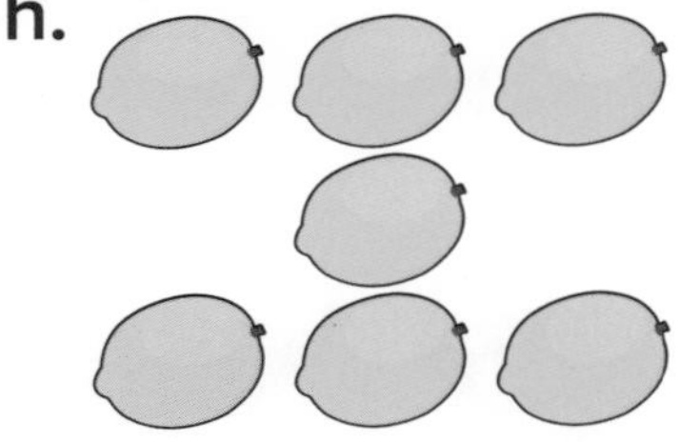
7 lemons

i.

6 peaches

Step Ahead Look at these telephone numbers. Loop the numerals that do not match the numerals on page 12.

Aidan	521-6Ƨ62
Brianna	929-20Ⴈ9
Michael	934-4ƐƐ2
Mia	52ɗ-8701

1.4 Matching Representations for 1 to 10

How can you quickly figure out how many fingers are raised without counting each one?

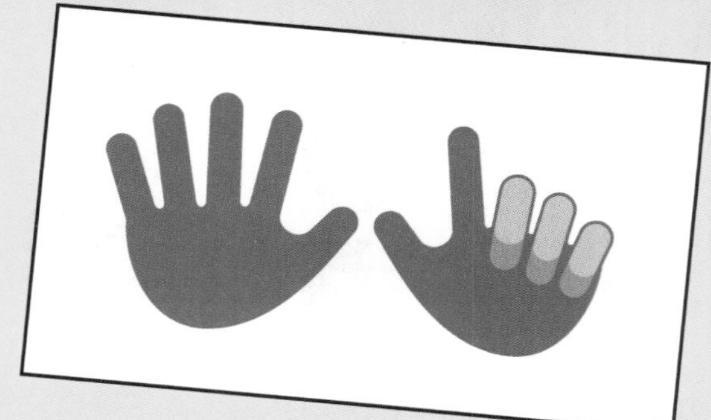

I know there are 10 fingers on 2 hands. Three fingers are down so it's 3 less than 10.

What is another way?

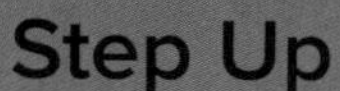

Step Up 1. Write the number of fingers that are raised.

a.

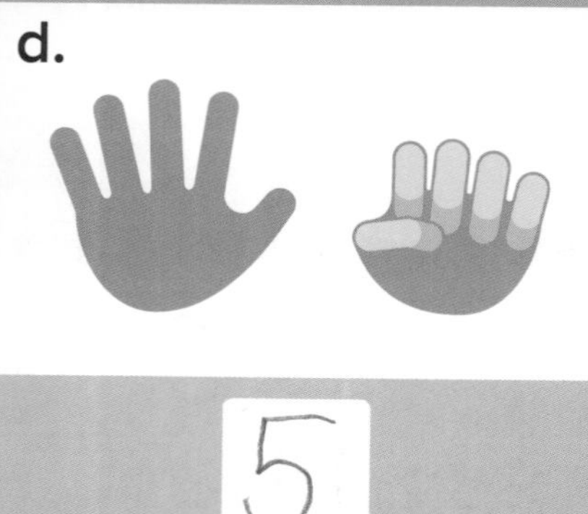

b.

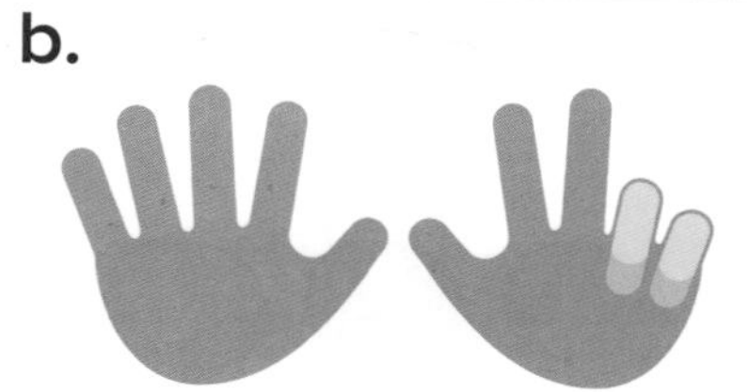

c.

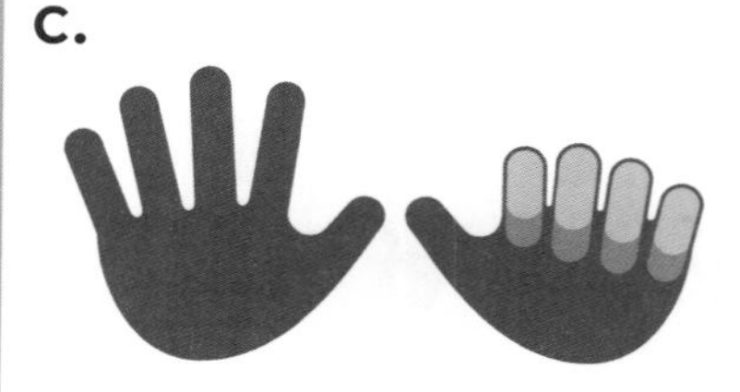

d.

e.

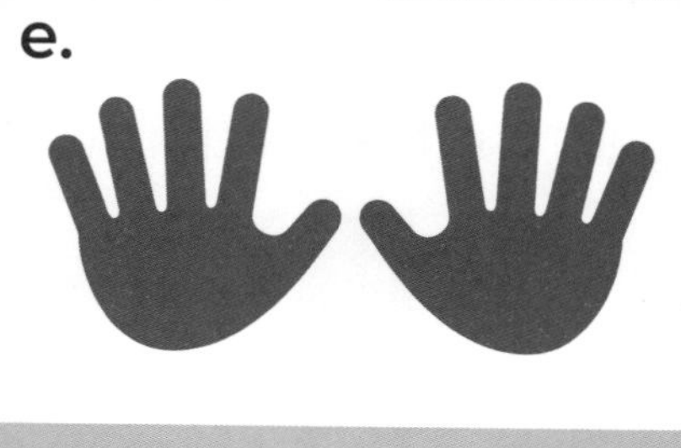

f.

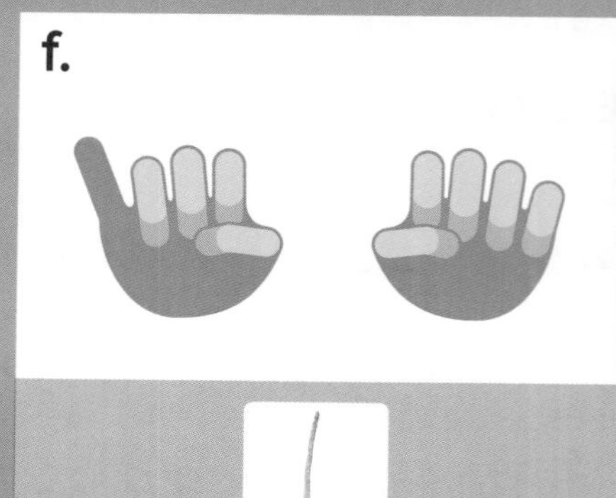

2. a. Write the matching numeral in the box beside each picture.

1 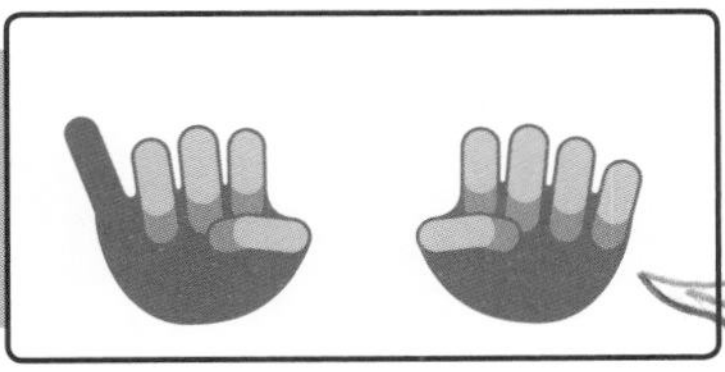

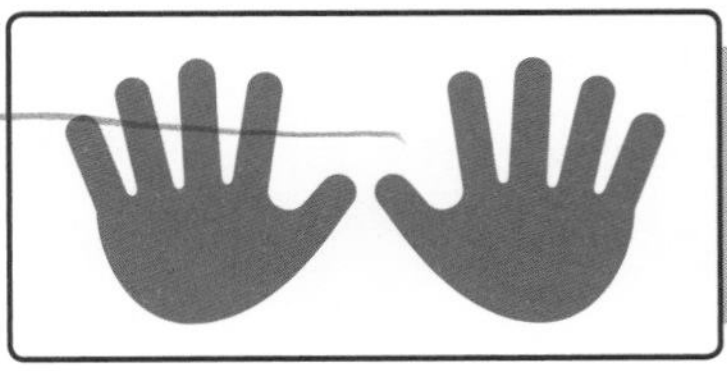 10

ten

one

7 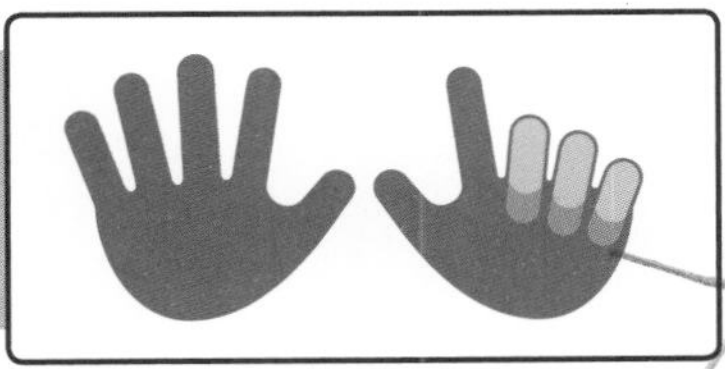

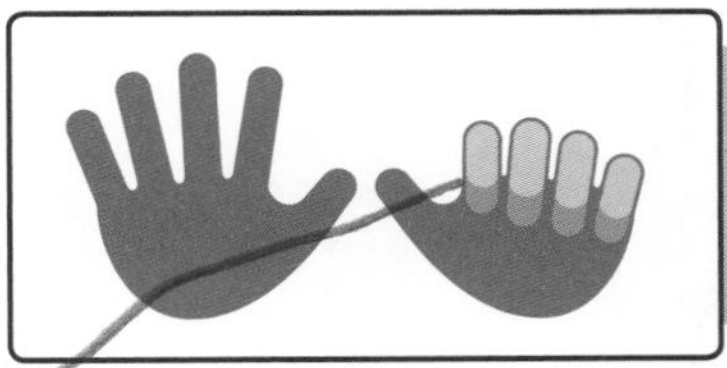 6

three

seven

3 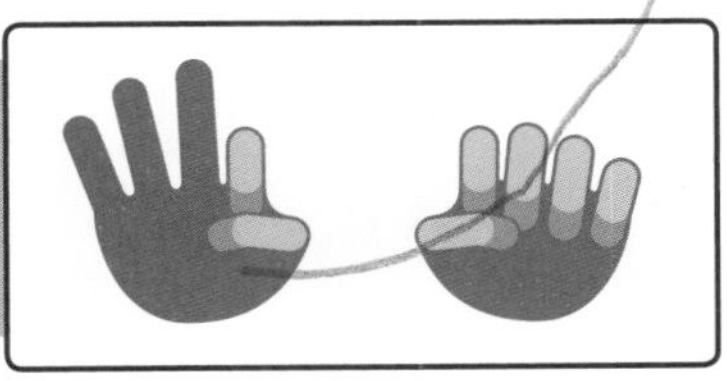

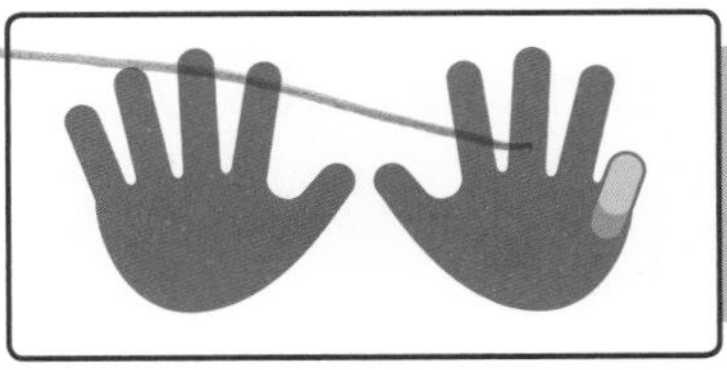 9

nine

six

4 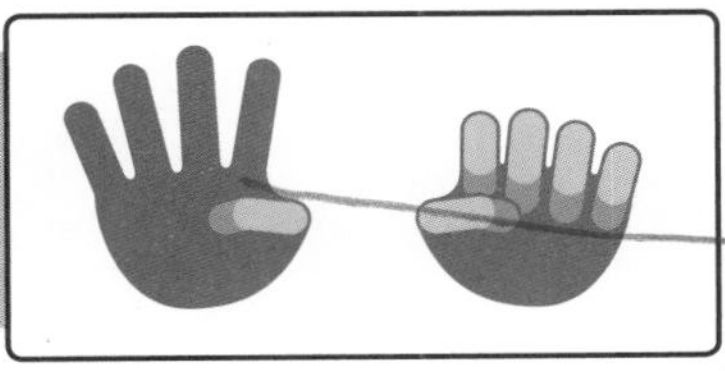

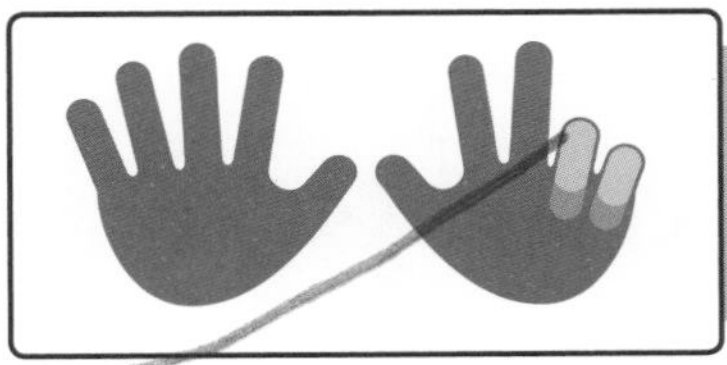 8

two

four

2 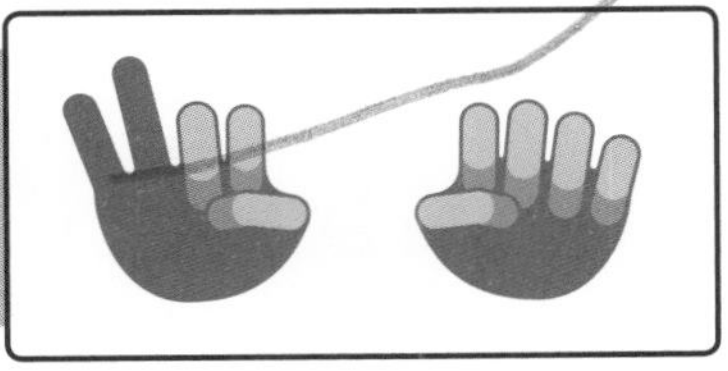

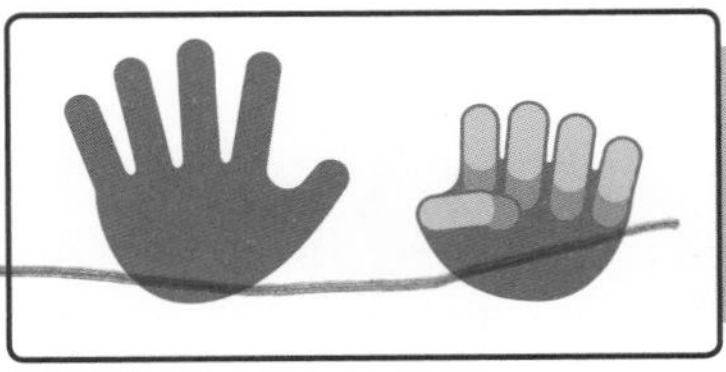 5

eight

five

b. Then draw a line from each picture to its matching number name.

Step Ahead

Count and write the number of letters in each number name.
Loop one number name that you think is special.

one	3	two	3	three	5	four	4	five	4
six	3	seven	5	eight	5	nine	4	ten	3

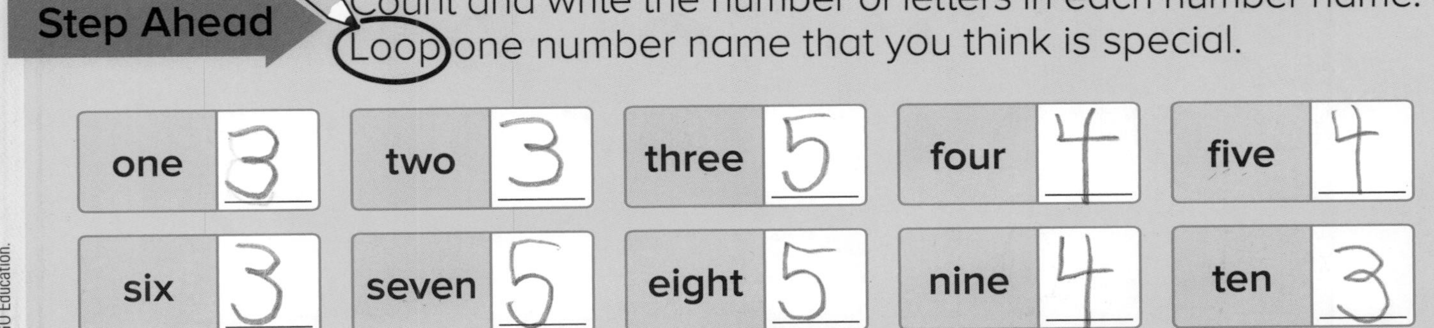

1.5 Recognizing Quantities by Sight

Look at this card.

Figure out the number of shapes on these cards without counting each one.

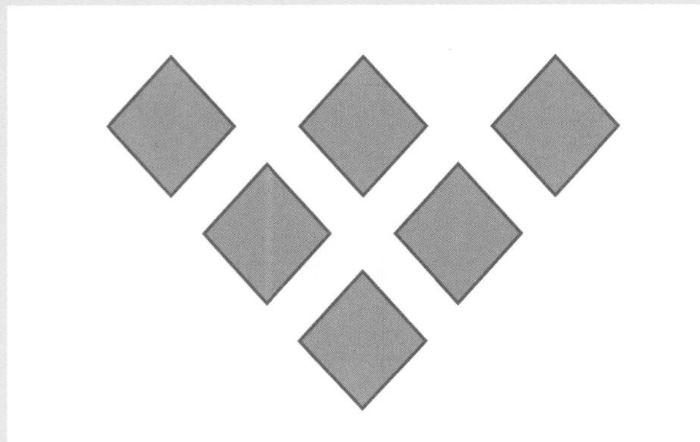

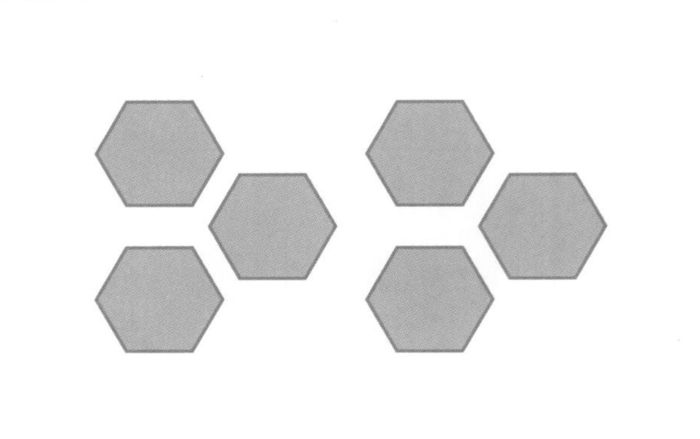

Step Up

1. Figure out the number of shapes without counting each one. Write the numeral.

a.

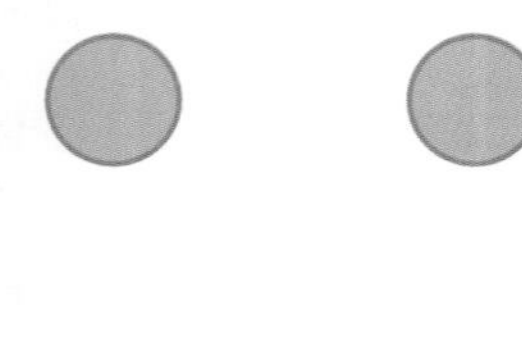

b.

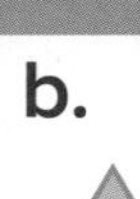

c.

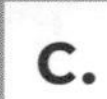

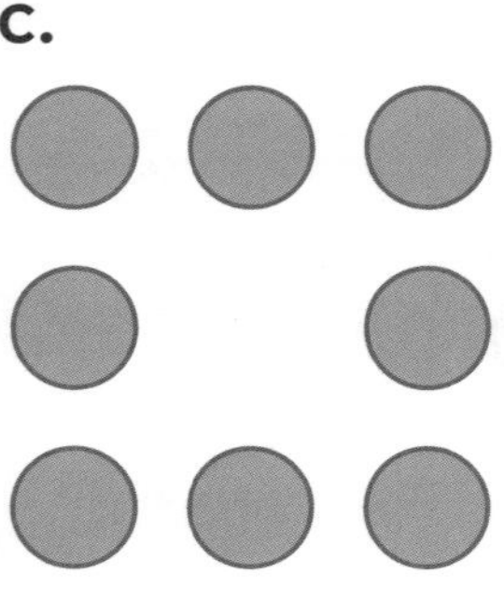

d.

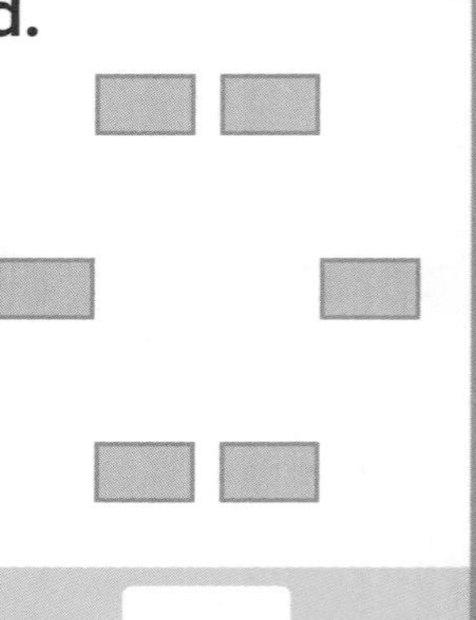

2. Write the number of shapes without counting each one.

a.

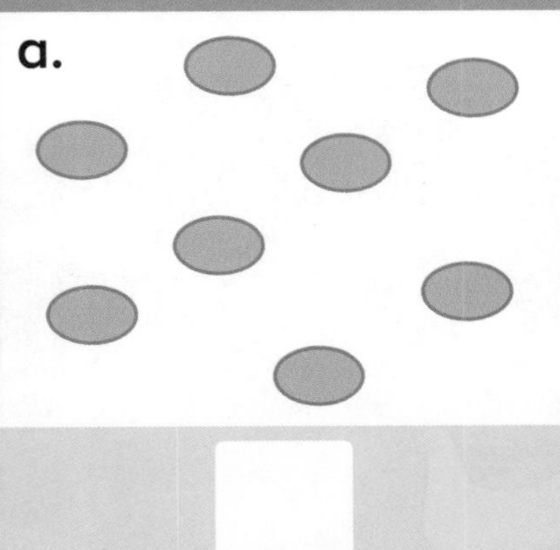

b.

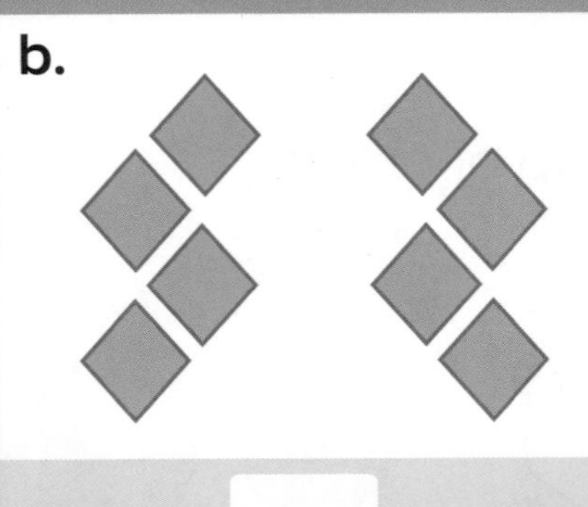

c.

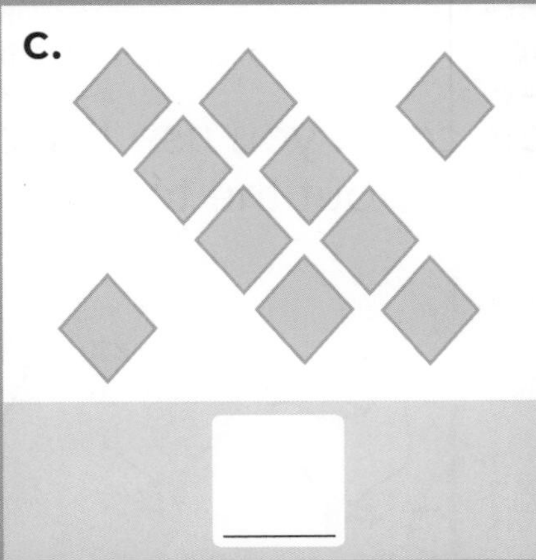

d.

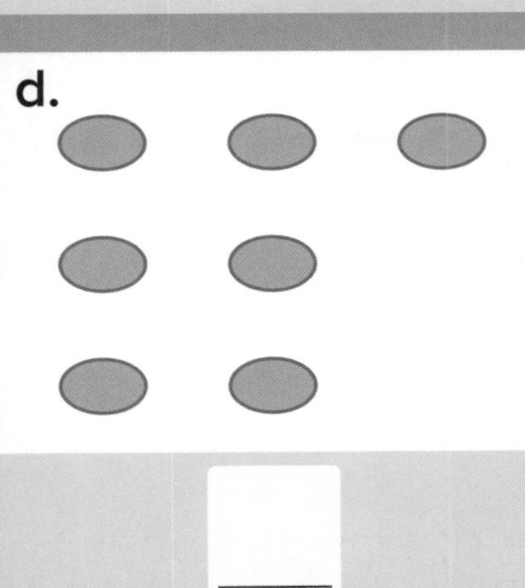

e.

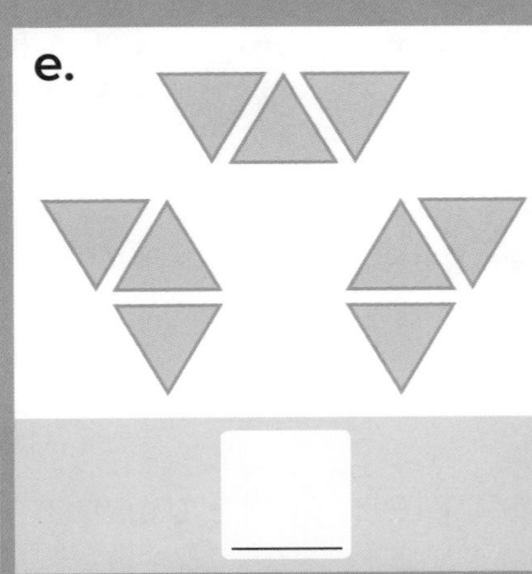

f.

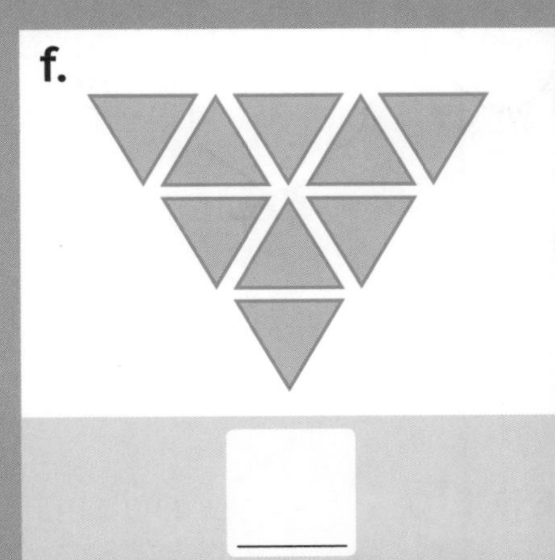

Step Ahead Figure out the number on each card without counting each shape. Color the cards that you found easy to figure out.

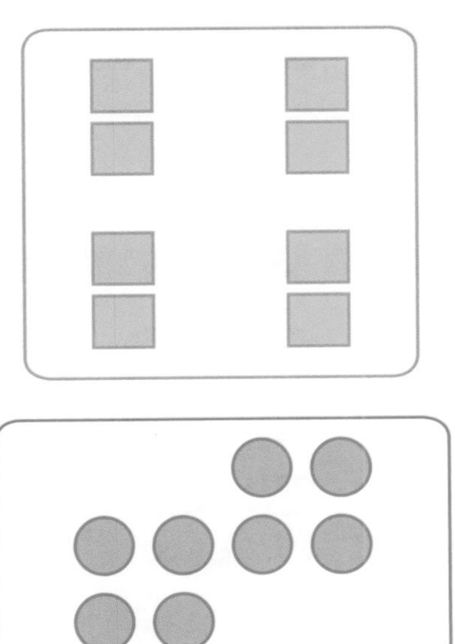

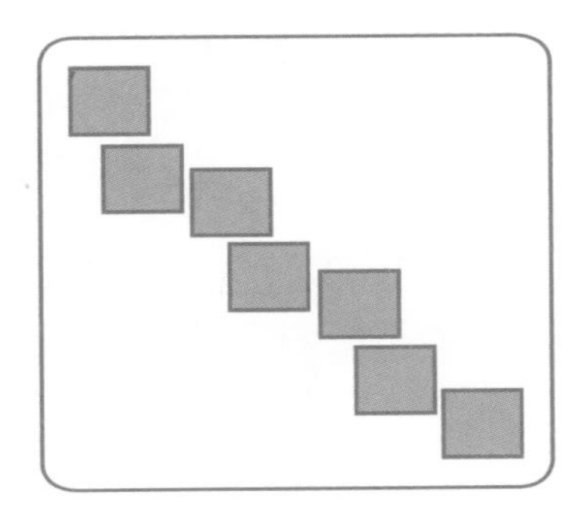

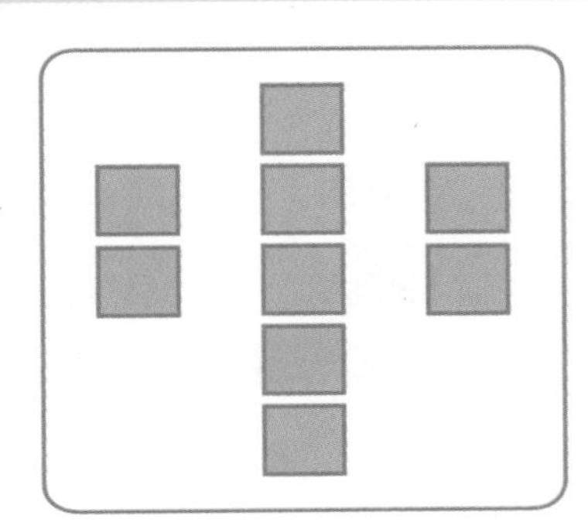

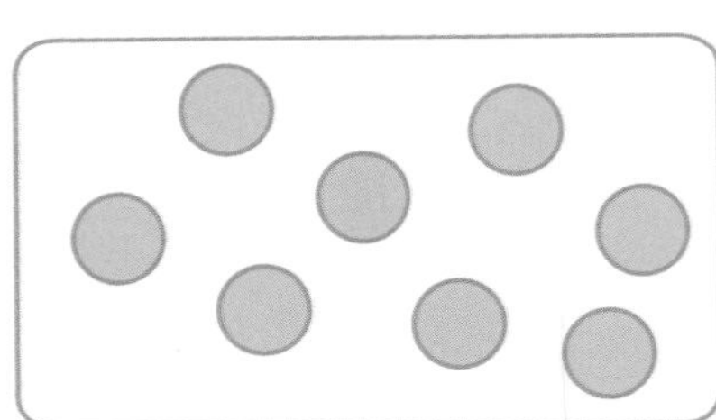

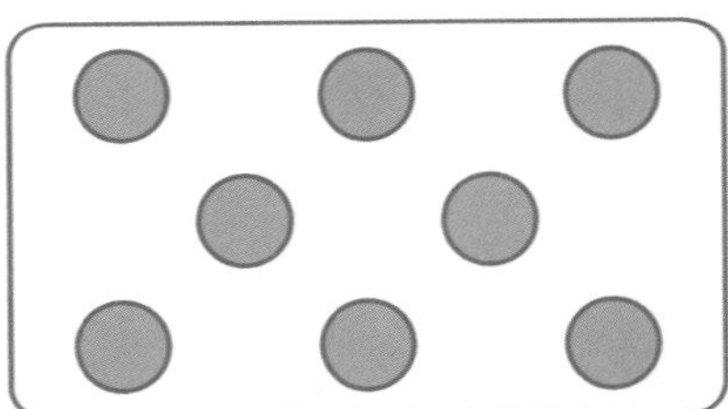

1.6 Analyzing Teen Numbers

Loop a group of ten chickens.

How could you use the group of ten to figure out the total?

Step Up I. Loop a group of ten. Write the number of tens and ones.

a. 1 ten 1 ones

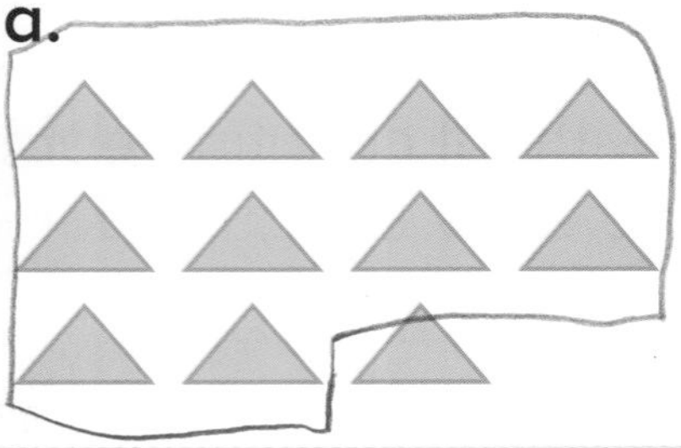

b. 1 ten 4 ones

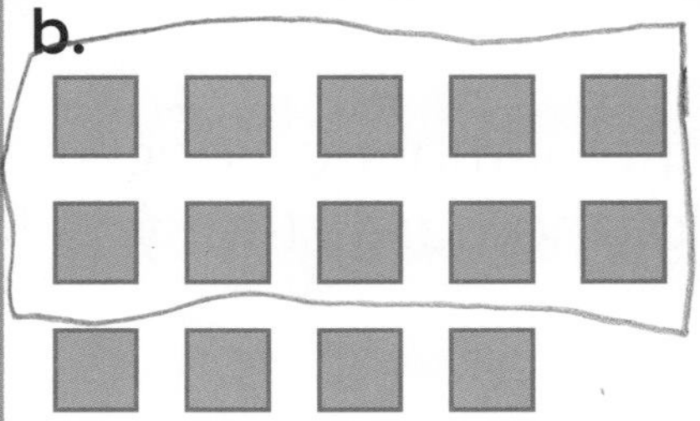

c. 1 ten 3 ones

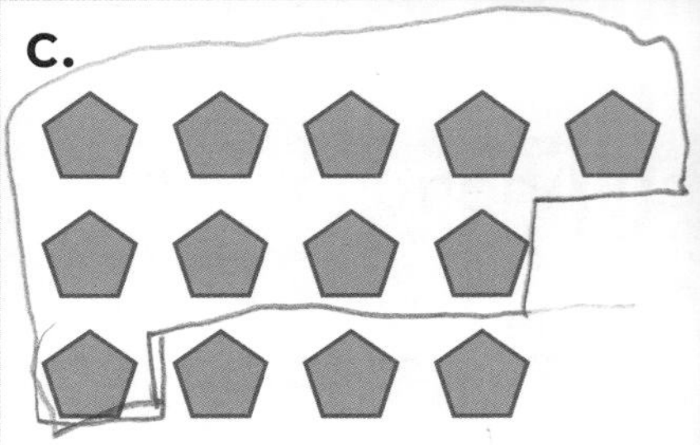

d. 1 ten 0 ones

e. 1 ten 2 ones

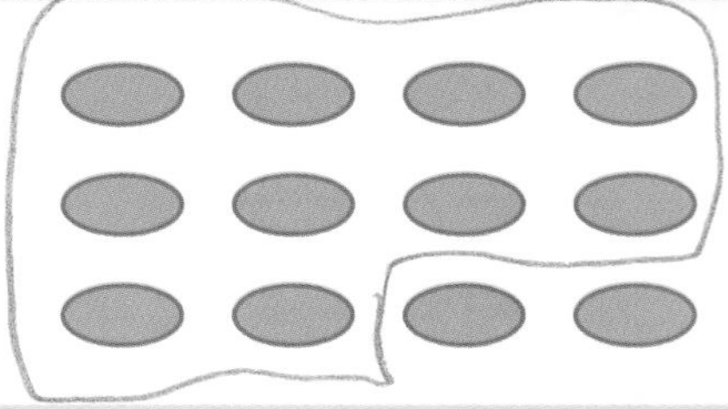

2. Loop a group of ten fingers. Then write the number of tens and ones.

a. 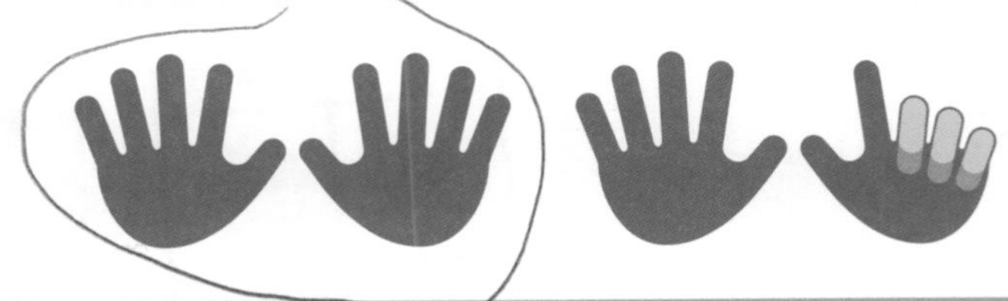

1 ten 7 ones

b. 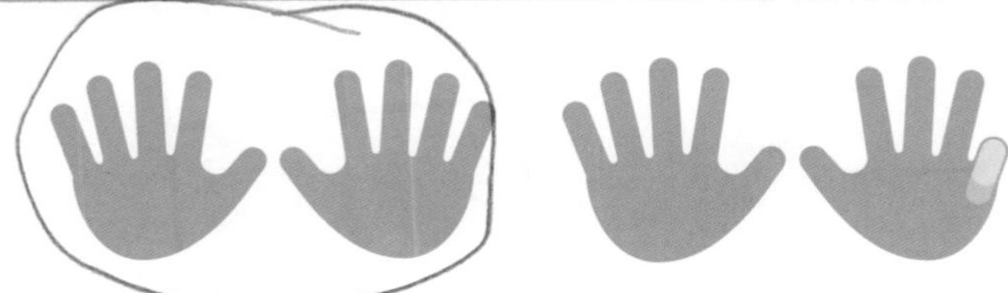

1 ten 9 ones

c. 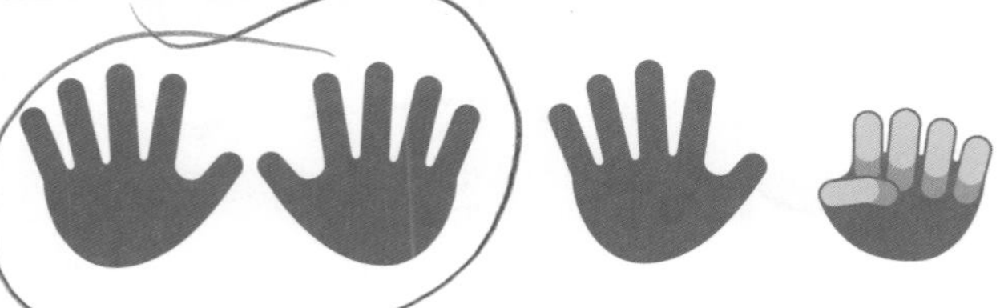

1 ten 5 ones

d. 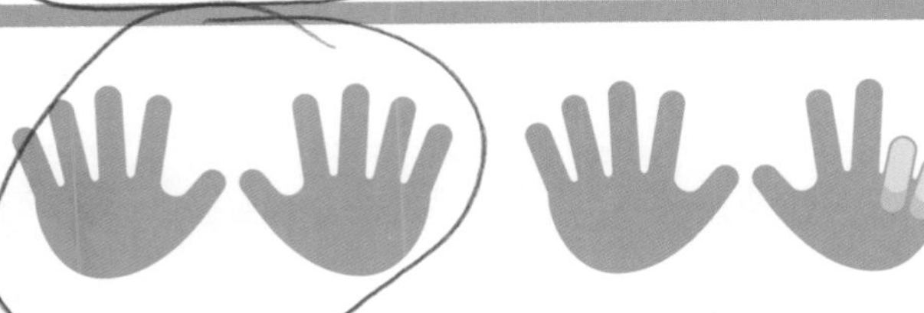

1 ten 8 ones

Step Ahead **a.** Loop a group of ten on each card.

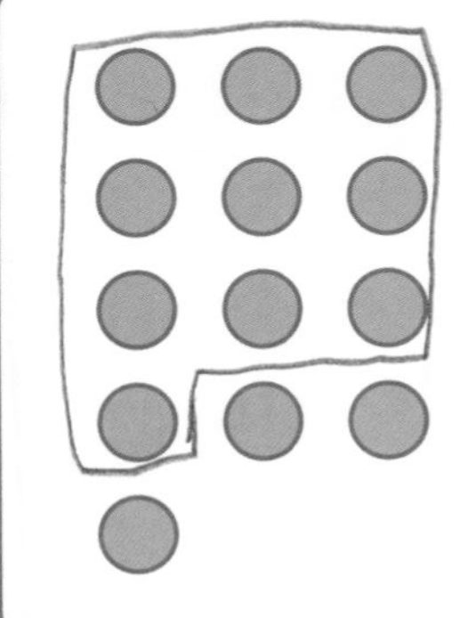

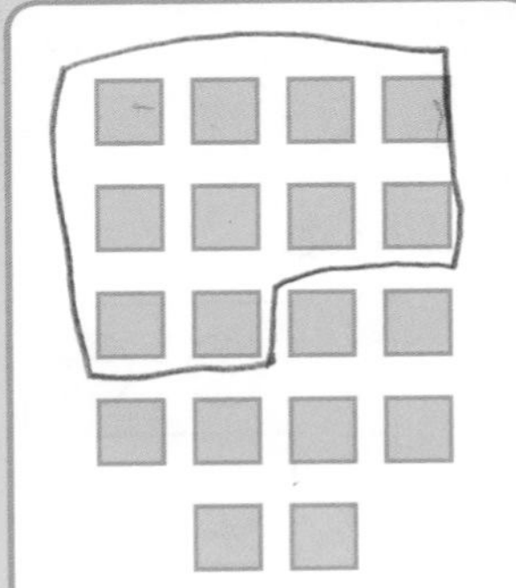

b. Write what you notice.

1.7 Representing Teen Numbers

How many ● are on this frame?

How do you know?

How could you use the frame and counters to show 12, 15, or 18?

Look at the picture below.
Write the number of counters.

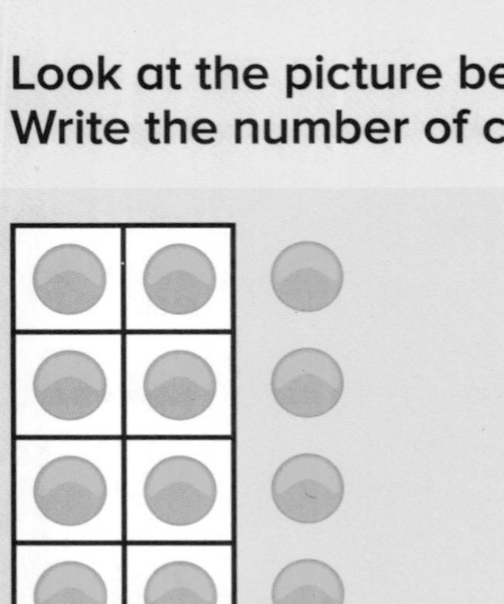

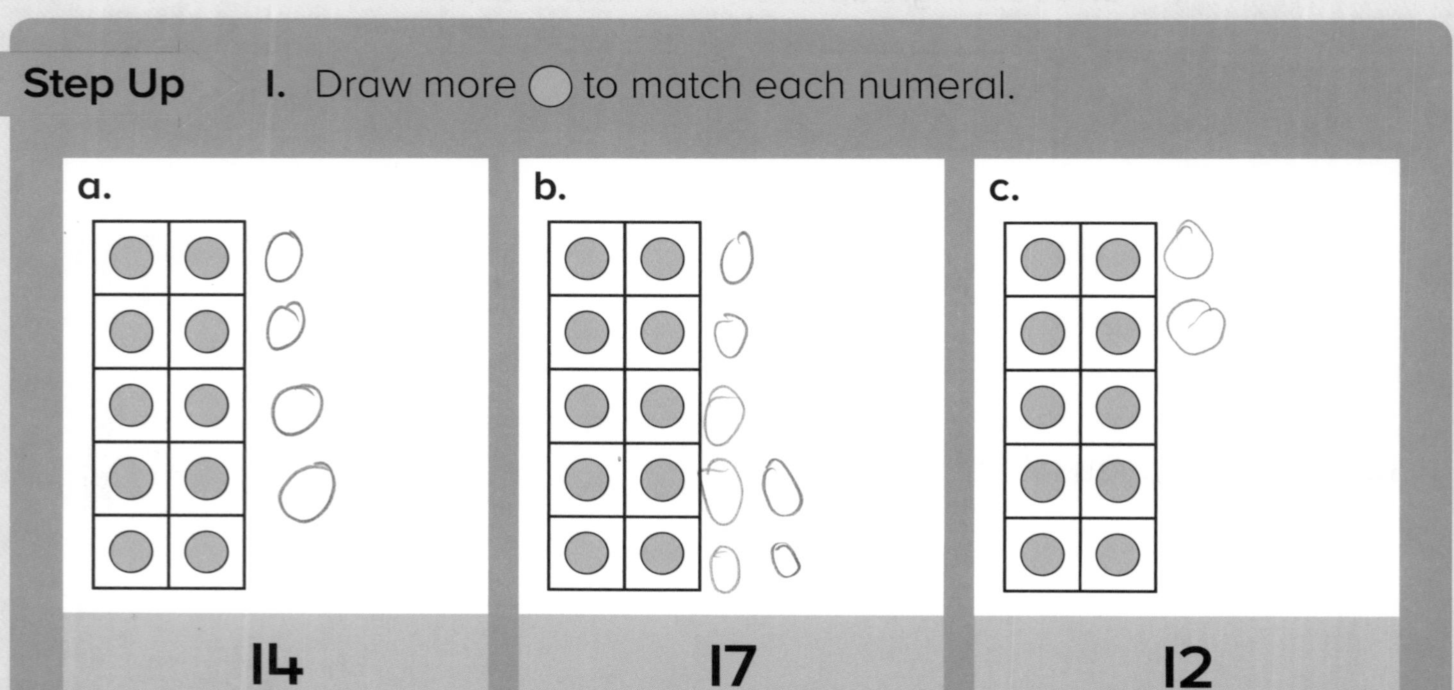

2. Draw ◯ to match each numeral. Remember to fill the ten-frame first.

a.

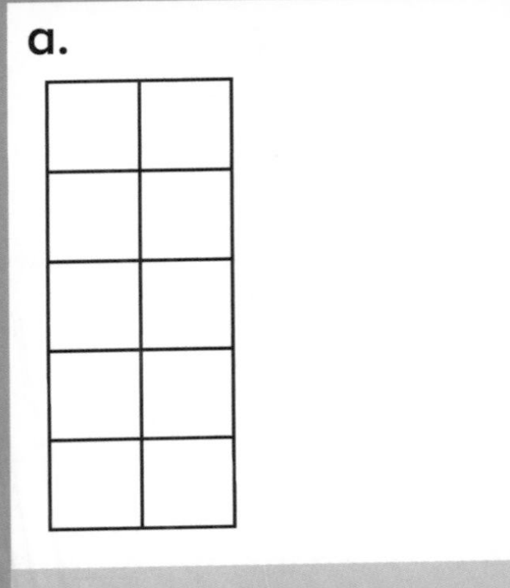

10

b.

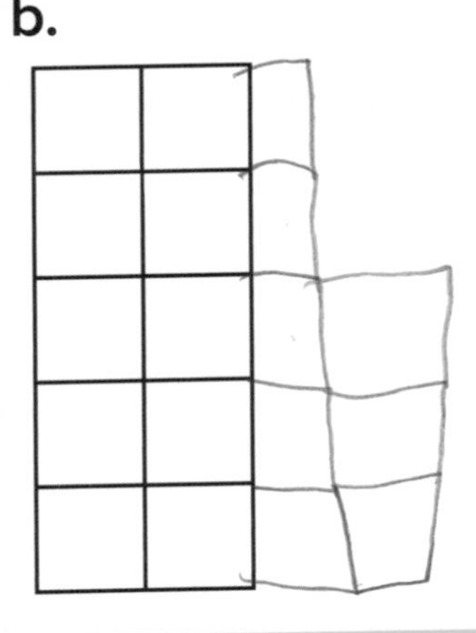

18

c.

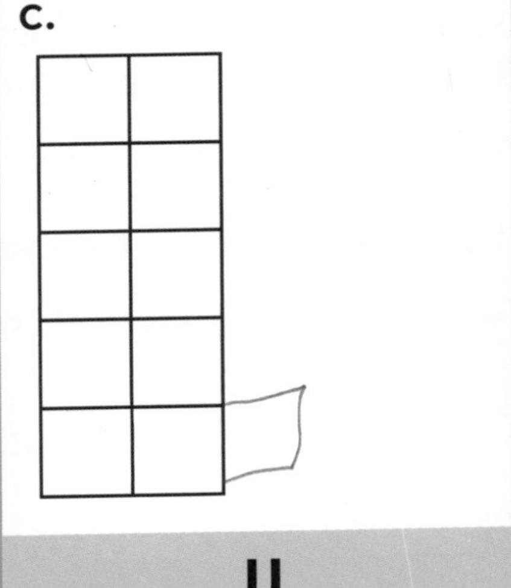

11

d.

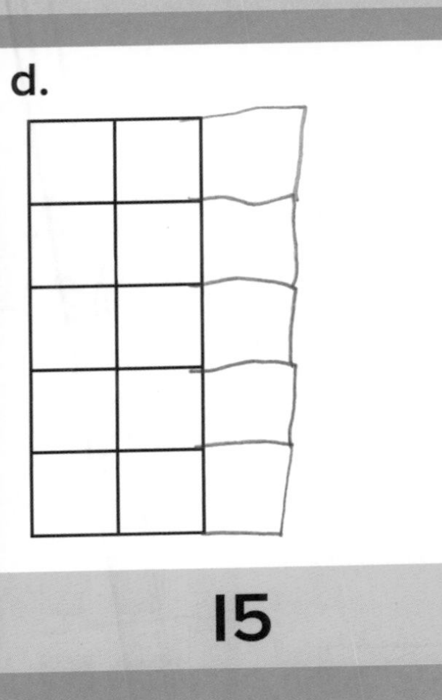

15

e.

13

f.

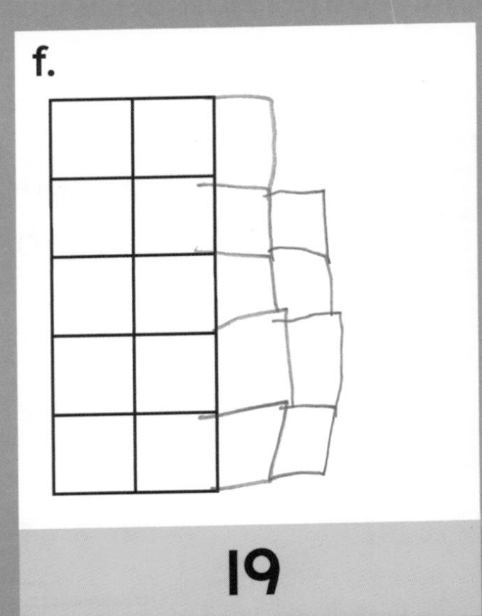

19

Step Ahead

This number of counters can be shown another way. Draw them using the frame. Then write the total.

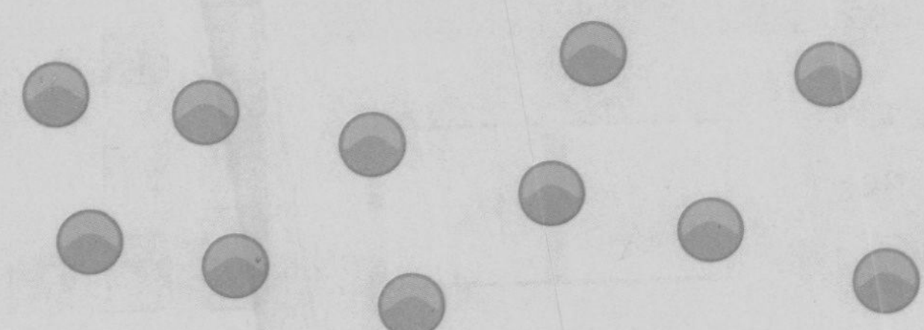

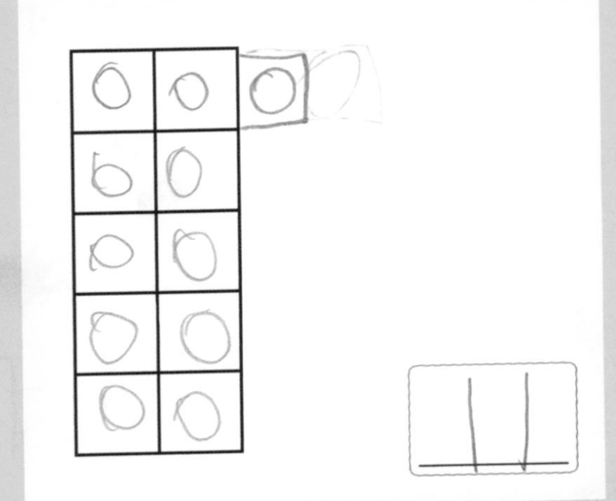

1.8 Writing Teen Numbers

Look at this picture of blocks.
What number does it show? How do you know?

Which blocks show the ones?

What do the other blocks show?

Write the number on this expander.

1 tens 7 ones

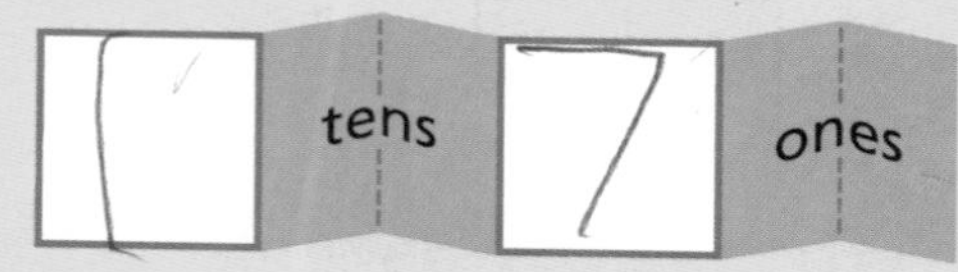

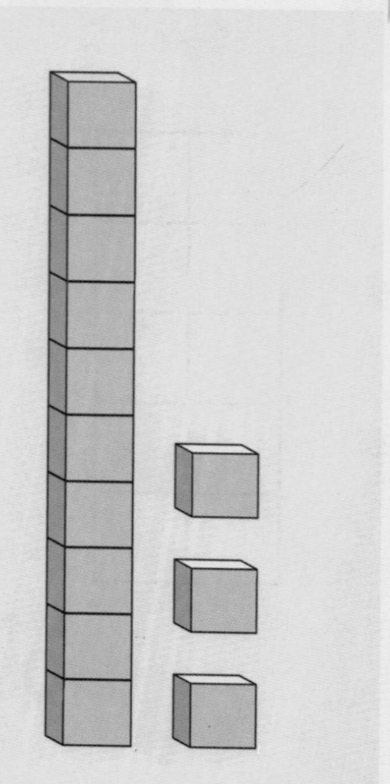

Which other numbers have one ten and some ones?

Step Up

1. Look at the block picture. Write the matching number on the open and closed expanders.

a.

1 tens 7 ones

1 7

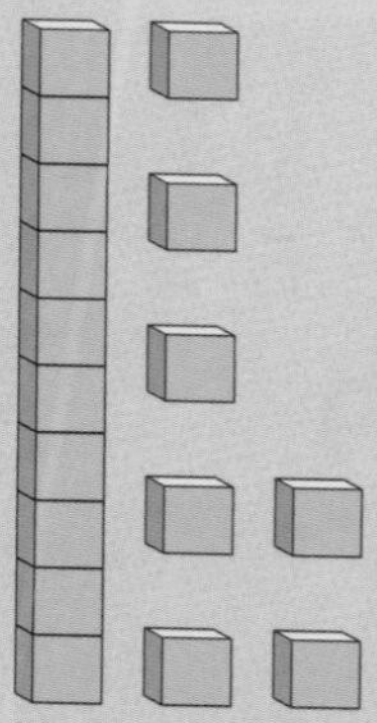

b.

1 tens 8 ones

1 8

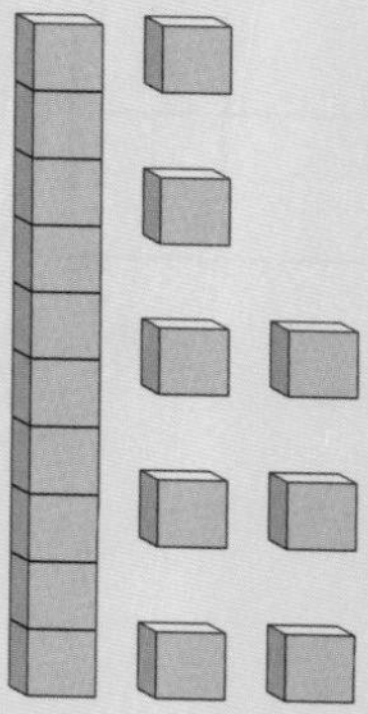

c.

1 tens 4 ones

1 4

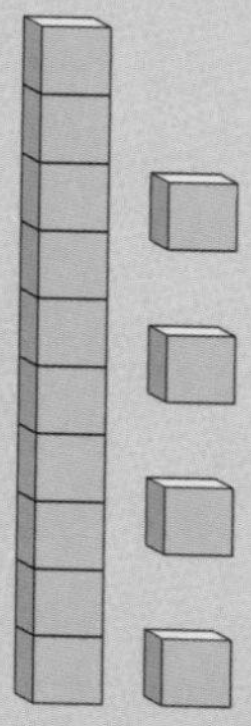

d.

1 tens 6 ones

1 6

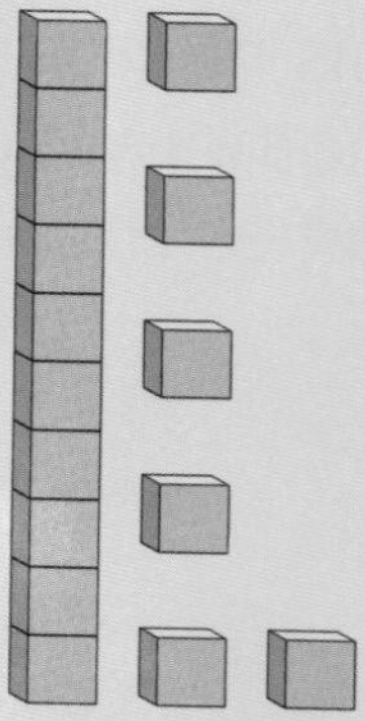

2. Draw more blocks to show the number of tens and ones.

a. 1 tens 6 ones

b. 1 tens 4 ones

c. 1 tens 7 ones

d. 1 tens 9 ones

e. 1 tens 5 ones

f. 1 tens 8 ones

Step Ahead Look at each picture. Think about the number it shows. Write what you notice.

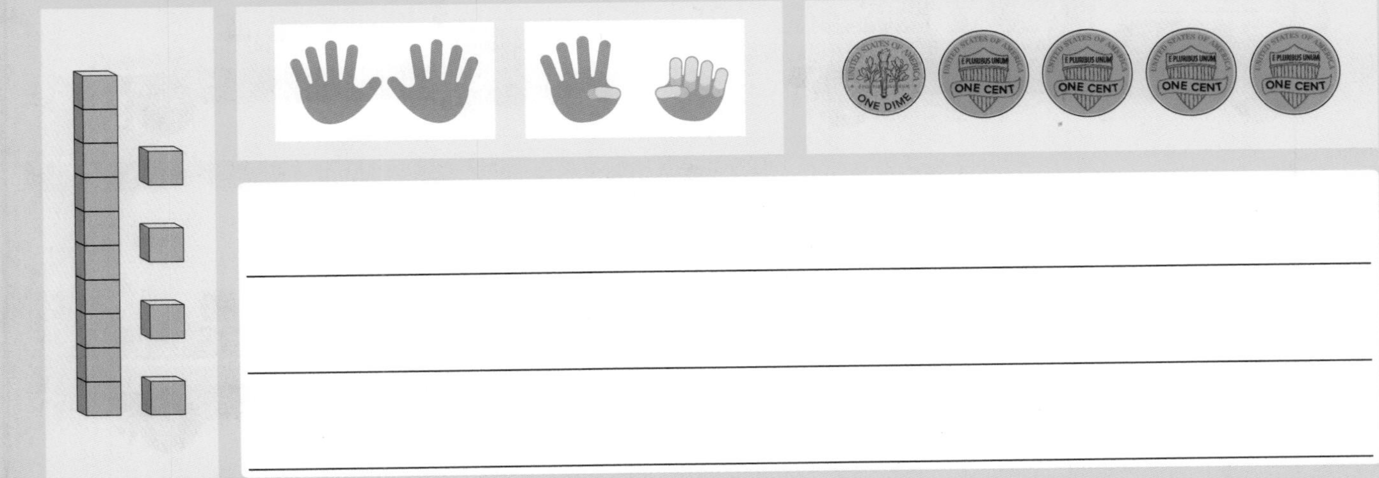

1.9 Comparing Teen Numbers

Look at this picture. What do you see?

Why are the pans not balanced?

How many blocks are on the left pan?

How many blocks are on the right pan?

Which number is greater?

How do you know?

What is another way you could show which number is greater?

Step Up 1. Write the number of boxes on each truck.
Loop the truck in each pair that has the greater number.

a. ____ or ____

b.  ____ or ____

c.  ____ or ____

2. Write a numeral that is **more than** and a numeral that is **less than** each numeral.

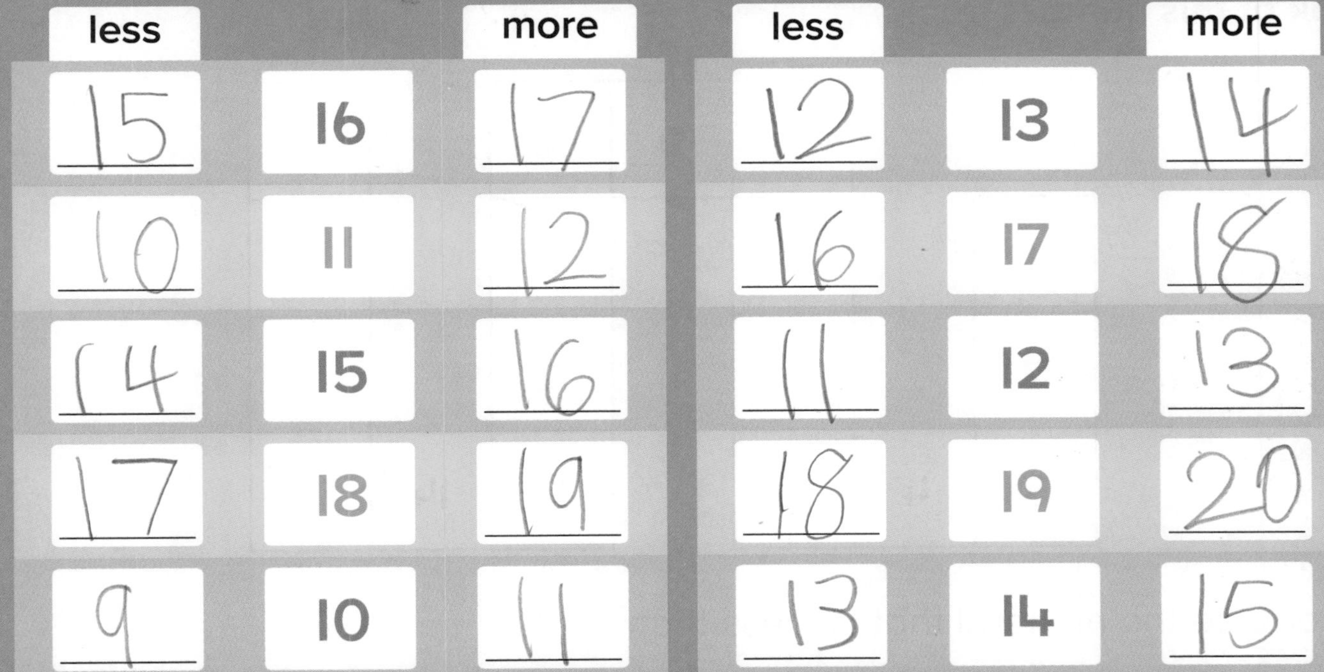

less		more	less		more
15	16	17	12	13	14
10	11	12	16	17	18
14	15	16	11	12	13
17	18	19	18	19	20
9	10	11	13	14	15

Step Ahead Write the amount of money in each wallet. For each card, color the wallet that holds the greater total value.

a.

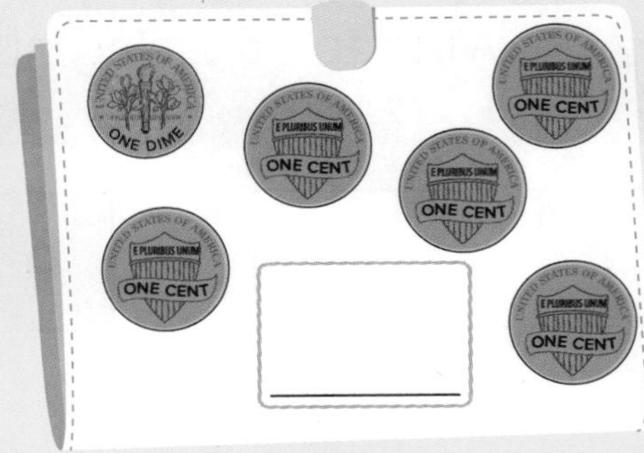

b.

1.10 Ordering 1 to 19

Look at this number track.

			9	10		
1		7		11		17
2		6		12		16
3	4	5		13	14	

Color blue the numeral that is 1 less than 12.

Color red the numeral that is 2 more than 5.

Color green the numeral that is between 12 and 14.

Write the missing numerals on the track.

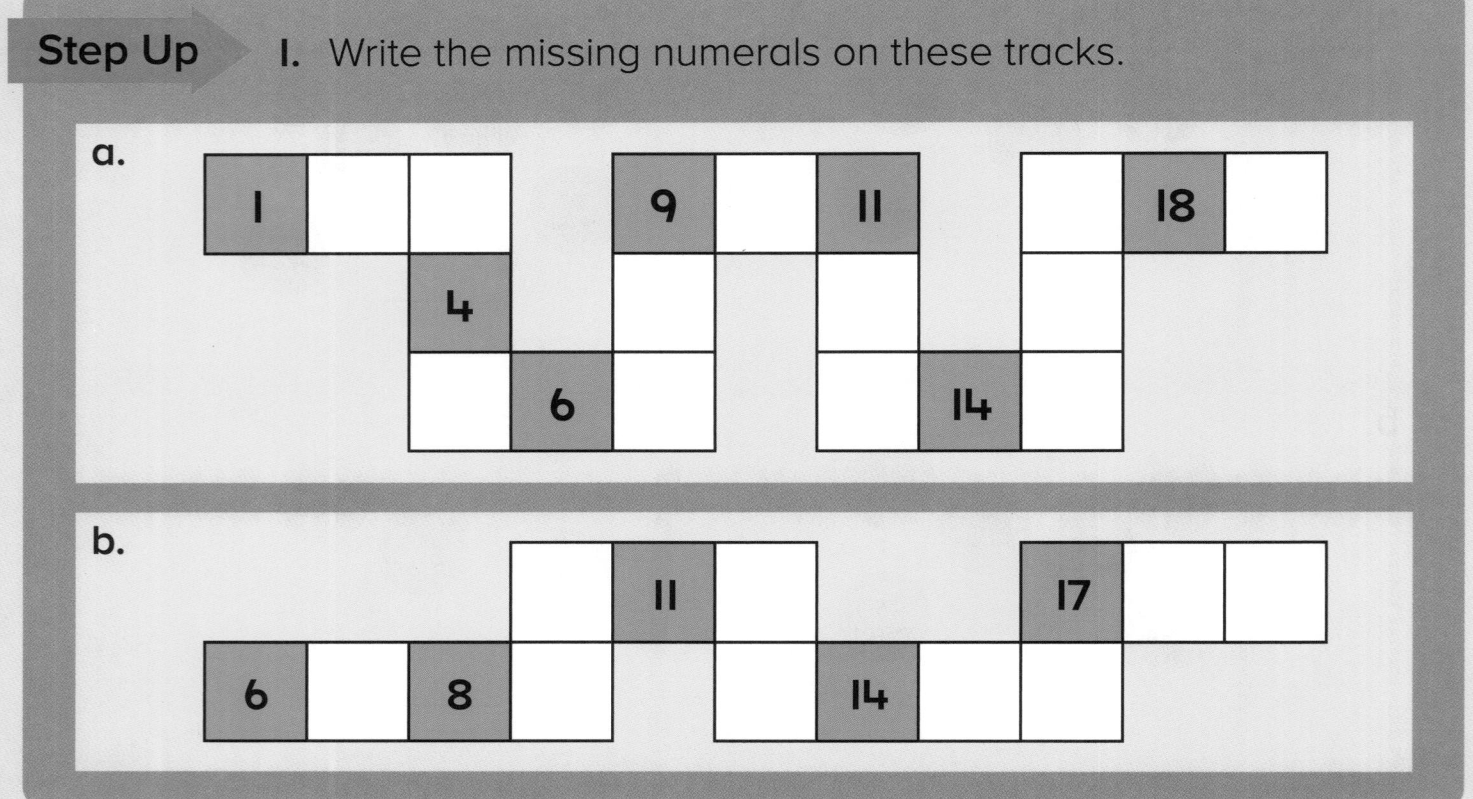

Step Up 1. Write the missing numerals on these tracks.

a.

1				9		11			18	
		4								
			6				14			

b.

			11				17		
6		8				14			

2. Write the number of cubes you see.
Draw one more cube. Then write the new total below the cubes.

a. I see ______

New total ______

b. I see ______

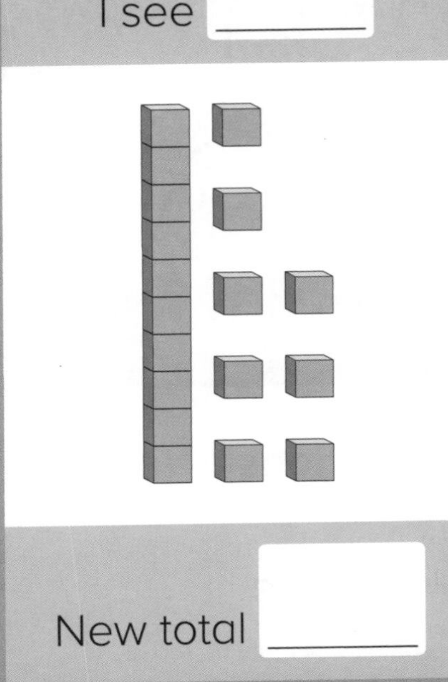

New total ______

c. I see ______

New total ______

3. Write these numerals in order from **least** to **greatest**.

a.

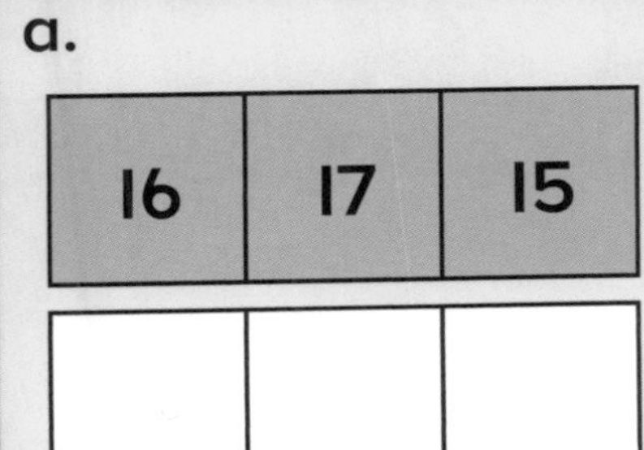

16	17	15

b.

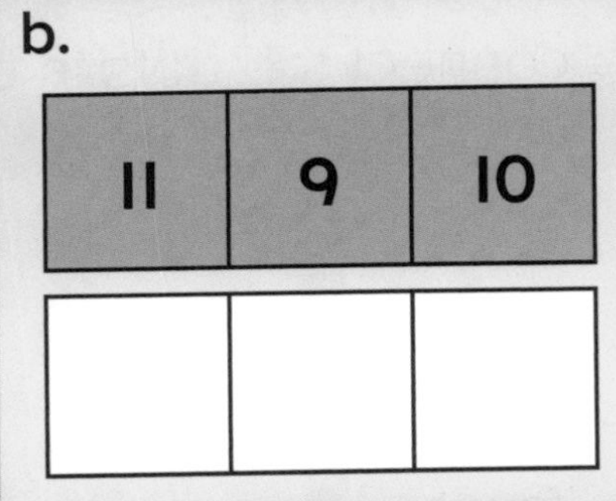

11	9	10

c.

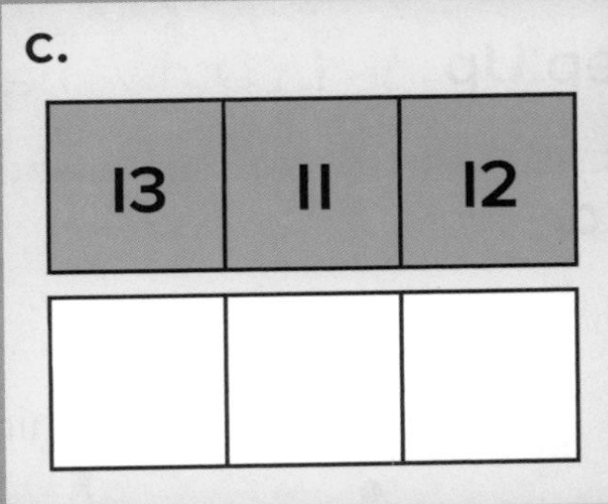

13	11	12

Step Ahead Read the clues.
Then shade the ◯ beside the correct statement.

Clues
Sam is 9 years old.
Maria is 15 years old.
Jose is 11 years old.

- ◯ Sam is oldest.
- ◯ Jose is older than Sam.
- ◯ Maria is younger than Sam.
- ◯ Maria is the youngest.

1.11 Reading Ordinal Number Names

What is happening in this picture?

Which athlete finished first? How do you know?

Look at this toy.

Which ring went on first?

Which ring went on third?

How could you describe the positions of the other two rings?

Where else would you use words like **first, second,** and **third**?

Step Up 1. Draw lines to connect the dots in order.

a.

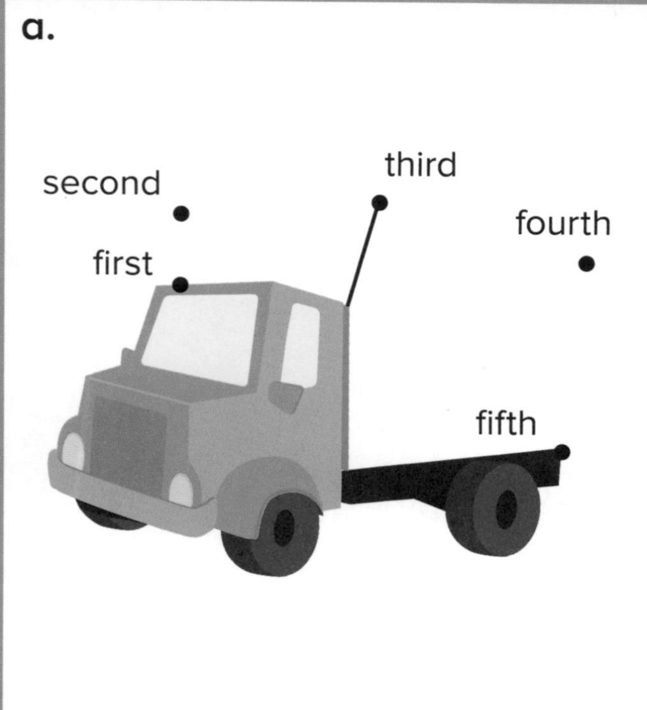

b.

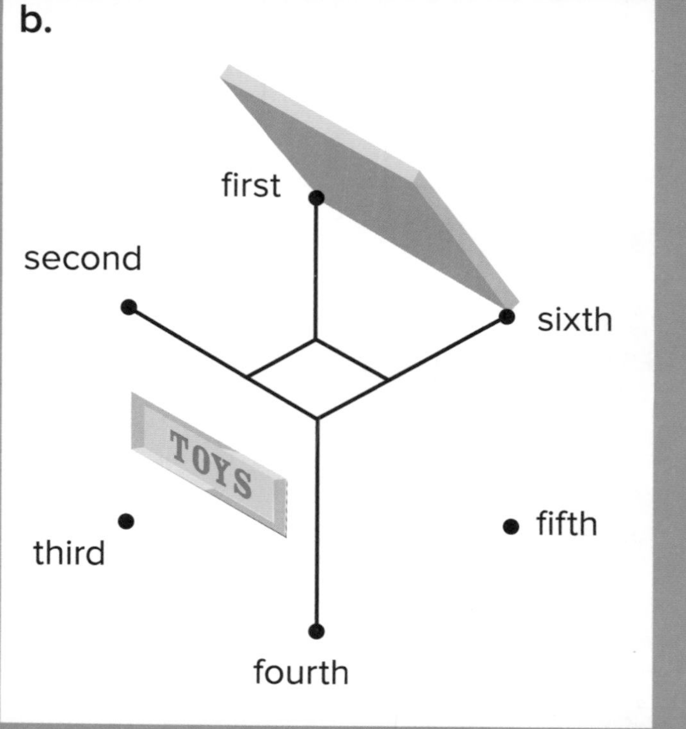

2. Draw ⌒ to connect the dots in order.

a.

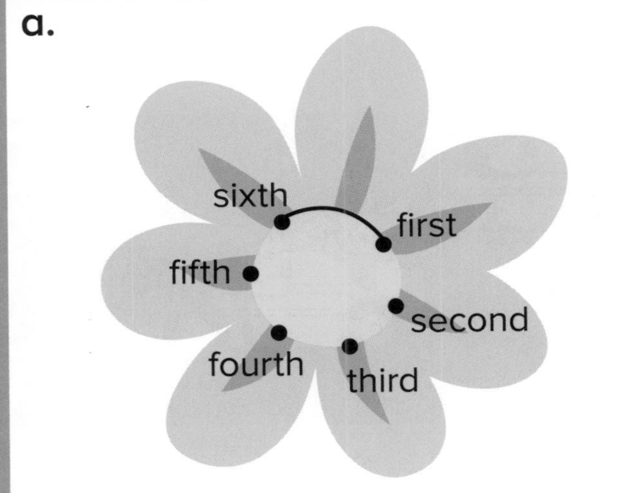

b.

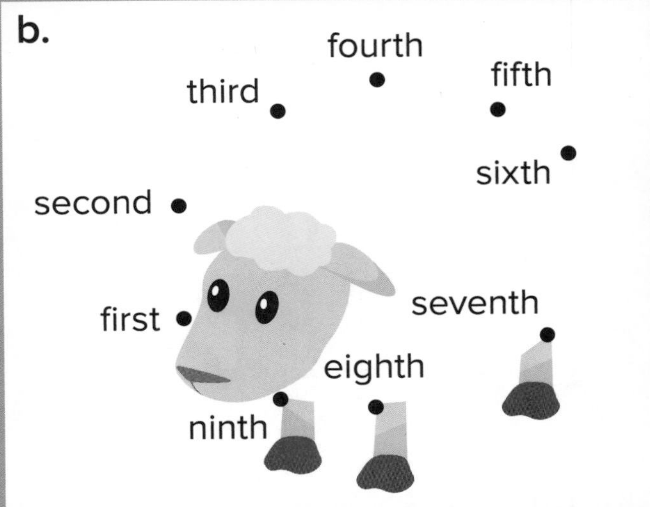

3. The **first** scoop of frozen yogurt is strawberry. Color these scoops.

a. Color the second scoop blue.

b. Color the fourth scoop red.

c. Color the third scoop green.

Step Ahead Draw 🙂 in the **first**, **third**, **fifth**, **seventh**, and **ninth** positions. Then draw 🙁 in the other positions to make a pattern.

start here ◯ ◯ ◯ ◯ ◯ ◯ ◯ ◯ ◯ ◯

Write the name of the last position. ____________

1.12 Matching Ordinal Number Names and Symbols

Describe the order of the cars in this race.

FINISH

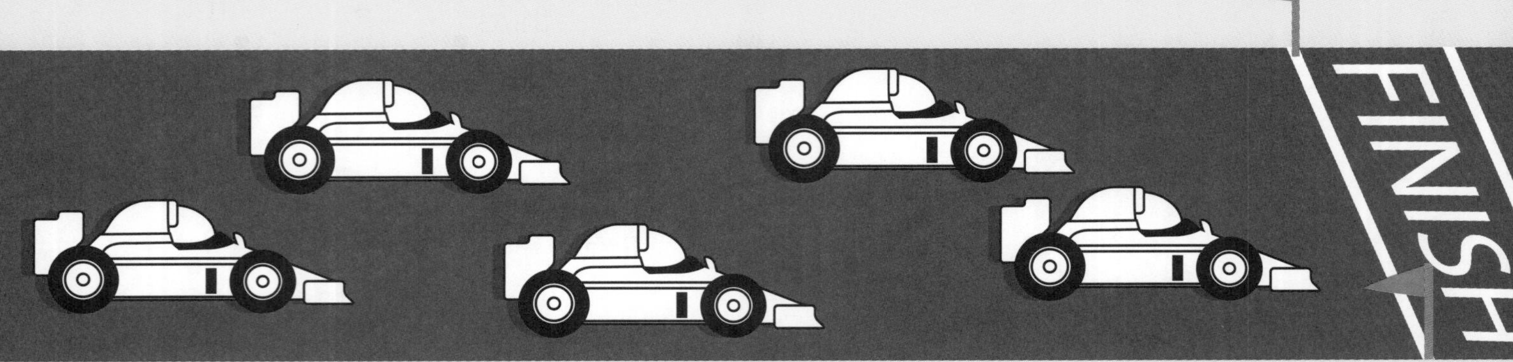

Color green the car that will finish 2nd. Color blue the car that will finish last. Color yellow the car that will finish 3rd. Color red the car that will finish first. In which position will the other car finish? How do you know?

Step Up **1.** Draw lines to connect cars and their ribbons.

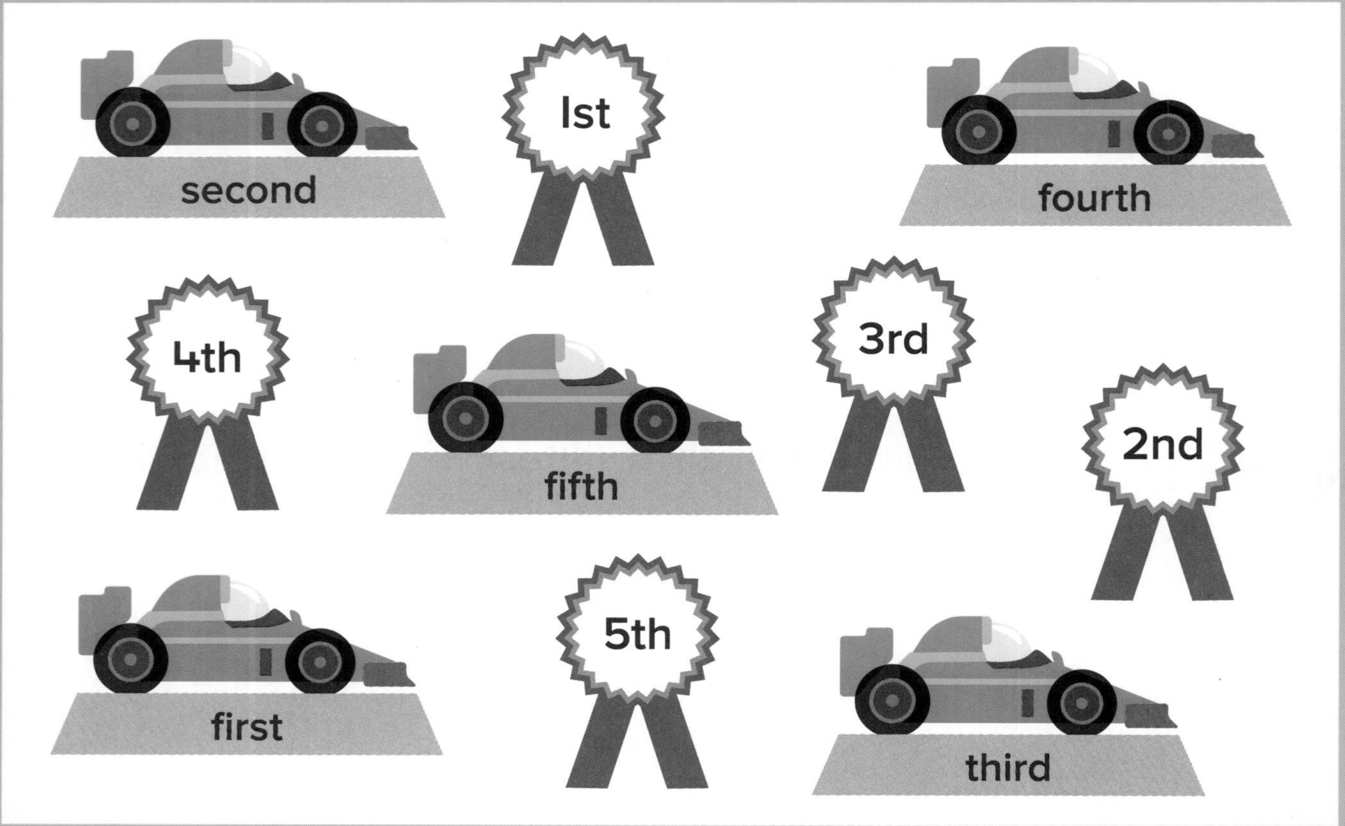
second
1st
fourth
4th
fifth
3rd
2nd
first
5th
third

2. The first plane is blue. Color other planes to match.

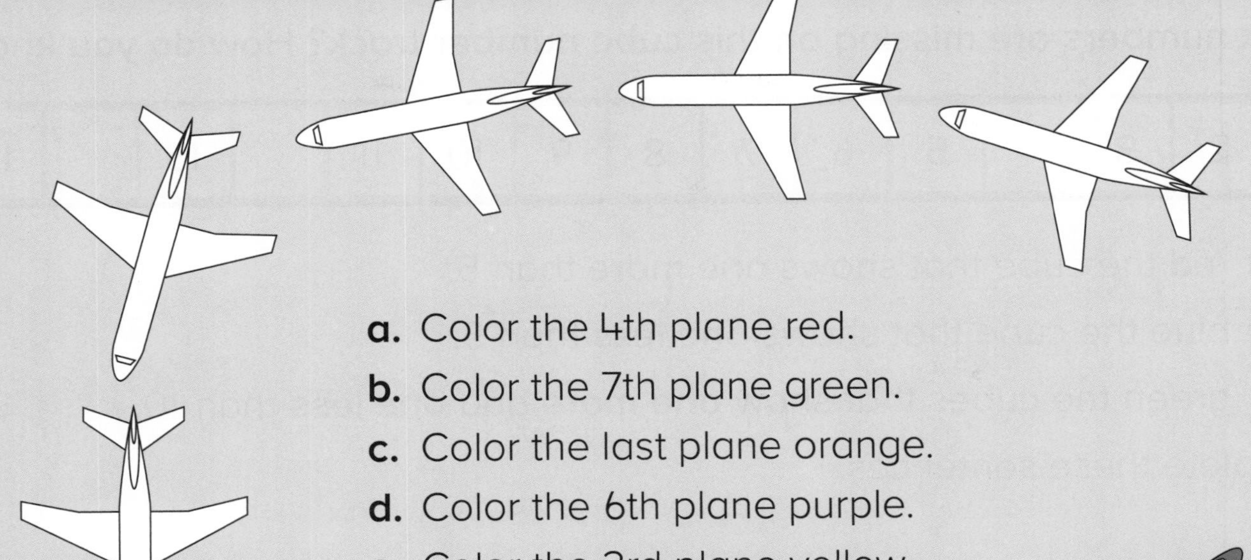

a. Color the 4th plane red.

b. Color the 7th plane green.

c. Color the last plane orange.

d. Color the 6th plane purple.

e. Color the 3rd plane yellow.

f. Color the 8th plane brown.

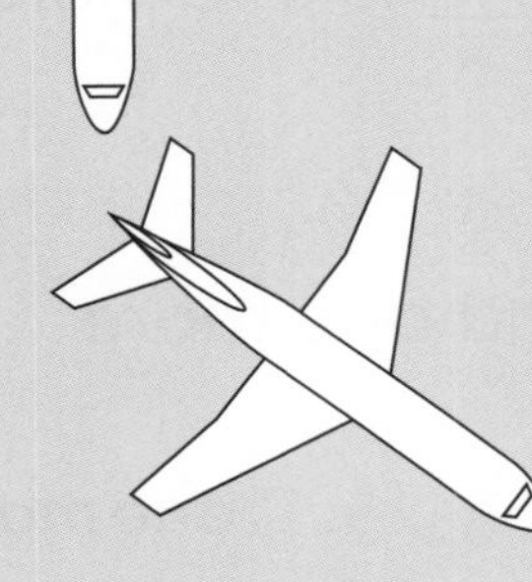
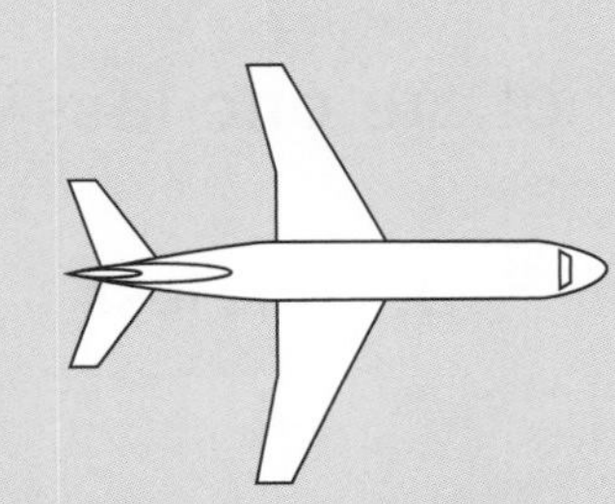

g. In which positions are the two white planes?

__________ __________

Step Ahead In each race, Australia finished two places after the USA. Write the missing positions for each race.

Australia	USA
6th	____

Australia	USA
____	1st

Australia	USA
4th	____

Australia	USA
____	3rd

Australia	USA
10th	____

Australia	USA
____	7th

2.1 Identifying One More and One Less

What numbers are missing on this cube number track? How do you know?

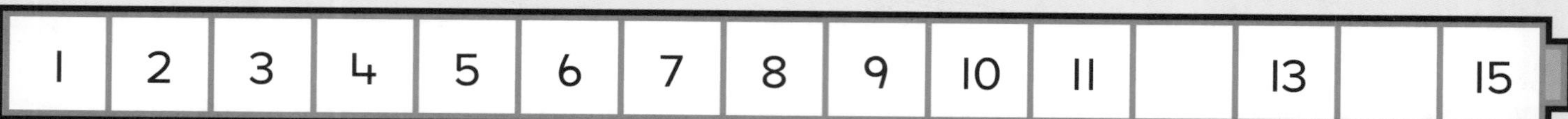

Color red the cube that shows **one more** than 5.

Color blue the cube that shows **one less** than 5.

Color green the cubes that show **one more** and **one less** than 10.

Complete these sentences.

7 is one less than ____.

13 is one less than ____.

____ is one more than 3.

Step Up 1. Write the numerals that are **one less** and **one more**.

	one less		one more
a.		6	
b.		3	
c.		5	
d.		9	
e.		4	
f.		2	

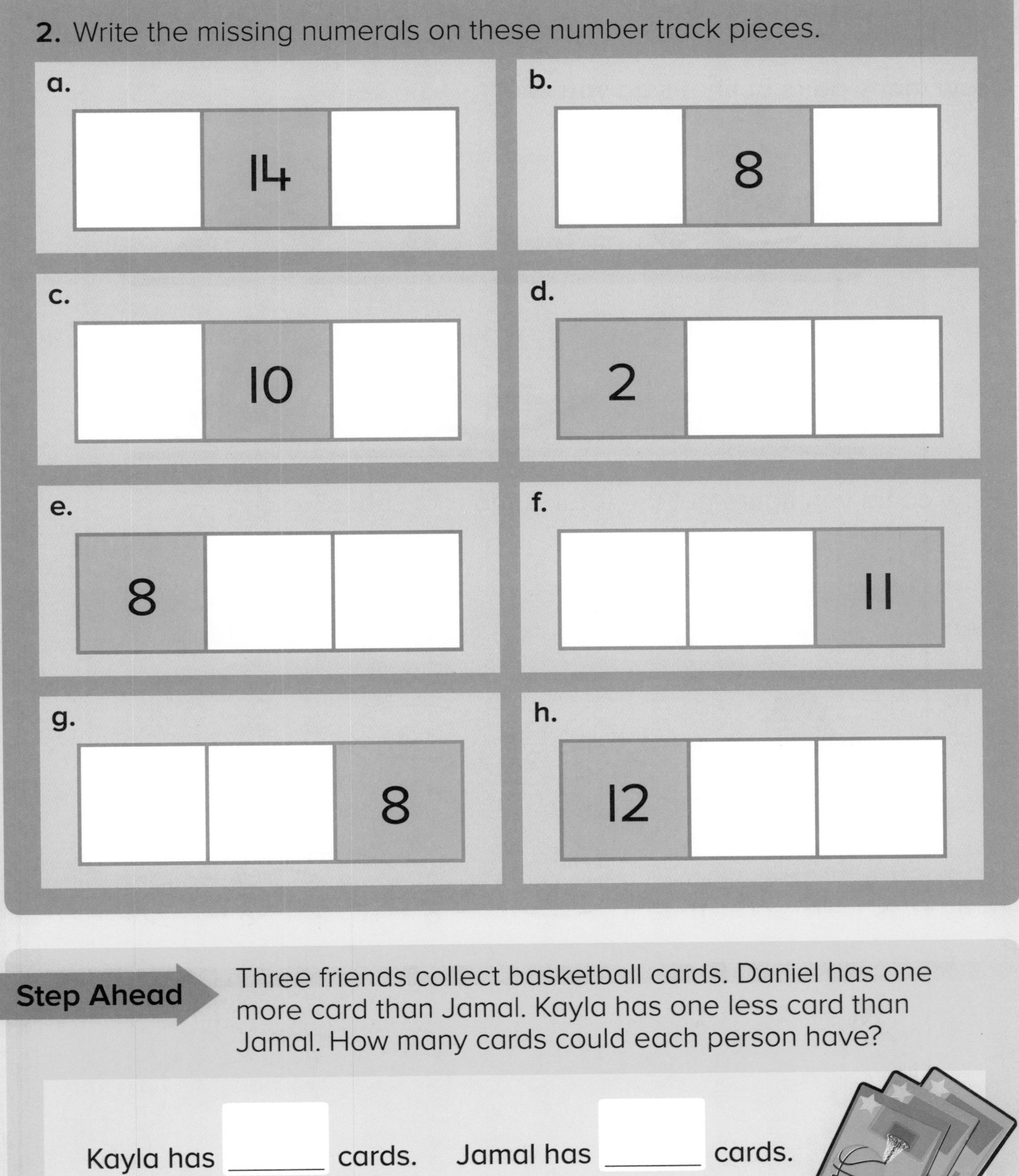

Step Ahead Three friends collect basketball cards. Daniel has one more card than Jamal. Kayla has one less card than Jamal. How many cards could each person have?

Kayla has ______ cards. Jamal has ______ cards.

Daniel has ______ cards.

2.2 Counting in Steps of 2

How many pairs of shoes do you see?

How could you figure out the total number of shoes?

Step Up 1. Draw jumps of 2. Color the numbers you land on.

a.

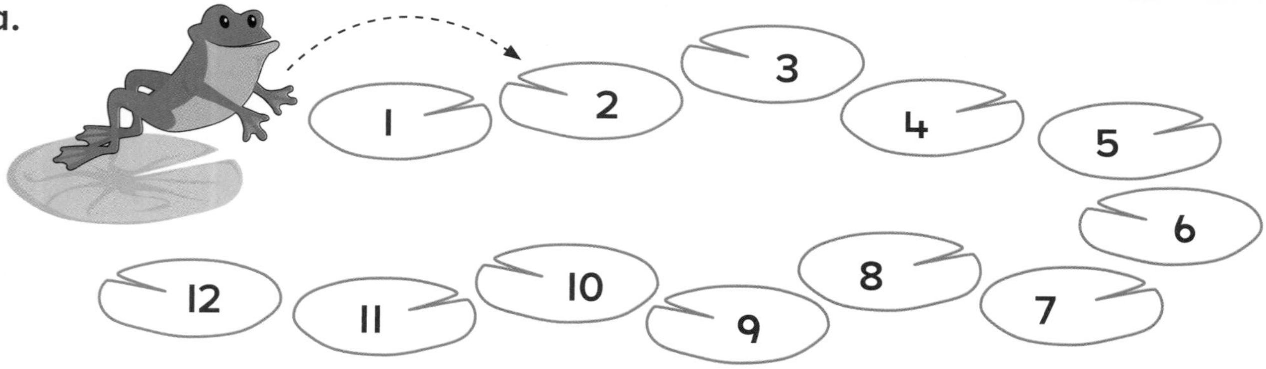

1 2 3 4 5 6 7 8 9 10 11 12

b.

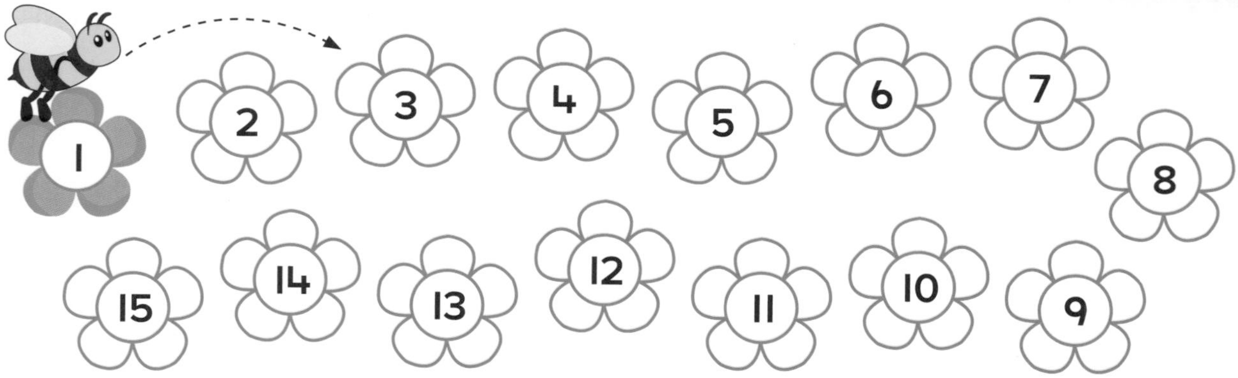

1 2 3 4 5 6 7 8 9 10 11 12 13 14 15

2. Draw jumps of 2. Color the numbers you land on.

a.

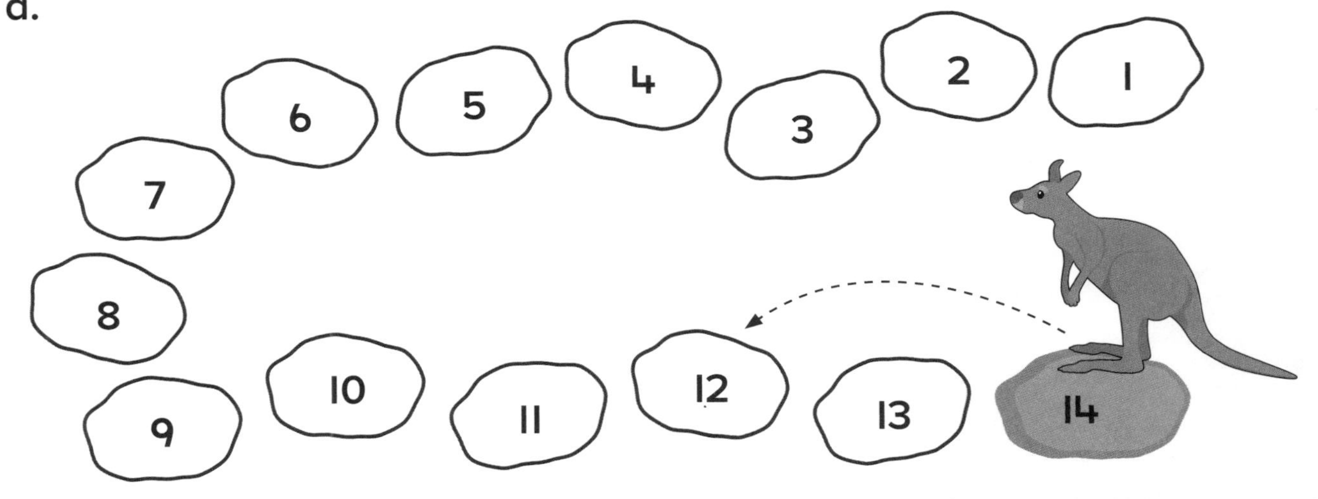

b.

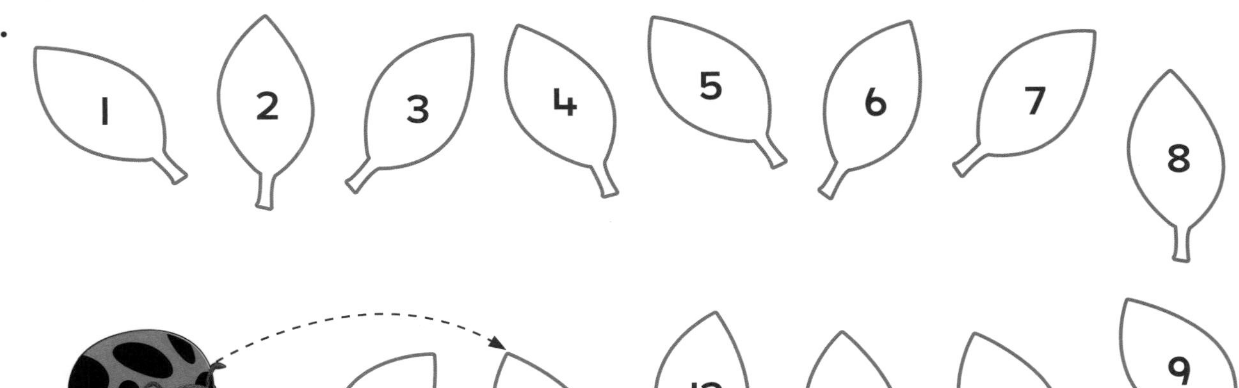

Step Ahead These number patterns were made with jumps of 2. Write the missing numerals.

a. 2 4 ___ ___ 10

b. ___ 6 ___ 10 ___

c. ___ 3 ___ 7 ___

d. 3 ___ ___ 9 ___

2.3 Counting On from 5

What is a quick way to figure out the total number of fingers raised?

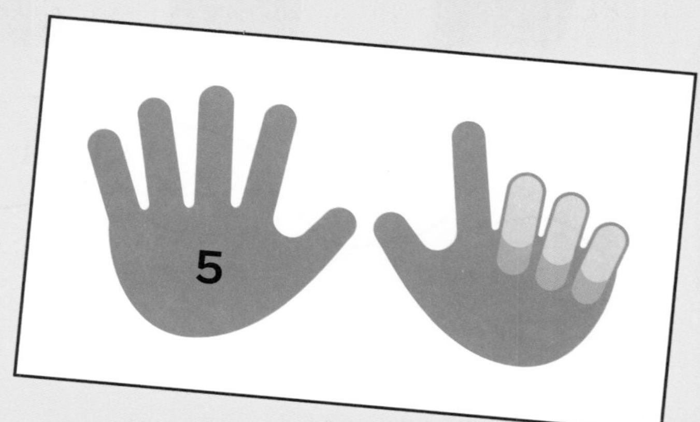

I counted on from 5.

Use your quick way to figure out the total number of cubes.

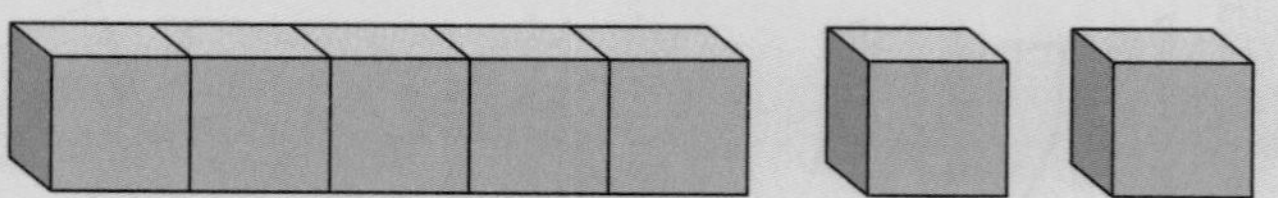

Step Up 1. Start at 5 and count on. Write the numbers **you say**.

a. 5 6 7 8

b. ___ ___

c. ___ ___ ___

2. Start at 5 and count on. Write the total.

a.

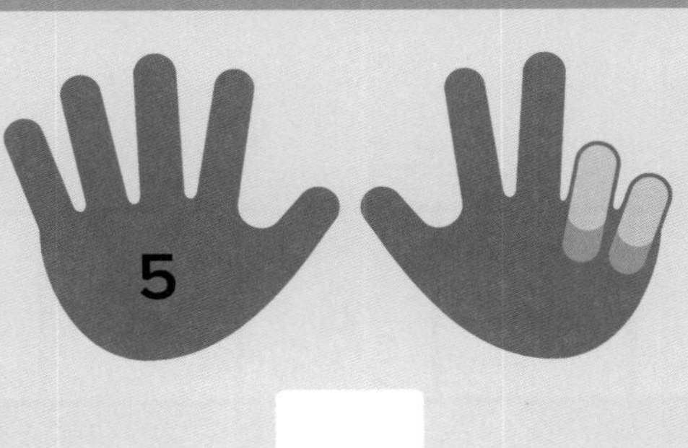

b.

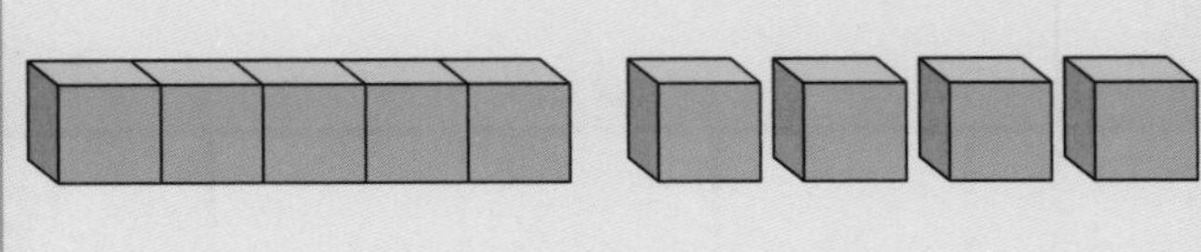

c.

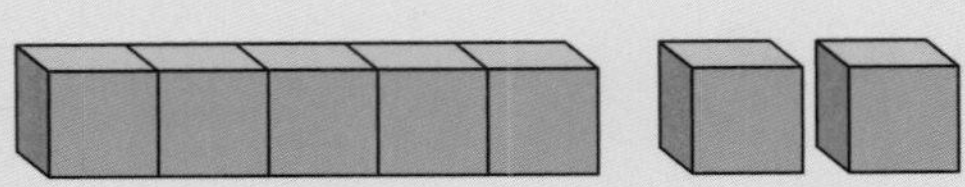

d.

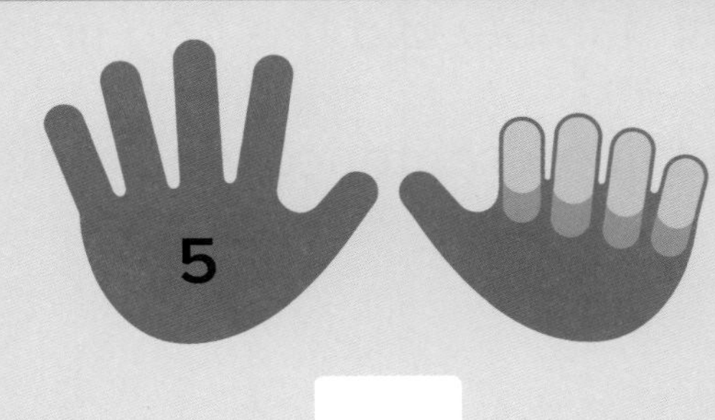

e.

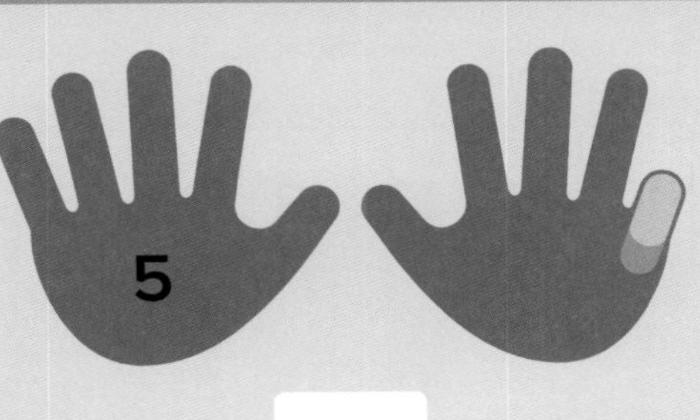

f.

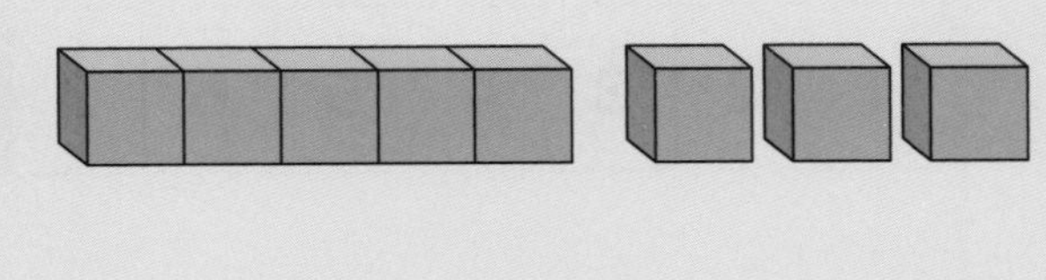

Step Ahead Write an addition sentence to match each picture.

a.

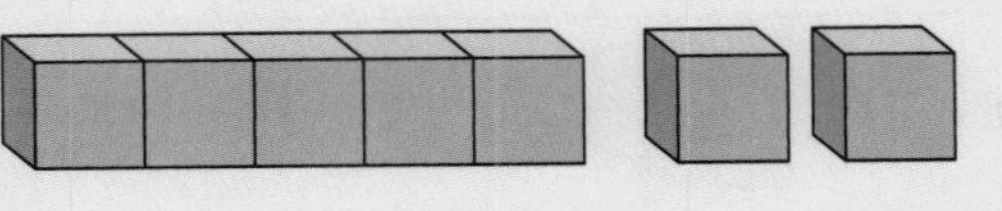

b.

2.4 Using a Number Track to Count On (to 15)

What is happening in this picture?

On what number did the frog start?

On what number did the frog finish? How many jumps did it make?

What addition sentence would match the picture?

___ + ___ = ___

Step Up 1. Count on 1. Then write the addition sentence.

a.

___ + ___ = ___

b.

___ + ___ = ___

c.

___ + ___ = ___

2. Count on 2. Then write the addition sentence.

a.

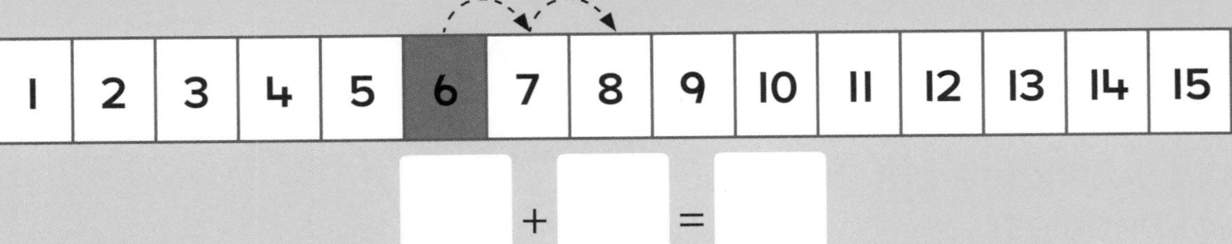

____ + ____ = ____

b.

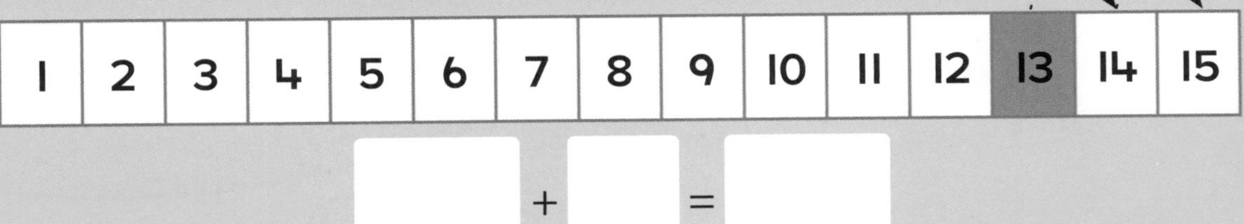

____ + ____ = ____

c.

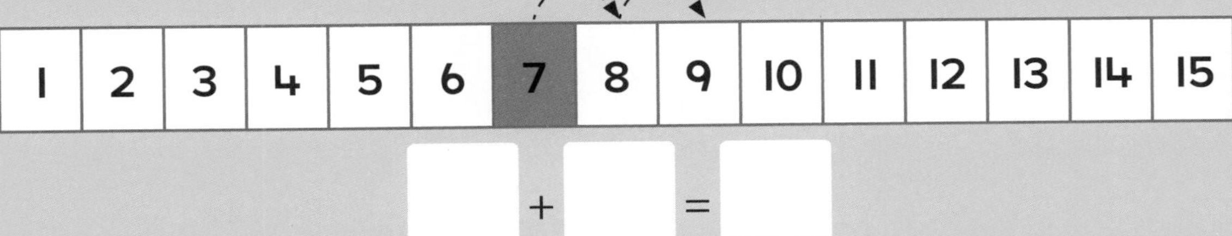

____ + ____ = ____

d.

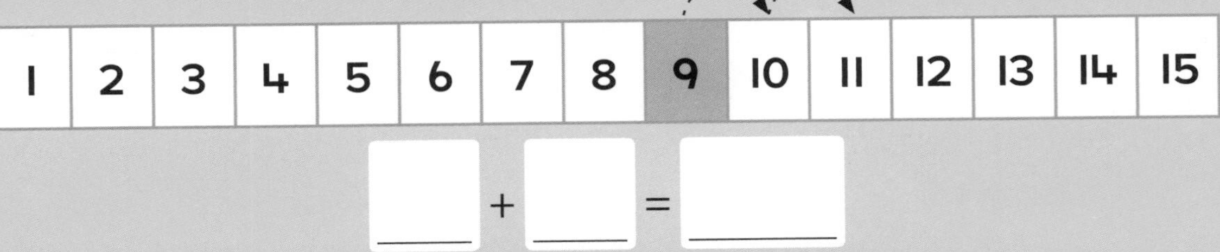

____ + ____ = ____

Step Ahead Draw jumps to match each addition sentence.

1	2	3	4	5	6	7	8	9	10	11	12	13	14	15

3 + 1 = 4

12 + 2 = 14

2.5 Using the Count-On Strategy with Coins

There are 6 pennies in this purse and some outside the purse.

How could you figure out the total number of pennies?

What addition sentence could you write?

___ + ___ = ___

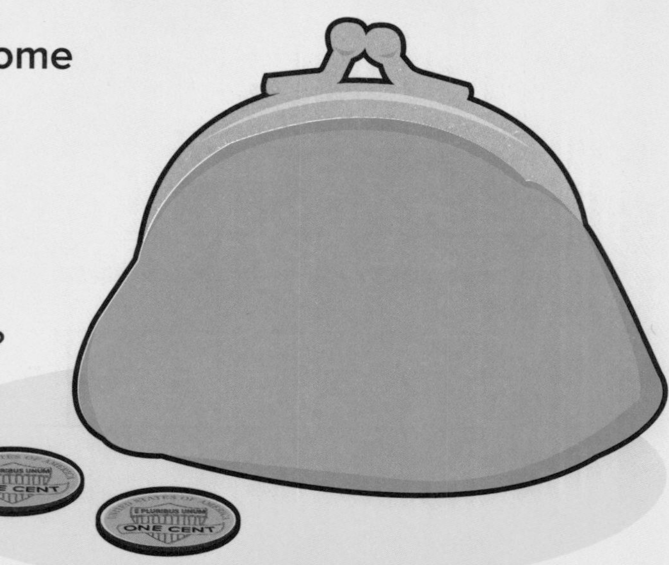

Step Up 1. Count on 1 or 2 pennies. Then write the addition sentence.

a.

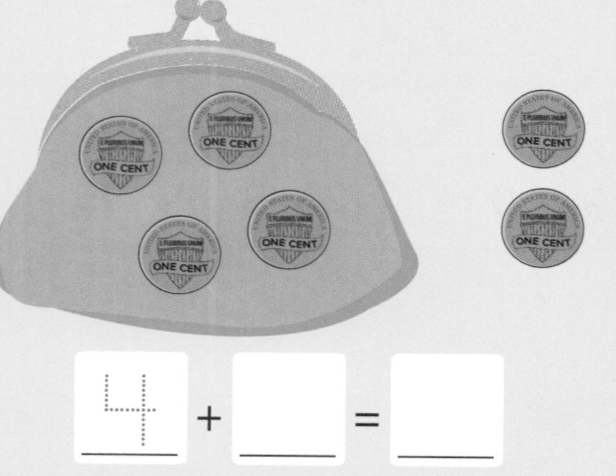

4 + ___ = ___

b.

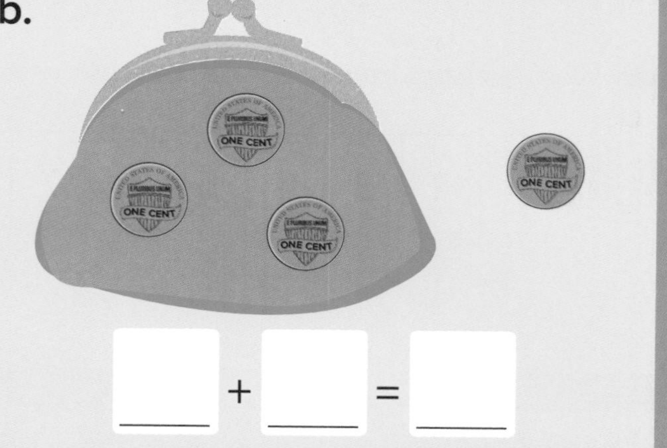

___ + ___ = ___

c.

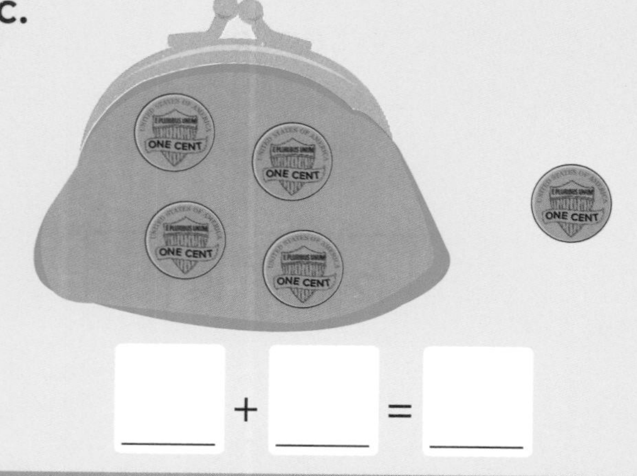

___ + ___ = ___

d.

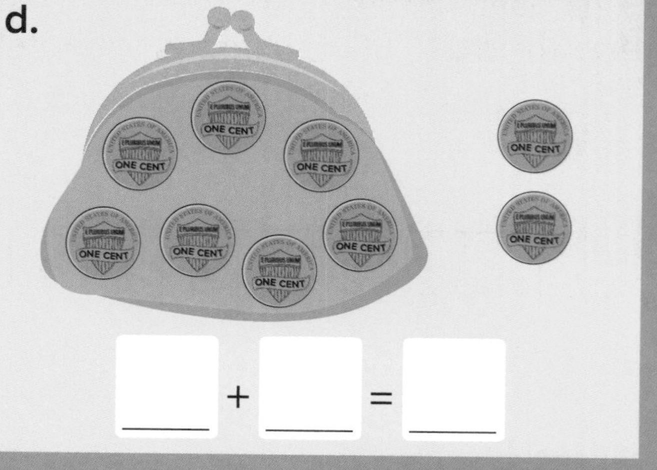

___ + ___ = ___

2. Figure out the total. Write the addition sentence.

a.

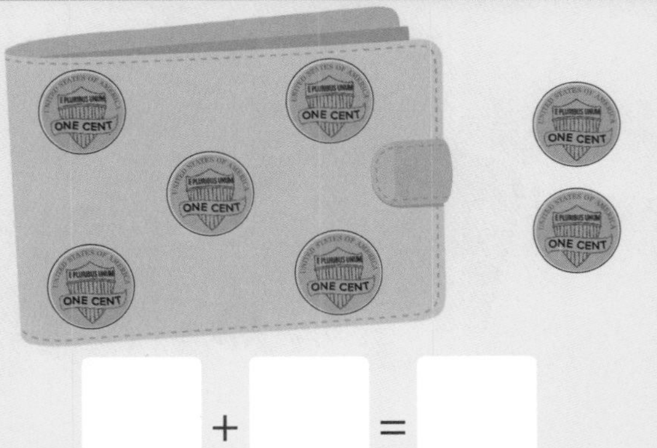

____ + ____ = ____

b.

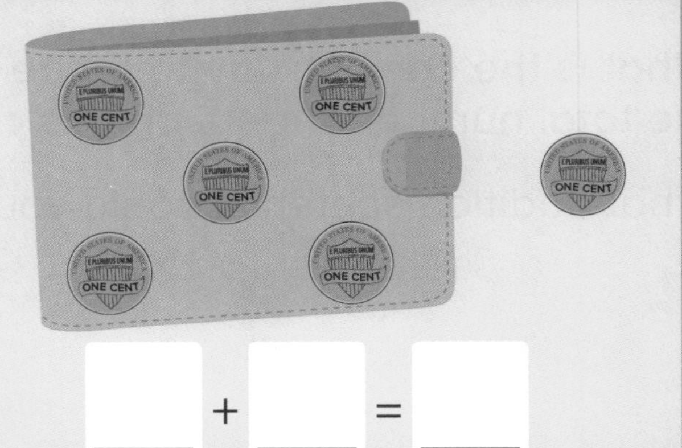

____ + ____ = ____

c.

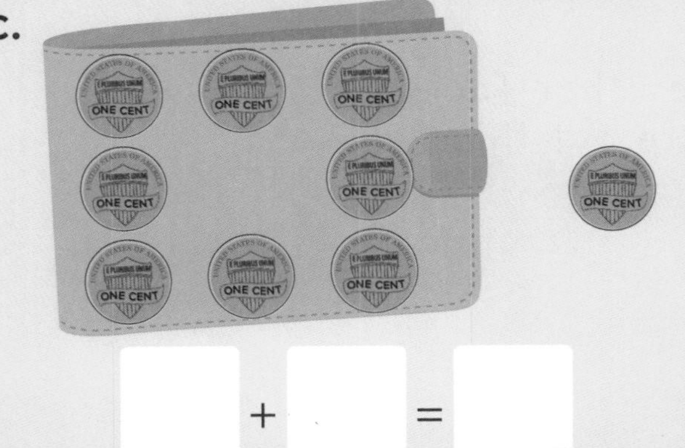

____ + ____ = ____

d.

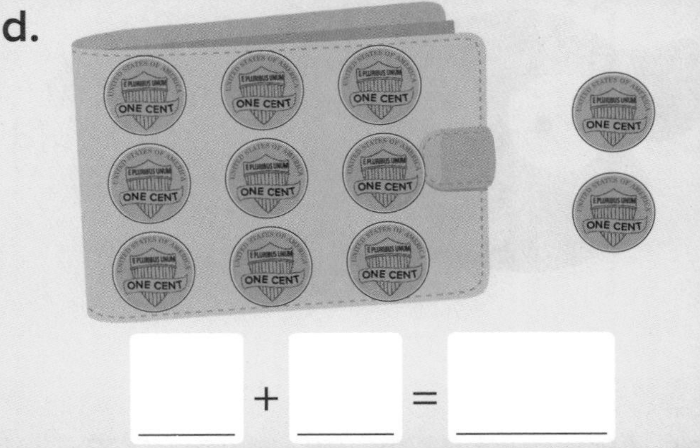

____ + ____ = ____

e.

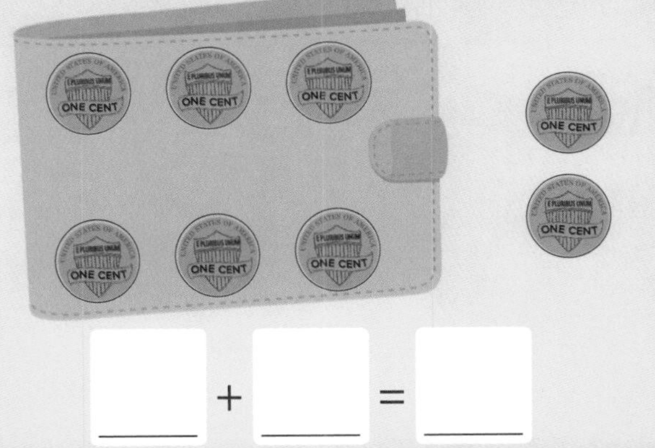

____ + ____ = ____

f.

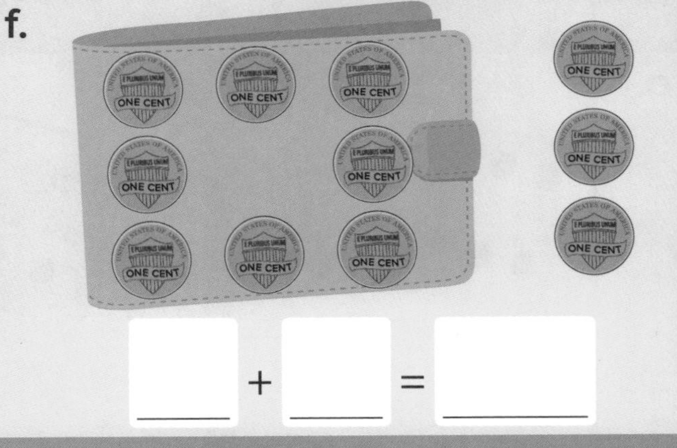

____ + ____ = ____

Step Ahead

There are 13 pennies in total.
How many are in the purse?

____ pennies

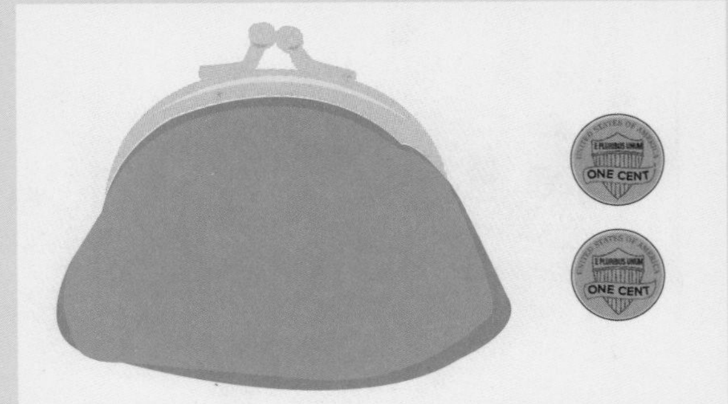

2.6 Using the Count-On Strategy

What is the easiest way to figure out the total number of dots on this card?

What addition sentence could you write?

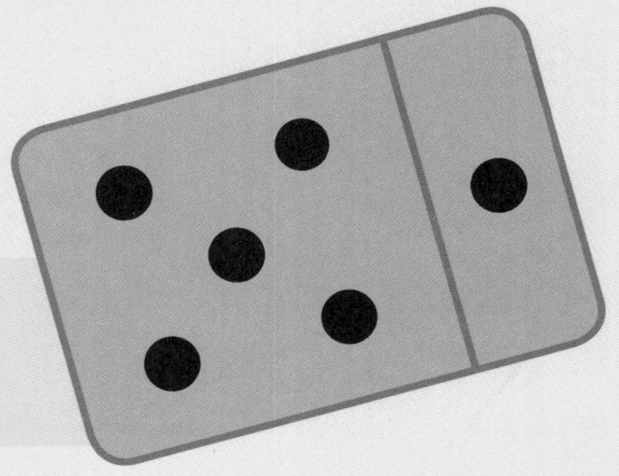

___ + ___ = ___

What are some other facts you could figure out this way?

Step Up 1. Count on 1 or 2. Then write the addition sentence.

a.

___ + ___ = ___

b.

___ + ___ = ___

c.

___ + ___ = ___

d.

___ + ___ = ___

e.

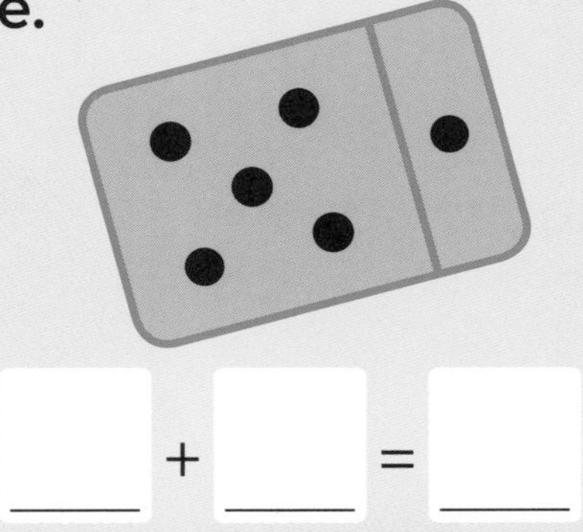

___ + ___ = ___

f.

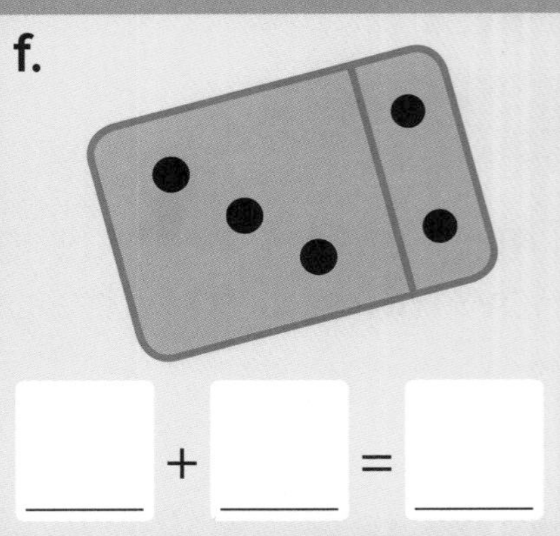

___ + ___ = ___

2. Write the addition sentence to match each card.

a.

2 + 5 = 7

b.

1 + 10 = 11

c.

2 + 9 = 11

d.

1 + 11 = 12

e.

0 + 8 = 8

f.

2 + 13 = 15

3. Count on 1 or 2. Then write the addition sentence.

a.

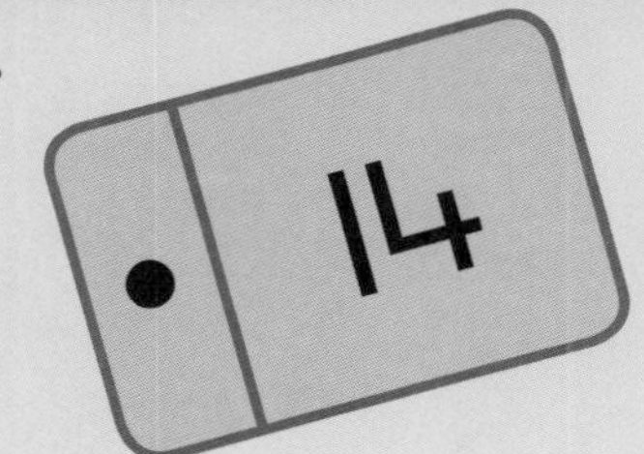

1 + 14 = 15

b.

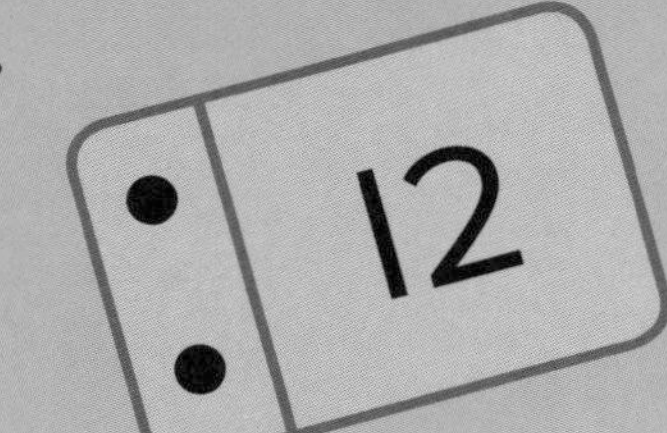

2 + 12 = 14

c.

2 + 15 = 17

Step Ahead Look at the total. Draw more dots on the card. Then complete the addition sentence.

a.

2 + 6 = 8

b.

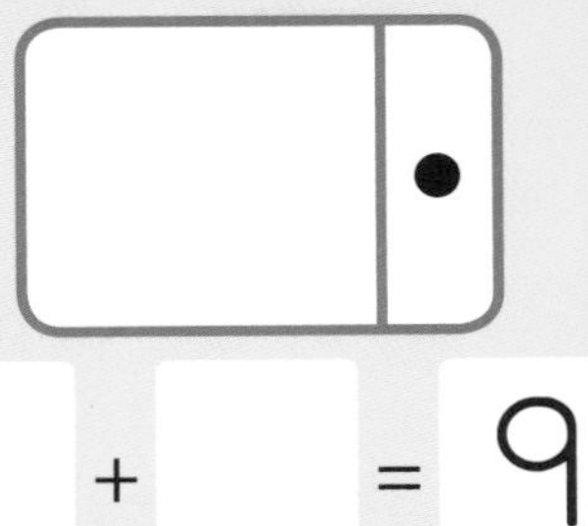

1 + ___ = 9

2.7 Using the Commutative Property of Addition with Count-On Facts

What do you notice about these pictures?

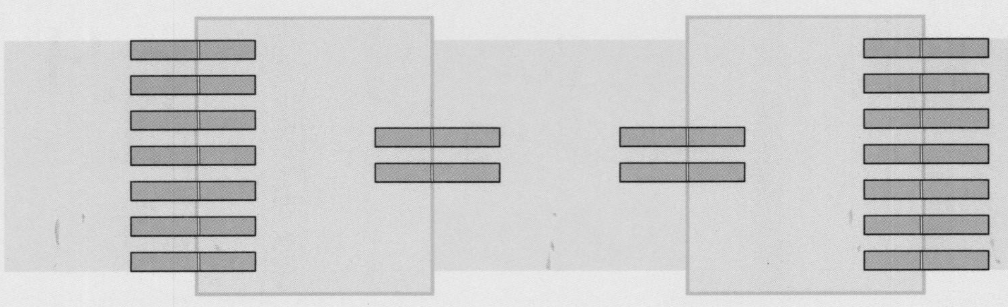

What addition fact would match each picture?

What number will you say first?

What number will you count on?

These facts are called turnaround facts.

Step Up 1. Complete the addition fact and its turnaround fact.

a.

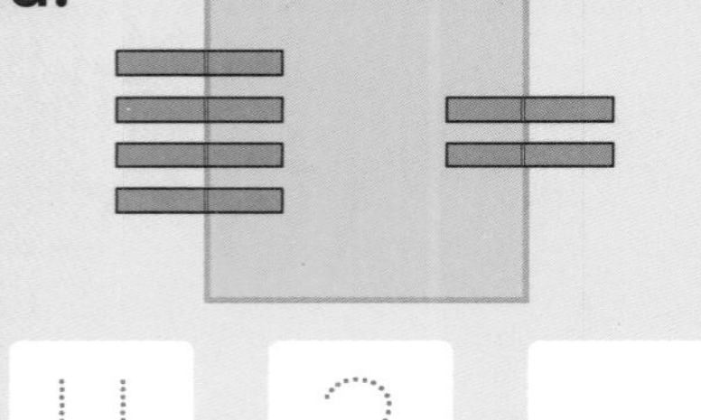

4 + 2 = ___

2 + ___ = ___

b.

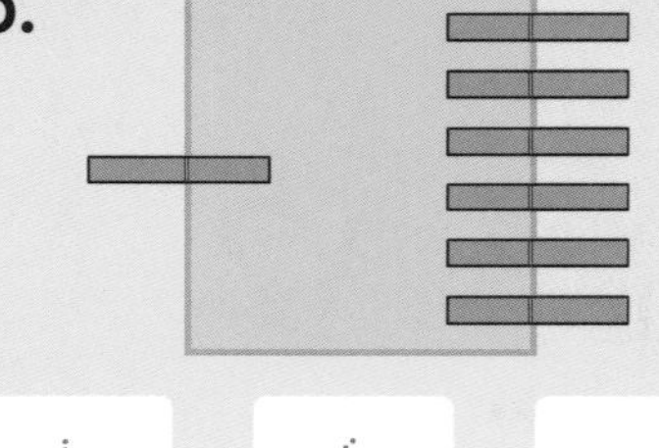

1 + 6 = ___

___ + ___ = ___

c.

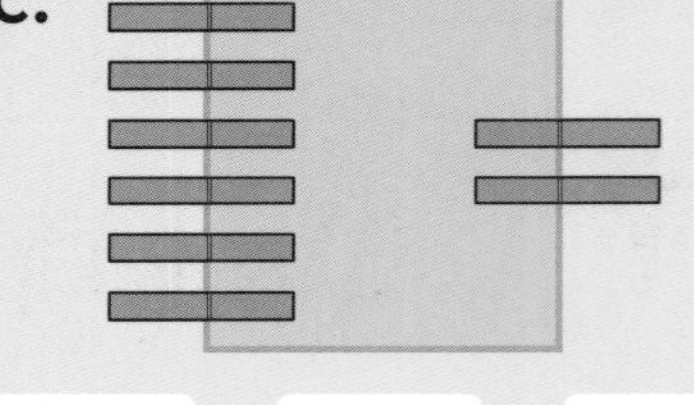

6 + 2 = ___

___ + ___ = ___

d.

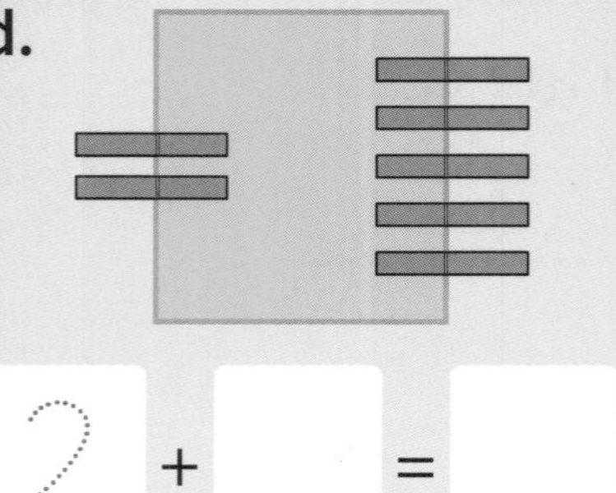

2 + ___ = ___

___ + 2 = ___

e.

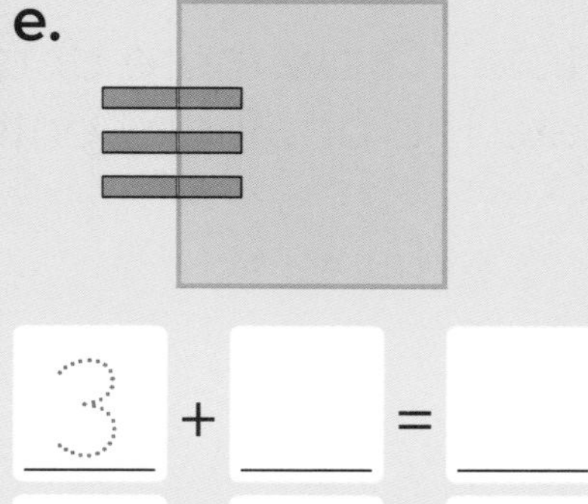

3 + ___ = ___

___ + ___ = ___

f.

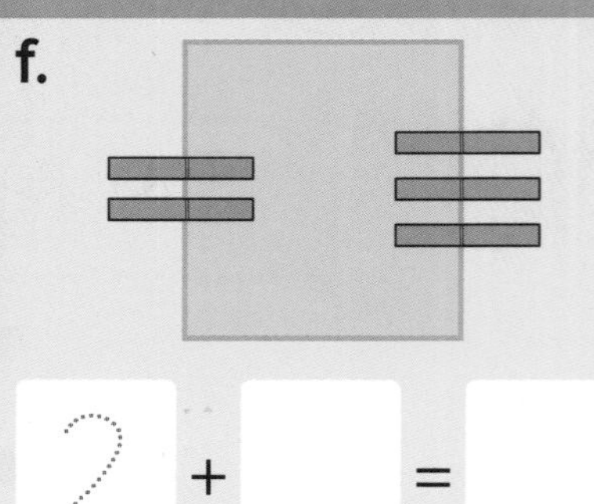

2 + ___ = ___

___ + ___ = ___

2. Write the addition sentence. Then write the turnaround.

a.

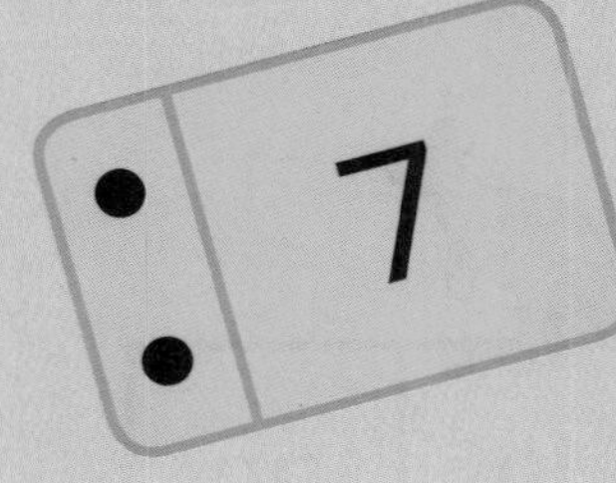

2 + 7 = 9

7 + 2 = 9

b.

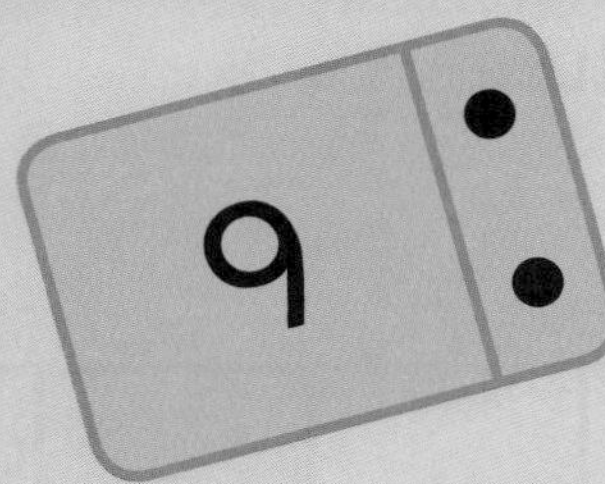

2 + 9 = 11

9 + 2 = 11

c.

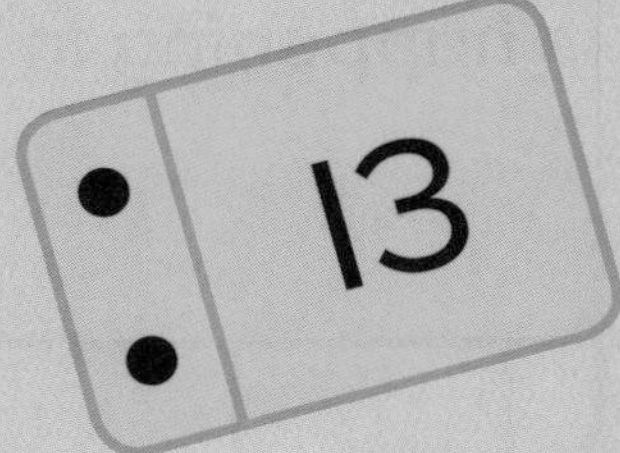

2 + 13 = 15

3 + 2 = 15

d.

2 + 17 = 19

17 + 2 = 19

e.

0 + 11 = 11

11 + 0 = 11

f.

1 + 15 = 16

15 + 1 = 16

Step Ahead Look at the total. Draw the dots on the card. Then write two addition facts to match.

a.

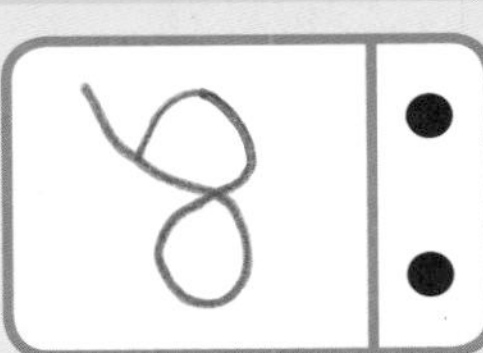

2 + 8 = 10

8 + 2 = 10

b.

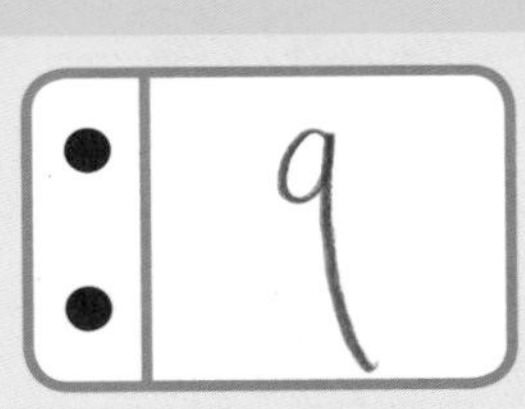

2 + 9 = 11

9 + 2 = 11

2.8 Using a Number Track to Count On (to 20)

What is happening in this picture?

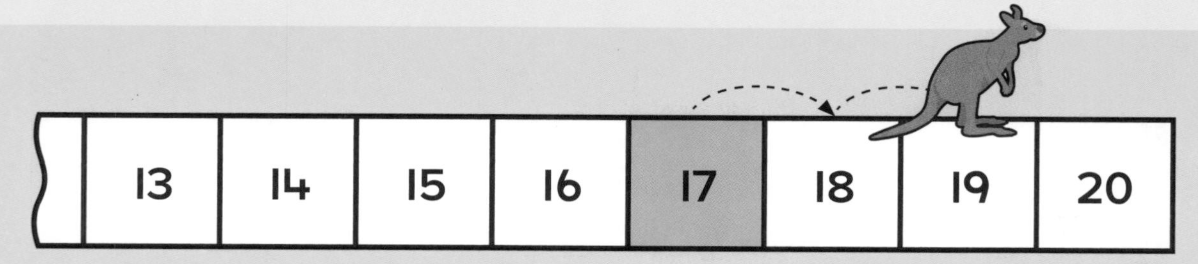

On what number did the kangaroo start?

On what number did the kangaroo finish? How many jumps did it make?

What addition sentence matches the picture? How do you know?

What is the turnaround fact?

Step Up 1. Count on 1 or 2. Then write the addition sentence.

a. | 11 | 12 | 13 | 14 | 15 | 16 | 17 | 18 | 19 | 20 | ____ + ____ = ____

b. | 11 | 12 | 13 | 14 | 15 | 16 | 17 | 18 | 19 | 20 | ____ + ____ = ____

c. | 11 | 12 | 13 | 14 | 15 | 16 | 17 | 18 | 19 | 20 | ____ + ____ = ____

d. | 11 | 12 | 13 | 14 | 15 | 16 | 17 | 18 | 19 | 20 | ____ + ____ = ____

2. Draw jumps to help you count on. Then write the addition sentence.

a. Count on **2**.

11	12	13	14	15	16	17	18	19	20

_____ + _____ = _____

b. Count on **1**.

11	12	13	14	15	16	17	18	19	20

_____ + _____ = _____

c. Count on **2**.

11	12	13	14	15	16	17	18	19	20

_____ + _____ = _____

d. Count on **1**.

11	12	13	14	15	16	17	18	19	20

_____ + _____ = _____

Step Ahead Add the number in the star to each number in the circles. Write the answers in the squares.

a.

+1

16 13 15 11 9

b.

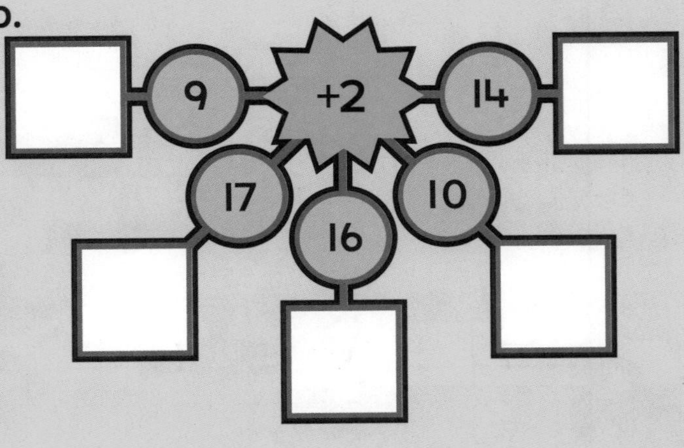

+2

9 14 17 16 10

2.9 Using Comparison Language to Describe Lengths

Look at the white car.

Which car is shorter? Which car is longer?

Which crane has the longest arm? Which is tallest? Which is shortest?

Look at all the purple windows.

Which window is the widest? Which is the narrowest?

What other lengths could you compare in the picture?

Step Up Your teacher will give you a sheet of pictures. Cut out the pictures and paste them in the spaces below to make true statements.

is longer than

is shorter than

is taller than

is wider than

is longer than

is narrower than

Step Ahead Draw a ribbon that is **longer and wider** than this red ribbon.

2.10 Counting Non-Standard Units to Measure Length

How could you use the blocks to measure the length of the pencil?

Does it matter which way the blocks are placed? Why?

Does it matter if gaps are left between the blocks? Why?

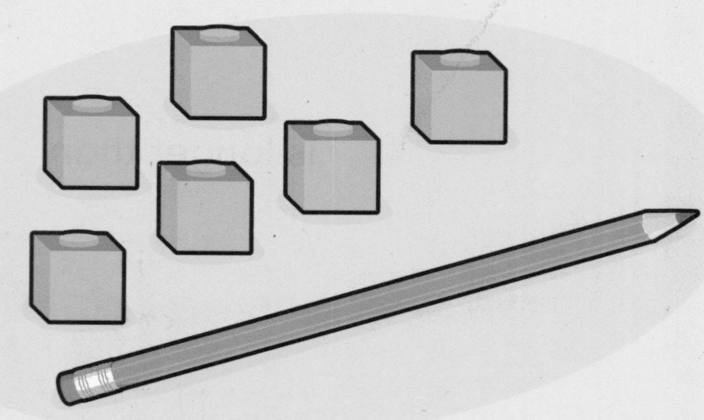

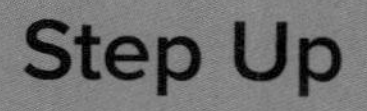

Step Up

1. Color the objects that are about the same length as this cube train.

2. Color the objects that are about the same length as this cube train.

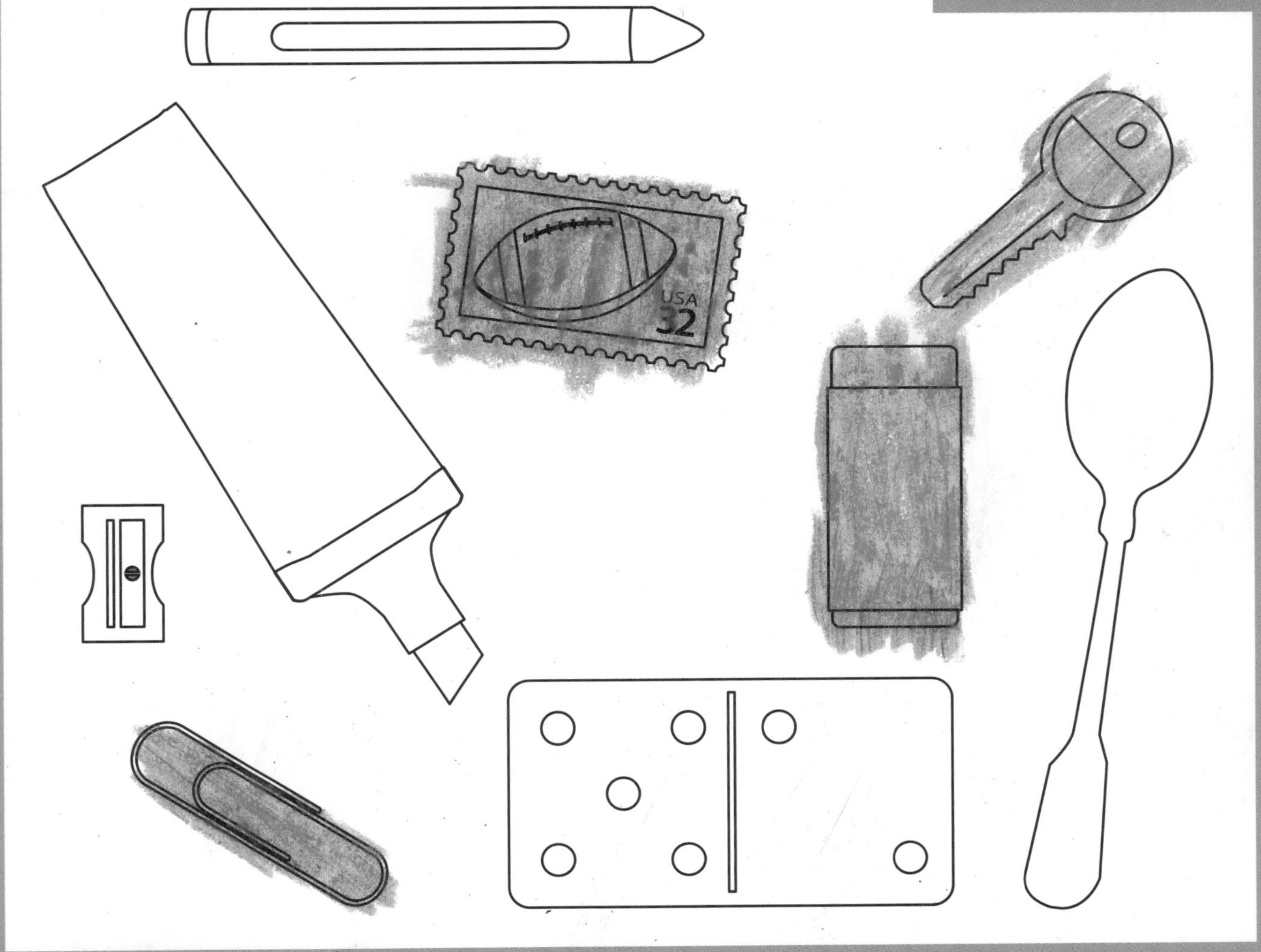

USA
32

Step Ahead List some more classroom objects that are about **5 cubes long**.

2.11 Measuring Length Using the Same Non-Standard Units

Paper ants were used to measure this leaf.

Is the measurement accurate?
How do you know?

How would you use the paper ants to measure the leaf?

Step Up 1. Use your paper ant trail to measure each leaf.
Write the number of ants.

a.

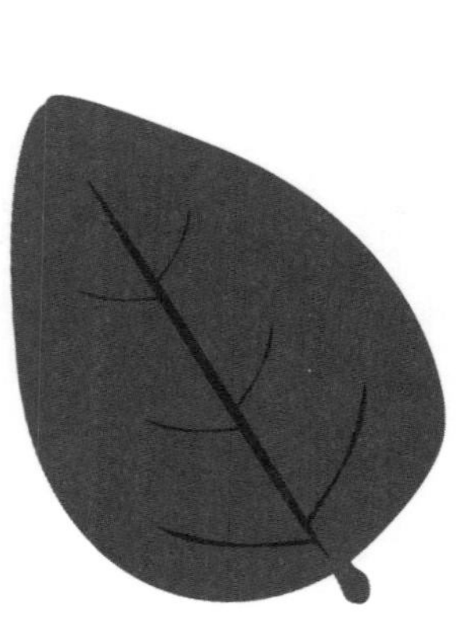

_____ ants long

b.

_____ ants long

2. Draw a leaf to match each length **exactly**.

6 ants long

3 ants long

Step Ahead

Your teacher will give you a leaf. Trace around the leaf in the space below. Then measure your leaf with your paper ant trail.

_____ ants long

2.12 Measuring Length Using Different Non-Standard Units

How many paper clips long is this toy truck?

How many cubes long is the truck? What do you notice?

Has the length of the truck changed?

What other objects could be used to measure the toy truck?

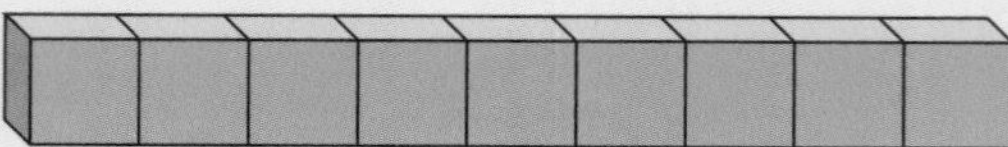

Step Up

1. Guess first, then measure the length of this pencil using the objects below.

Length of the pencil		
Measuring object	My guess	Measurement
a. cubes	______ cubes long	______ cubes long
b. 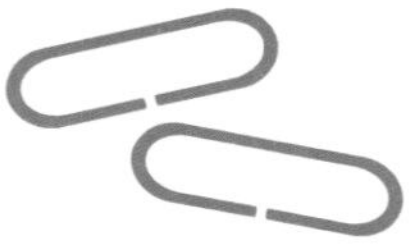 links	______ links long	______ links long
c. 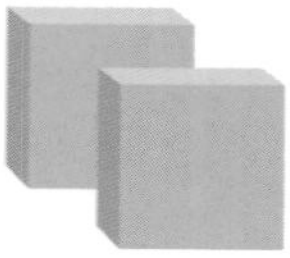 pattern blocks	______ blocks long	______ blocks long
d.  paper clips	______ clips long	______ clips long

2. Guess then measure the length of this whiteboard marker.

Length of the whiteboard marker		
Measuring object	My guess	Measurement
a. cubes	____ cubes long	____ cubes long
b. links	____ links long	____ links long
c. pattern blocks	____ blocks long	____ blocks long
d. paper clips	____ clips long	____ clips long

Step Ahead

Blake used paper clips to measure his toy truck. His truck was 2 paper clips long. Sara used a different object to measure the length of the same toy truck. She found that the truck was 4 objects long.

What do you know about the length of the object that Sara used to measure?

____

____

____

3.1 Naming Groups of Ten

Look at these number names.

What does the **teen** part mean?

sixteen eighteen seventeen

Look at these number names.

What does the **ty** part mean?

sixty eighty seventy

Look at these pairs of number names. What do you notice?

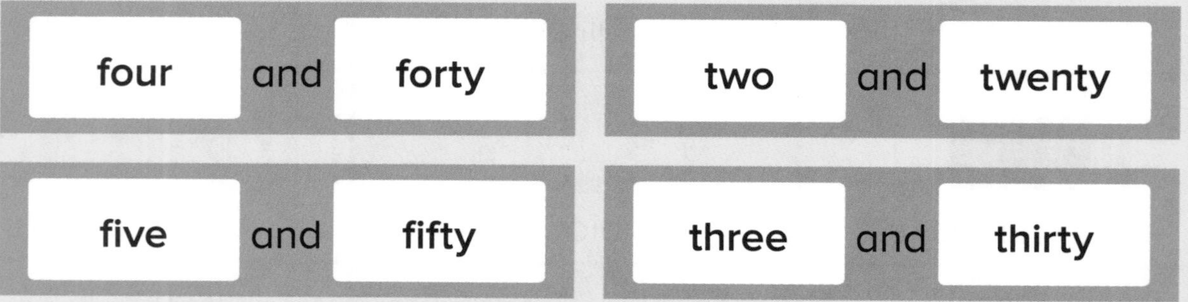

Step Up **1.** Count by tens. Write the missing number names.

a.	ten	twenty	____________	forty
b.	thirty	____________	fifty	sixty
c.	forty	fifty	____________	seventy
d.	sixty	____________	____________	ninety

2. Loop groups of ten. Write the number of tens.
Then write the number name.

a. ____ tens ____________

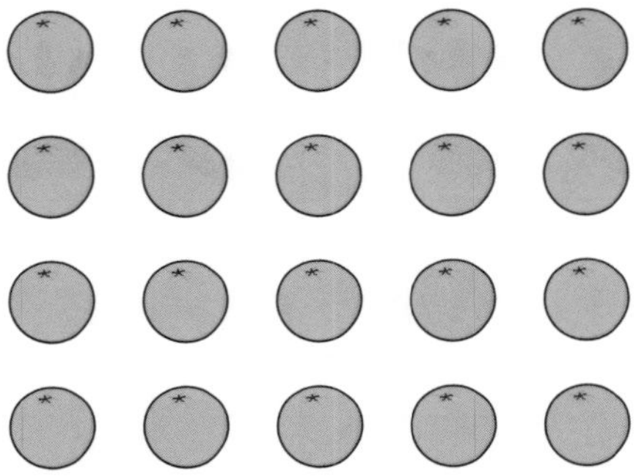

b. ____ tens ____________

c. ____ tens ____________

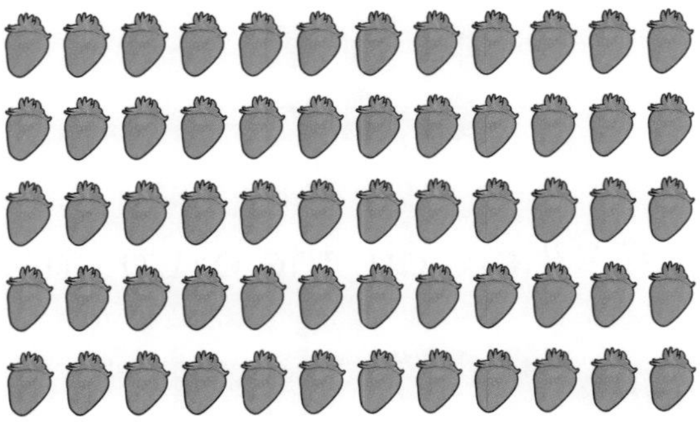

d. ____ tens ____________

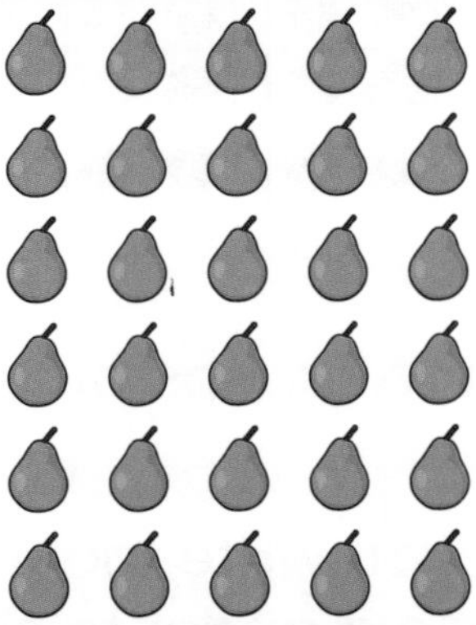

Step Ahead All these number names have been spelled incorrectly. Write each word to show the correct spelling to match the names on page 56.

a. **ninty** ____________

b. **fourty** ____________

c. **fivety** ____________

d. **thrity** ____________

3.2 Writing Tens and Ones (without Zeros)

These are different ways of showing tens and ones.

What number does each picture show? How do you know?

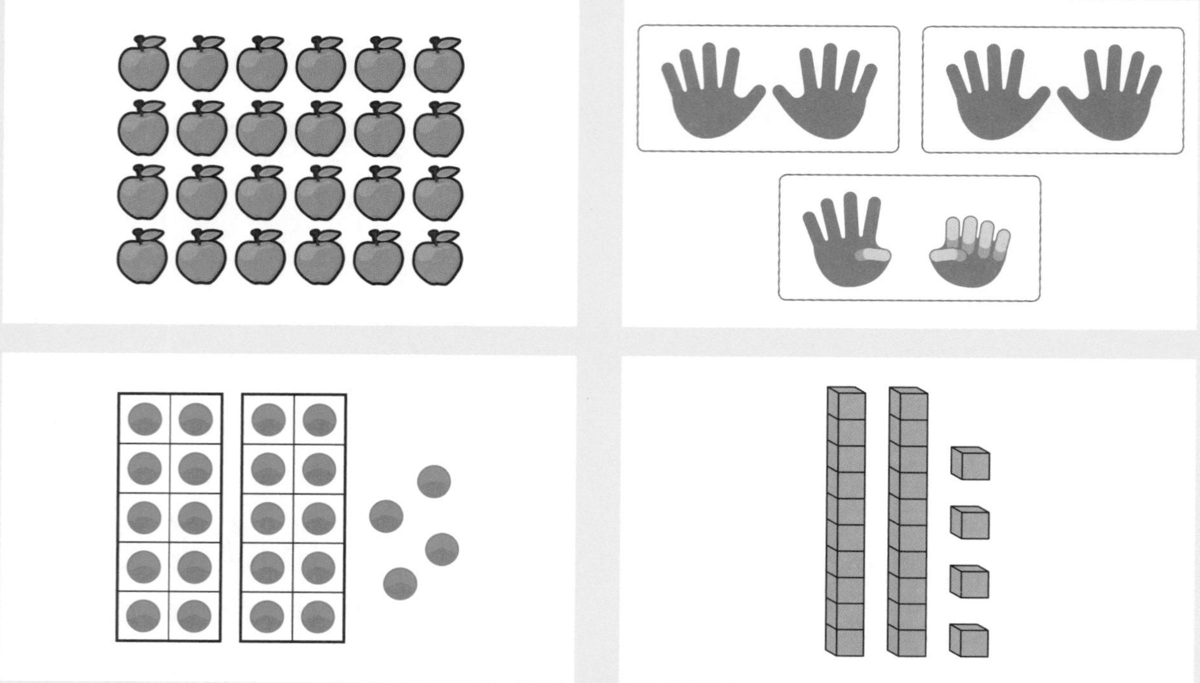

Where are the groups of ten in each picture? Where are the extra ones?

How would you write the number of tens and ones on this expander to show the same number?

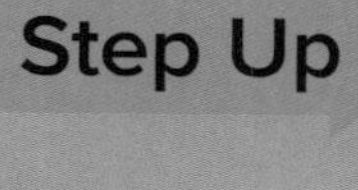

1. Write the matching number of tens and ones on the expander.

a.

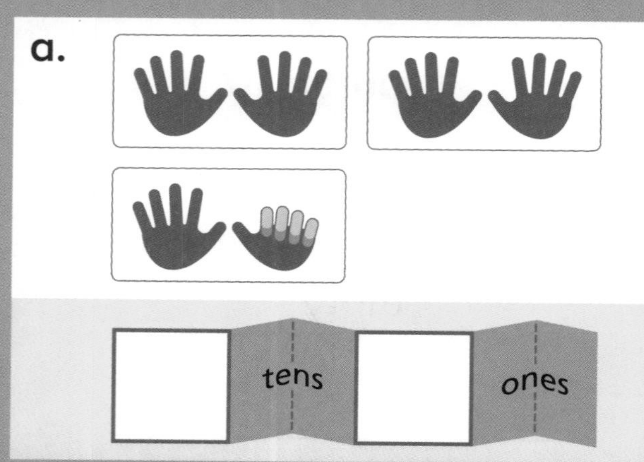

b.

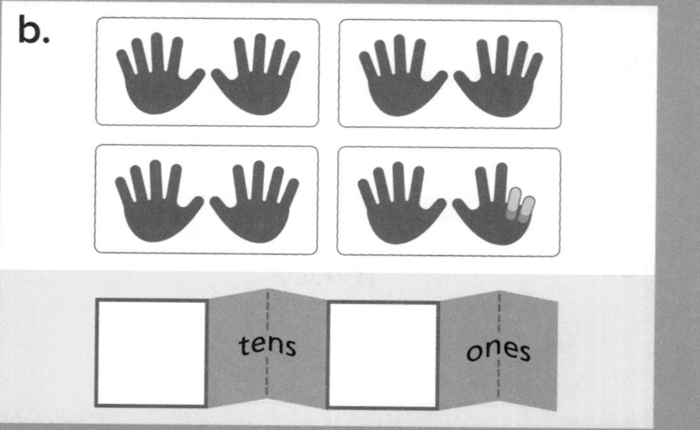

2. Write the matching number of tens and ones.

a.

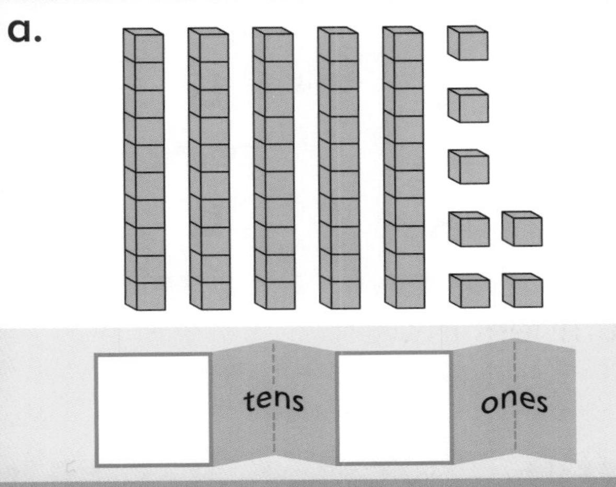

☐ tens ☐ ones

b.

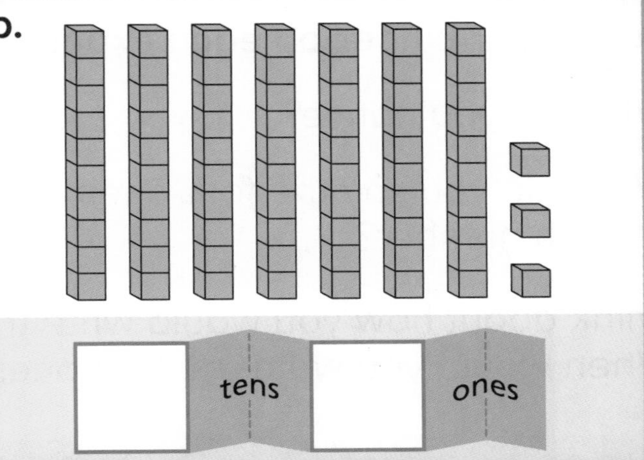

☐ tens ☐ ones

c.

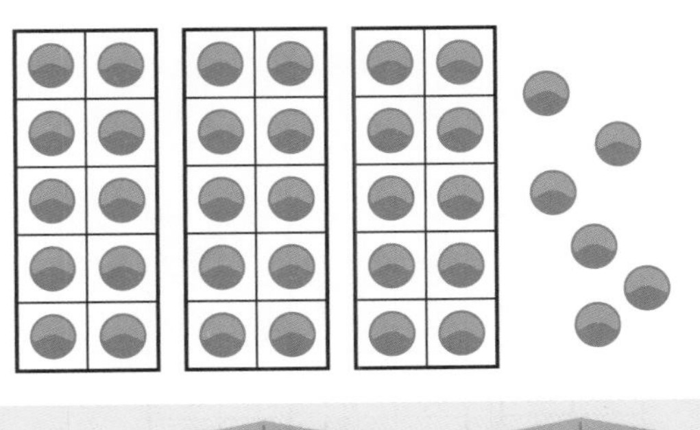

☐ tens ☐ ones

d.

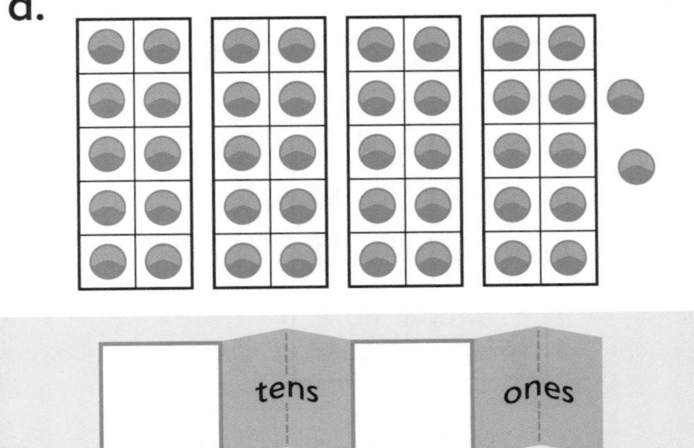

☐ tens ☐ ones

e.

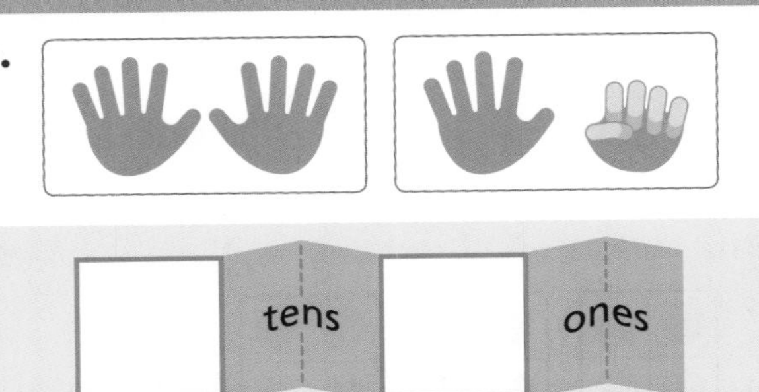

☐ tens ☐ ones

f.

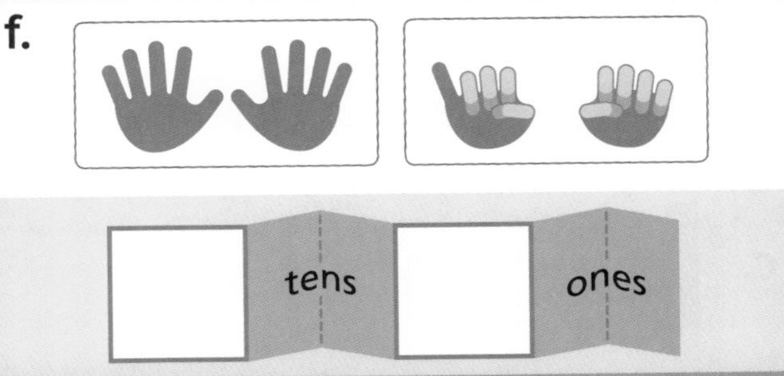

☐ tens ☐ ones

Step Ahead Write the number of tens and ones on the expander.

a. six tens and seven ones

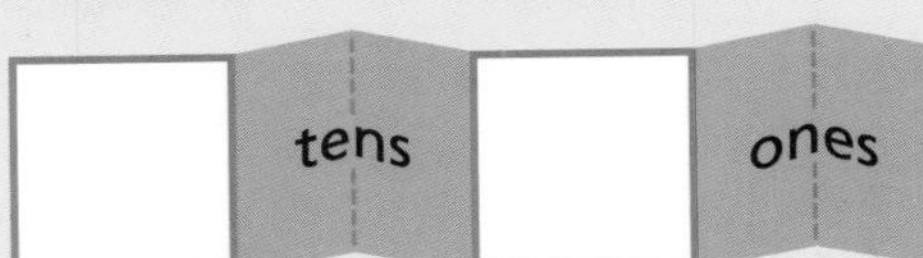

☐ tens ☐ ones

b. nine ones and three tens

☐ tens ☐ ones

3.3 Writing Tens and Ones, and Number Names

Read the number on each expander.

What do you notice?

When do you say the four ones in each number?

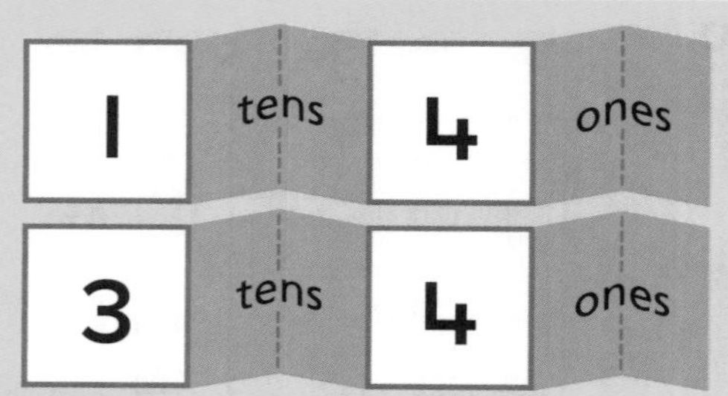

Think about how you would write these numbers in words. When would you write the four ones?

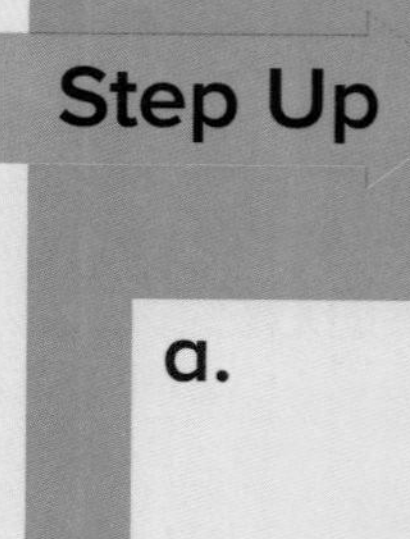

1. Look at the number of counters on and off the frames. Write the matching number on the expander. Then complete the number name.

a.

tens ones

twenty

b.

c.

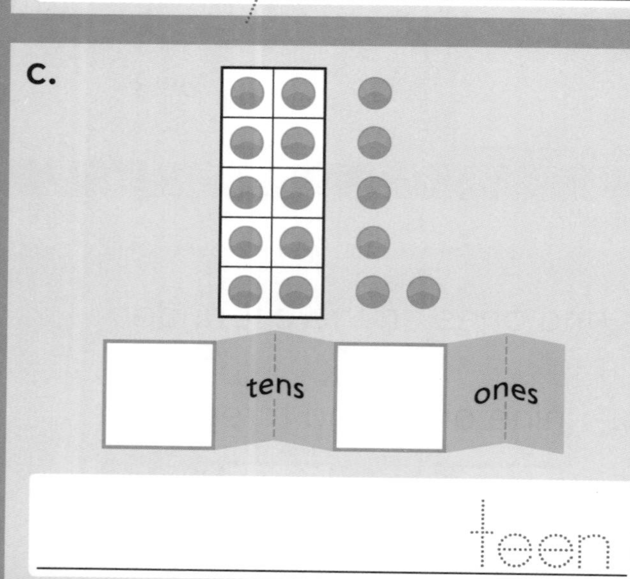

d.

2. Write the matching number on the expander.
Then write the number names.

a.

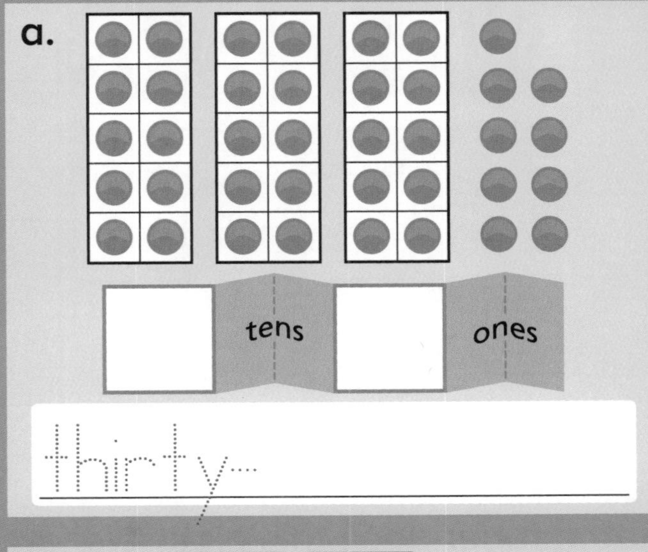

b.

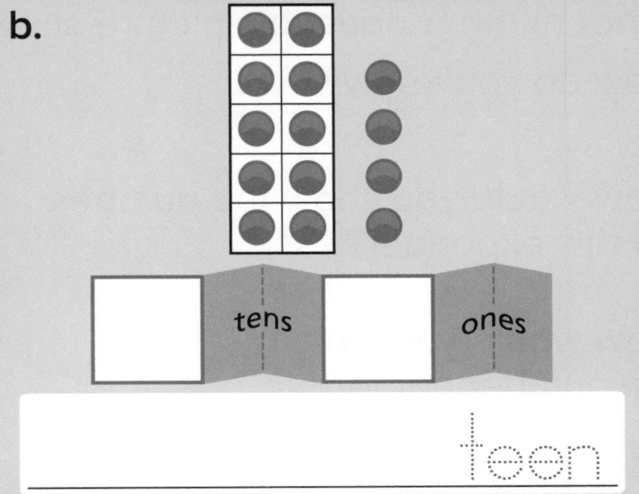

c.

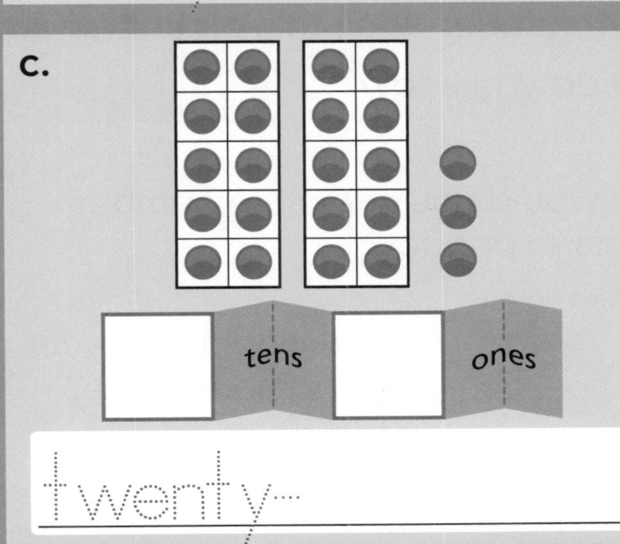

d.

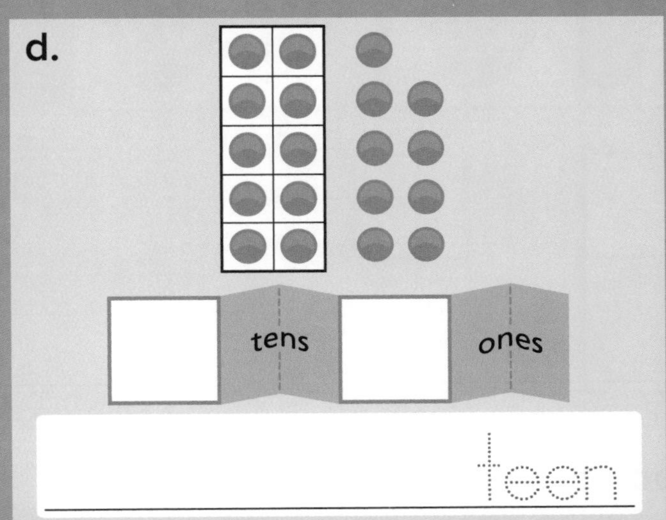

Step Ahead Read the number name.
Write the matching number on the expander.

a. **seventeen** tens ones

b. **sixty-three** tens ones

c. **twelve** tens ones

d. **ninety-two** tens ones

e. **seventy-two** tens ones

f. **fifty-seven** tens ones

3.4 Writing Tens and Ones (with Zeros)

What number does this picture show?
How do you know?

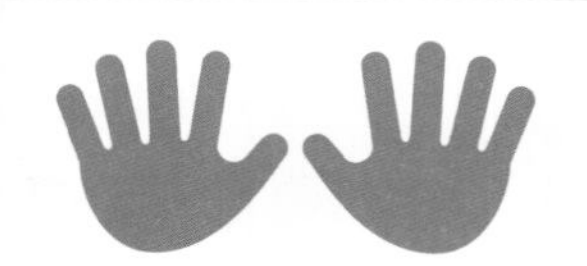
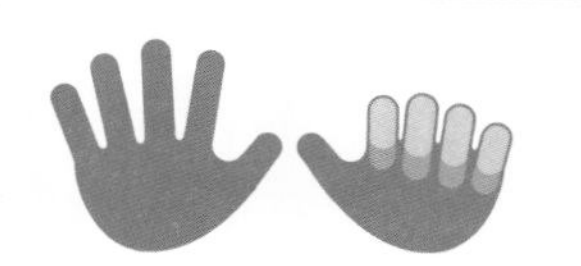

How would you show the number on this expander?

How would you write the number name?

____

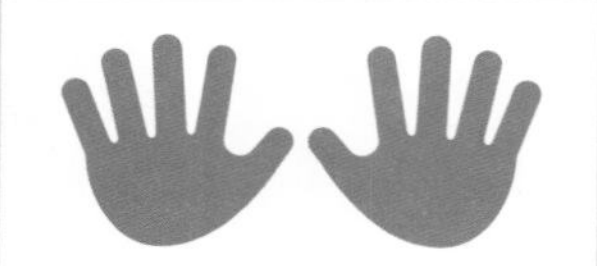

What number does this picture show?
How do you know?

How would you show the number on this expander?

____

How would you write the number name?

Look at these number names.

How many tens are in these numbers? How do you know?

ten eleven twelve thirteen fourteen fifteen
sixteen seventeen eighteen nineteen

How are these numbers different?

twenty thirty forty fifty
sixty seventy eighty ninety

Step Up Write the matching number of tens and ones on the expander. Then write the matching number name.

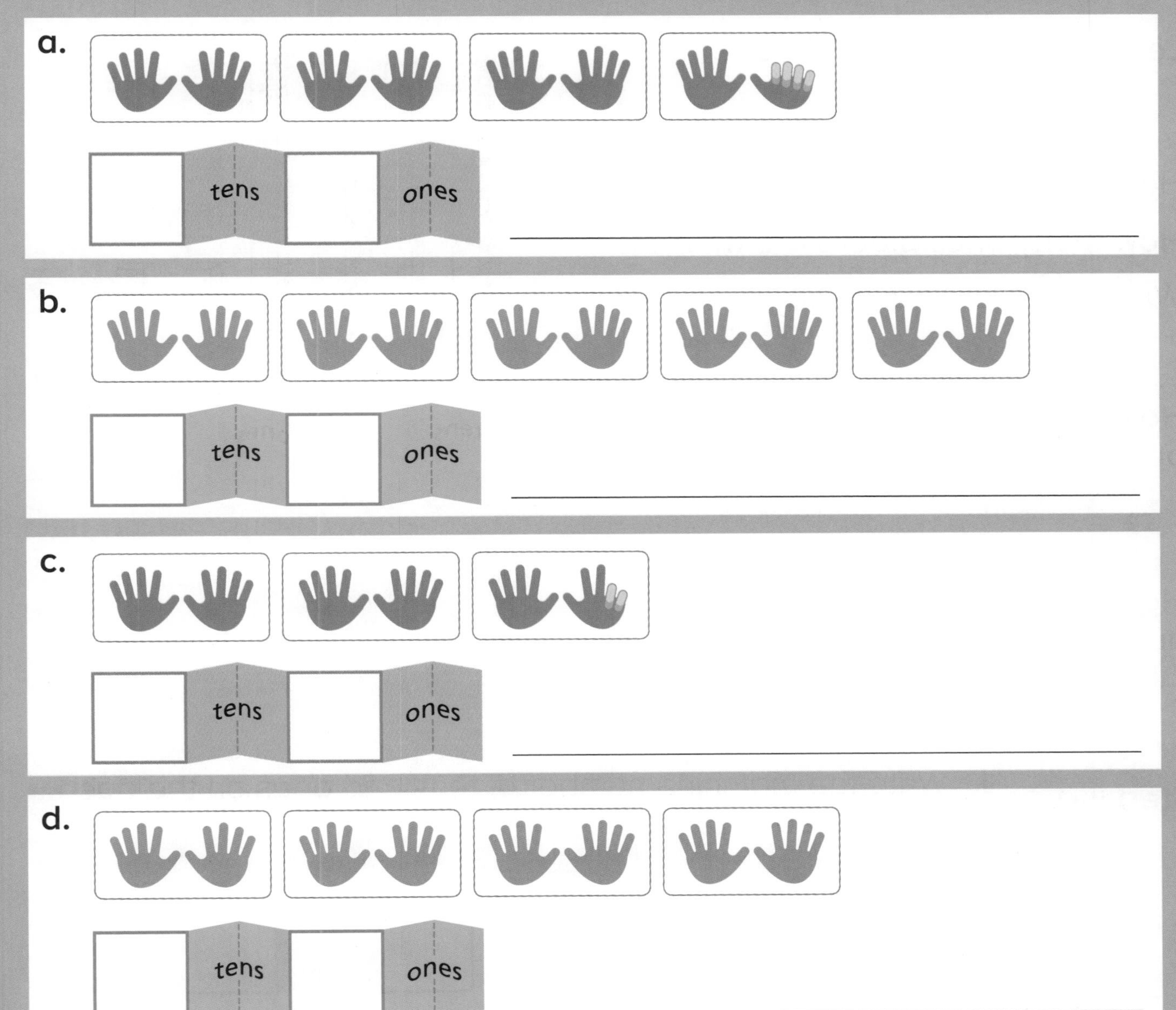

Step Ahead Look at the number of tens and ones. Write the matching number on the expander.

a. one ten and four ones

tens ones

b. eight tens and six ones

tens ones

3.5 Representing Tens and Ones

Look at this picture of blocks.

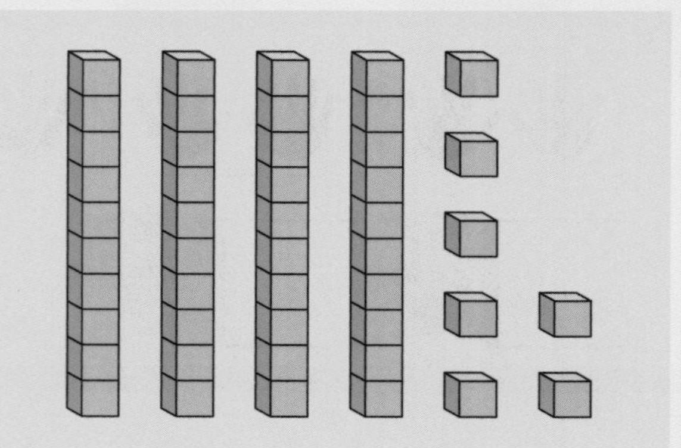

How many tens blocks are there?

How many ones blocks are there?

What number does it show?

How would you show the number on this open expander?

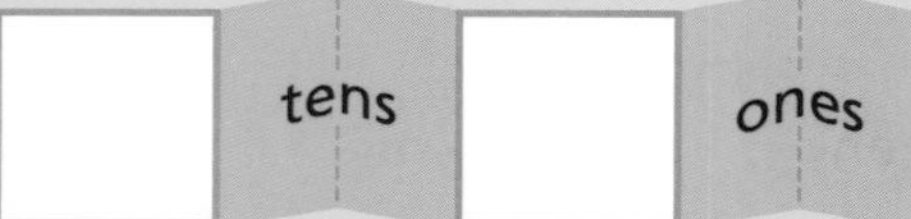

How would you show the same number on these expanders?

Step Up

1. Write the matching number of tens and ones on the open and closed expanders.

a.

tens

ones

b.

tens

ones

2. Color tens and ones to match the number on the expander.

a.

8 3

b.

1 4

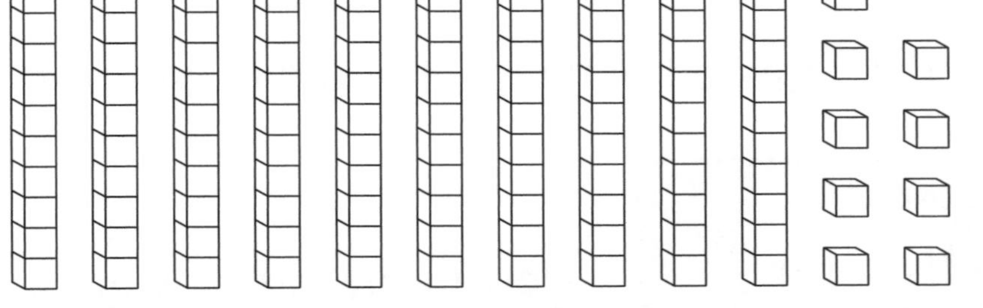

c.

6 0

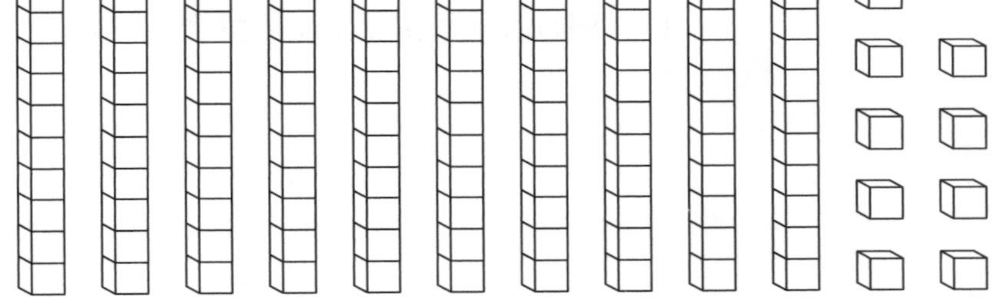

Step Ahead Write the number name to match each expander.

a. 9 4

b. 1 2

c. 3 6

3.6 Working with Ten as a Group

Look at these items. What do you notice?

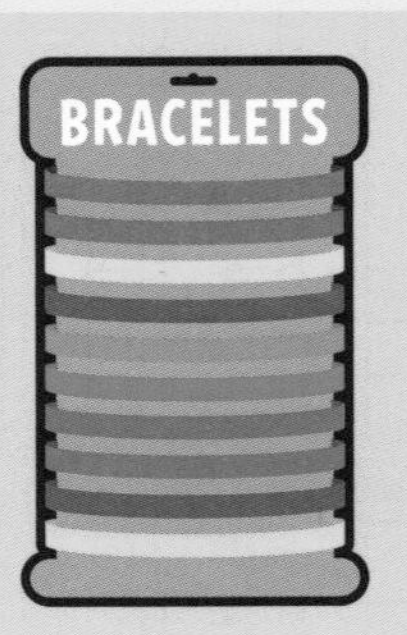

What are some other things that are in groups of 10?

How many marbles are in this pack?

How do you know?

How could you show 48 marbles?

I would use 4 packs of 10 plus 8 more marbles.

Step Up

1. Draw packs of 10 and some more marbles to match the number on the expander.

a.

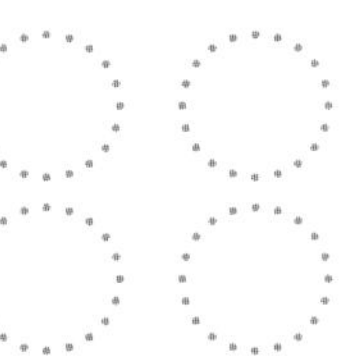

b.

2. Draw packs of 10 and some more marbles to match the number on the expander. Then write the number name.

a.

b.

c.

1 2

Step Ahead

Emily's teacher is making a name badge for each student in the class. There are 25 students in the class. The name badges are sold in packs of 10.

How many packs of badges will the teacher need to buy? Draw a picture to show your thinking.

3.7 Working with Tens and Ones (Dimes and Pennies)

Look at these coins.

How many pennies do you see?
How many cents is one penny worth?

How many dimes do you see?
How many cents is one dime worth?

What would you write on this expander to show the number of cents in total?

How do you know?

How would you show the same amount on these expanders?

What do you notice about the numbers on these expanders?

The expander shows the total number of cents.

Step Up **1.** Write the number of dimes and pennies.

There are ____ dimes and ____ pennies.

2. Write the number of dimes and pennies.
Then write the number of cents on the expanders.

a.

There are ____ dimes and ____ pennies.

[ ] tens [ ] ones

cents

b.

There is ____ dime and ____ pennies.

[ ] tens [ ] ones

[ ][ ] cents

c.

There are ____ dimes and ____ pennies.

[ ] tens [ ] ones

[ ][ ] cents

Step Ahead Write the total number of cents in words.

______________________________ cents

3.8 Introducing Time on the Hour (Analog Clocks)

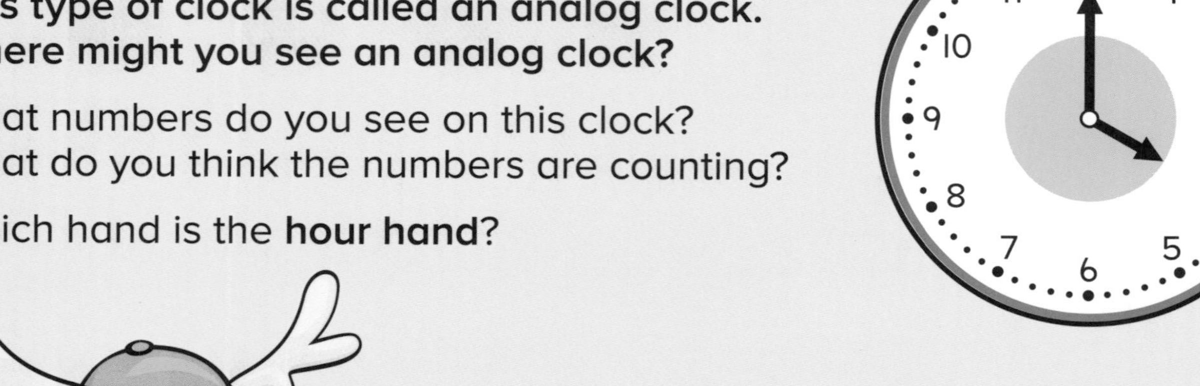

This type of clock is called an analog clock. Where might you see an analog clock?

What numbers do you see on this clock? What do you think the numbers are counting?

Which hand is the **hour hand**?

The short hand is the hour hand. It shows the name of the hour and counts the hours.

The long hand is called the **minute hand** because it counts the minutes.

When the minute hand is pointing to 12 it is the **start** of another hour.

This time is **on the hour** and is an **o'clock** time.

What time is the clock showing? How do you know?

Step Up **1.** Write each time.

a.

8:00 o'clock

b.

3:00 o'clock

c.

10:00 o'clock

2. The **minute** hand is the **long** hand. Draw the minute hand on each clock to show an hour time. Then write the time.

a.

2:00 o'clock

b.

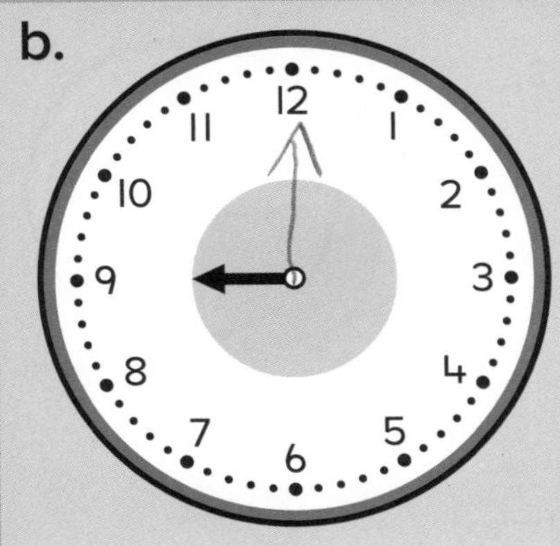

9:00 o'clock

c.

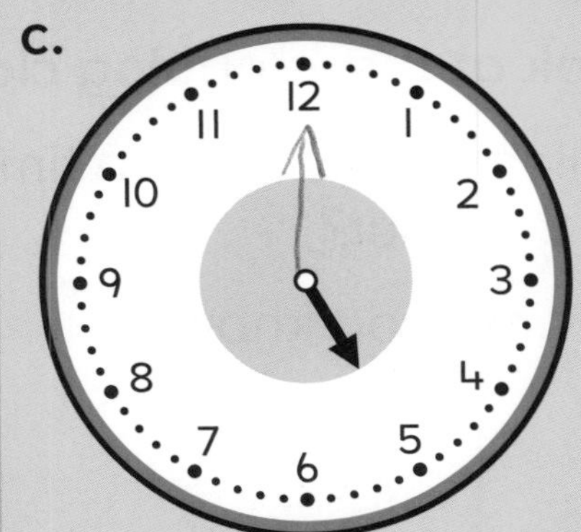

5:00 o'clock

d.

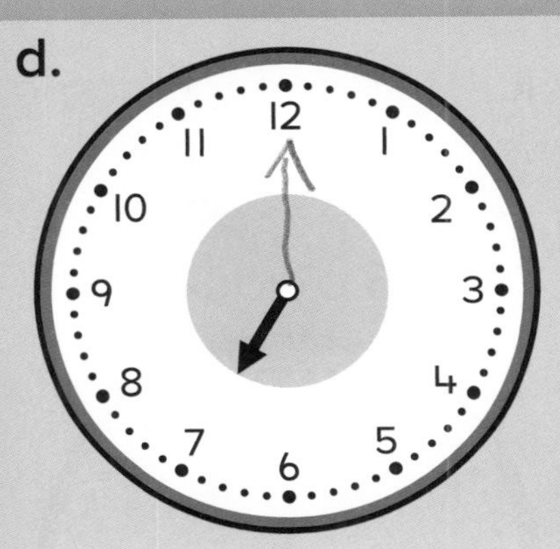

____ o'clock

e.

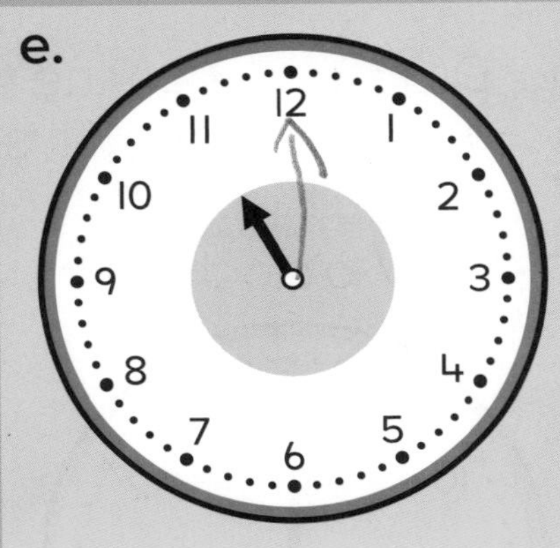

____ o'clock

f.

____ o'clock

Step Ahead Loop the clocks that show a time on the hour.

3.9 Working with Time on the Hour (Analog Clocks)

Look at these analog clocks.

Which clocks show a time on the hour?

How do you know?

What time does this clock show?

How do you know?

Step Up

1. Read the time. Draw a ◡ on the clock if it shows the same time. Draw a ⌒ on the clock if it shows a different time.

a. 3 o'clock

b. 7 o'clock

c. 5 o'clock

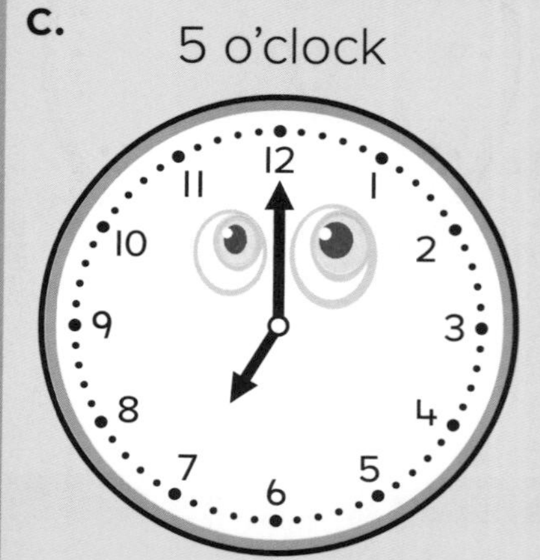

d. 2 o'clock

e. 6 o'clock

f. 10 o'clock

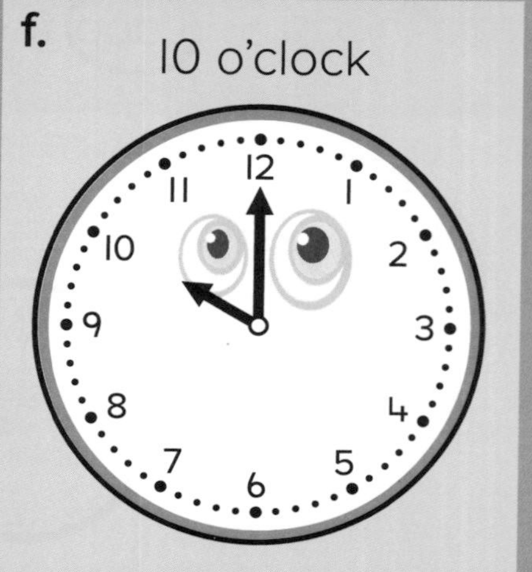

2. Draw hands on the clock to show the time.

a. 9 o'clock

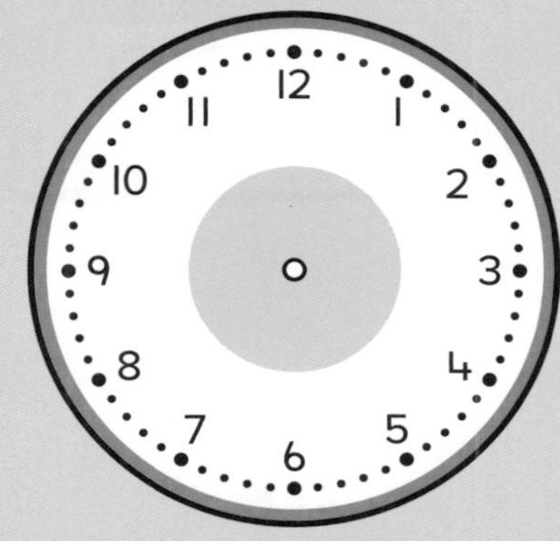

b. 5 o'clock

c. 1 o'clock

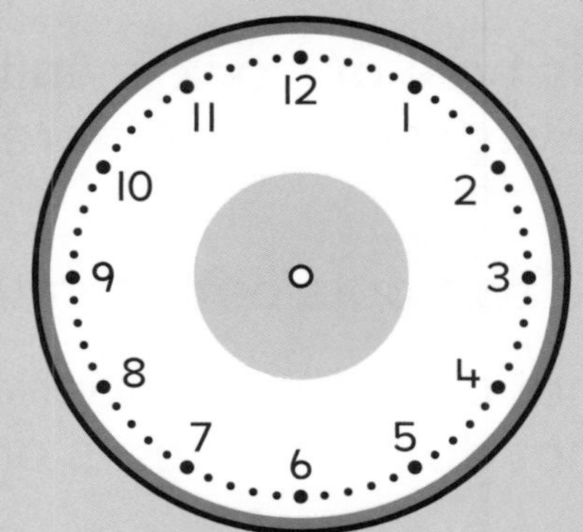

d. 11 o'clock

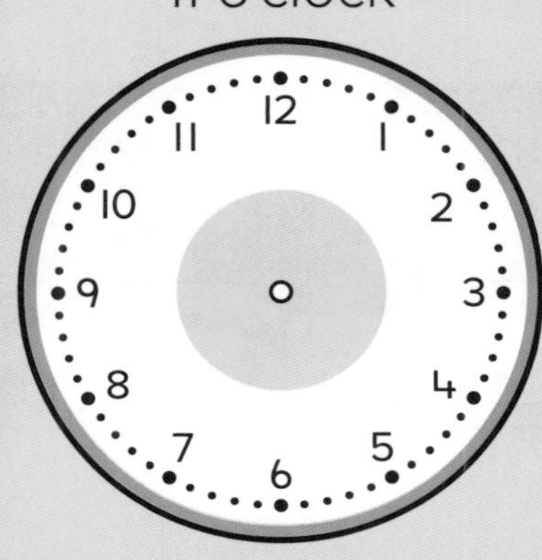

e. 6 o'clock

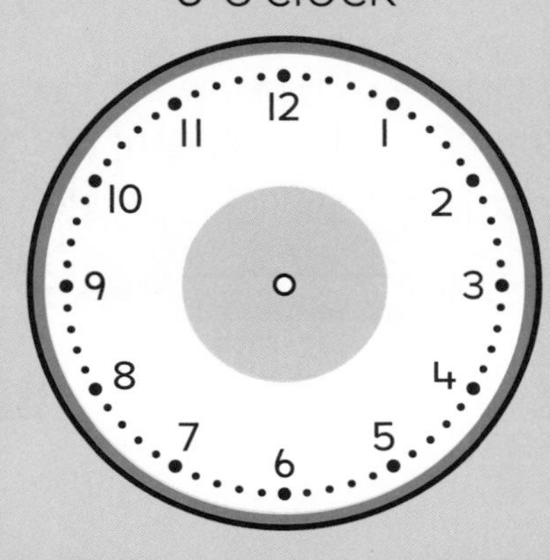

f. 4 o'clock

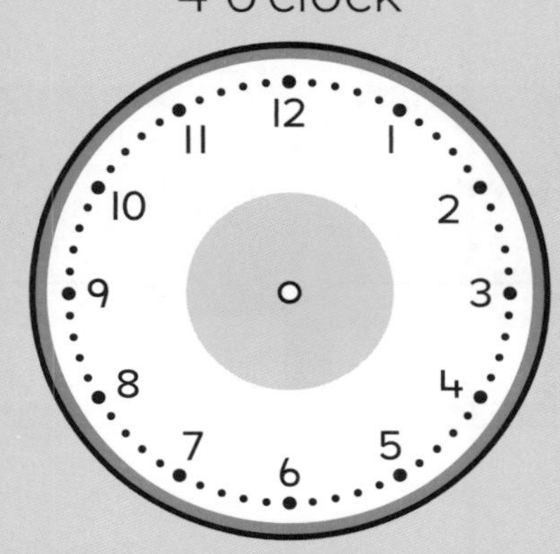

Step Ahead Complete these sentences to show what you would be doing at each of these morning times.

At 2 o'clock in the morning I am ______________________________

At 8 o'clock in the morning I am ______________________________

____

At 10 o'clock in the morning I am ______________________________

____

3.10 Reading Time on the Hour (Digital Clocks)

This type of clock is called a digital clock.
How is this clock different from an analog clock?

The two dots between the numbers is called a **colon**.

What does the number on the left side of the colon show?
What do the numbers on the right side show?

What do you know about the time on this clock?
What time is the clock showing?

Step Up

1. Draw a line to join each digital clock and each analog clock to a matching label.

1:00 8:00 5:00 9:00 3:00

8 o'clock 1 o'clock 3 o'clock 5 o'clock 9 o'clock

2. Draw lines to connect matching times.

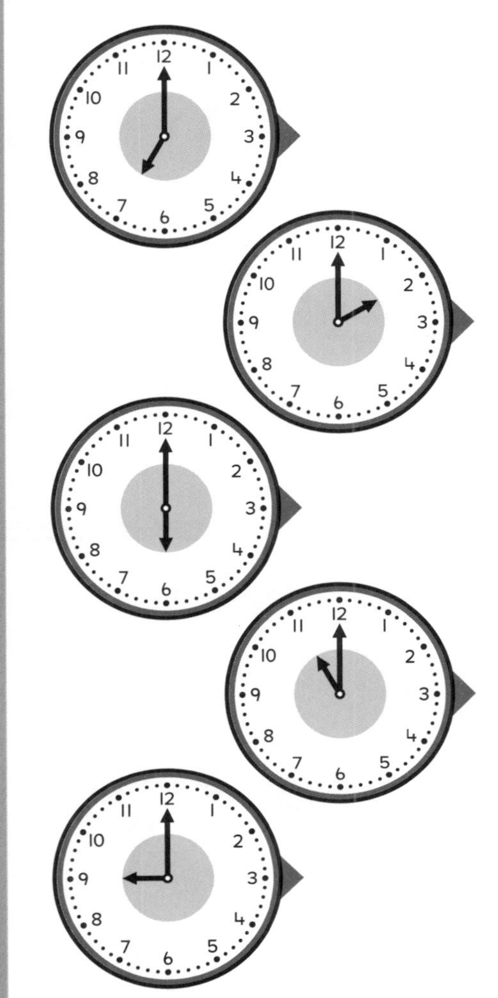

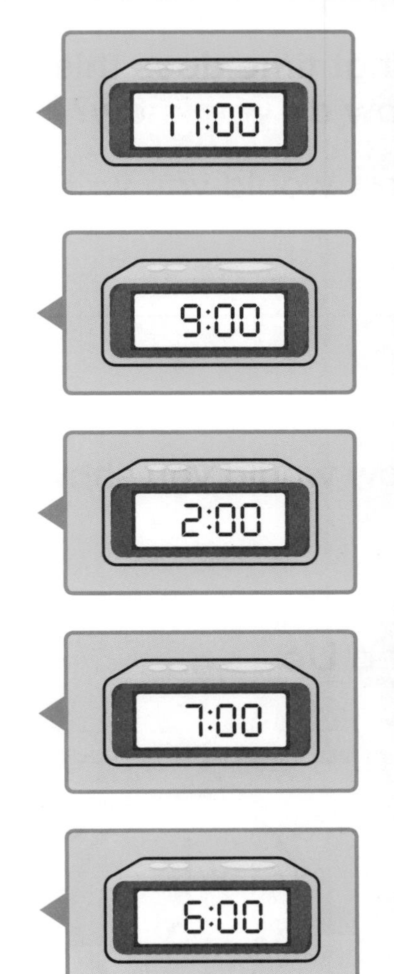

Step Ahead Write the time. Then complete the sentence.

a.

____ o'clock

One hour later will be ____ o'clock.

b.

____ o'clock

One hour later will be ____ o'clock.

c.

____ o'clock

One hour later will be ____ o'clock.

3.11 Reading and Writing Analog and Digital Times

What time does this clock show?
How do you know?

How would you write the time in words?

How would you show the same time on this digital clock?

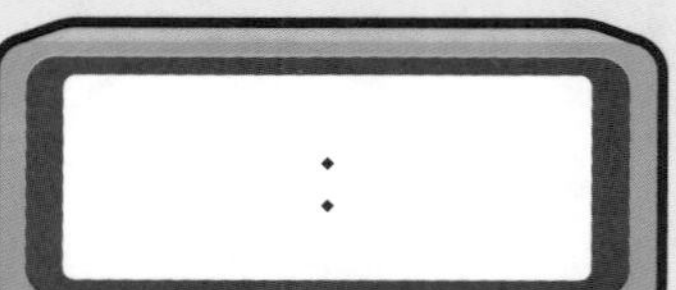

Step Up 1. Write each time on the digital clock.

a.

b.

c.

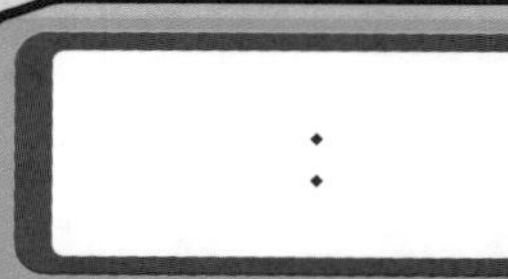

d.

e.

f.

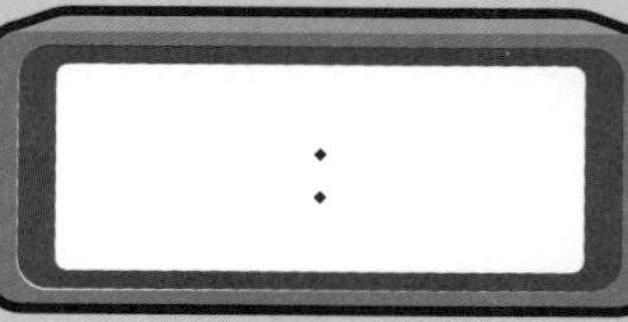

2. Draw the clock hands to show these times.

a. 9 o'clock

b. 10 o'clock

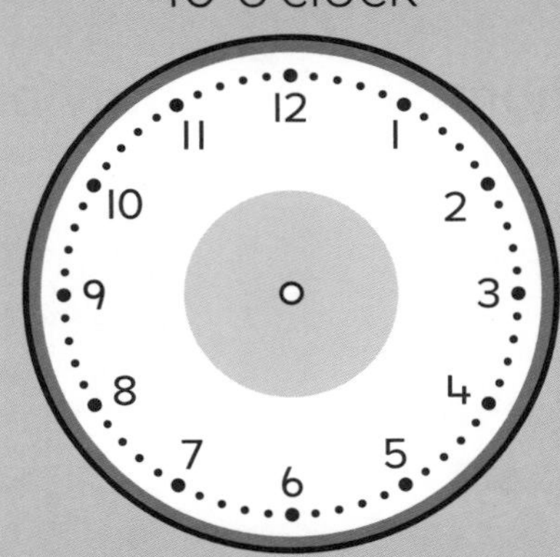

c. 5 o'clock

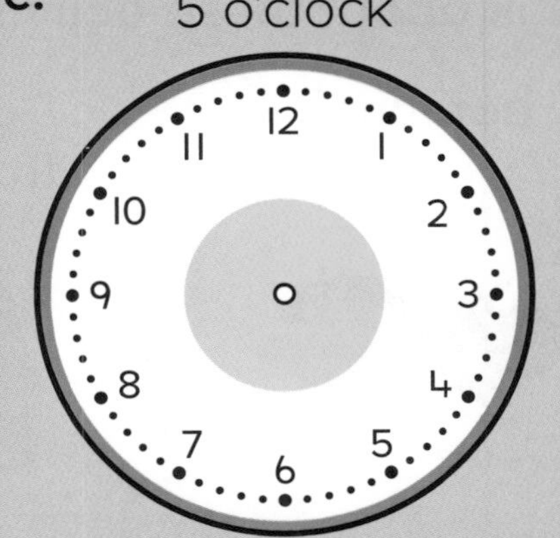

3. Write these times on the digital clocks.

a. 6 o'clock

b. 12 o'clock

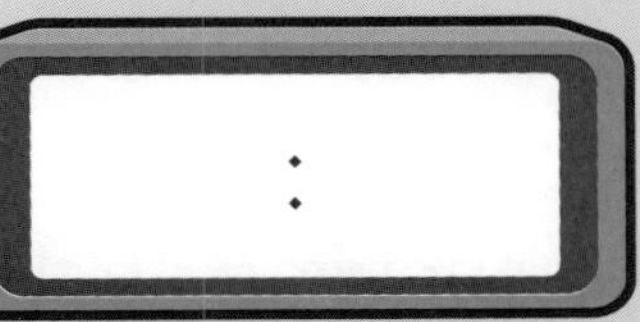

c. 3 o'clock

d. 11 o'clock

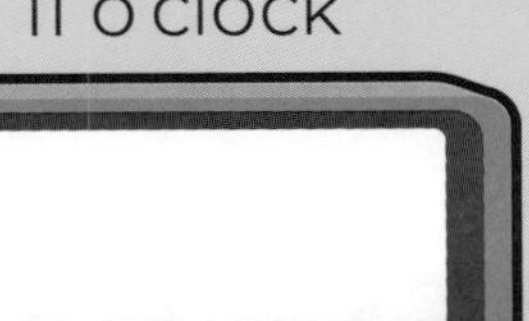

Step Ahead

Look at the analog clock.
Write the time that is **one hour before** and **one hour after**.

one hour before

one hour after

3.12 Sequencing Events

Think about these activities.

eat lunch	go home from school	play outside	wake up
			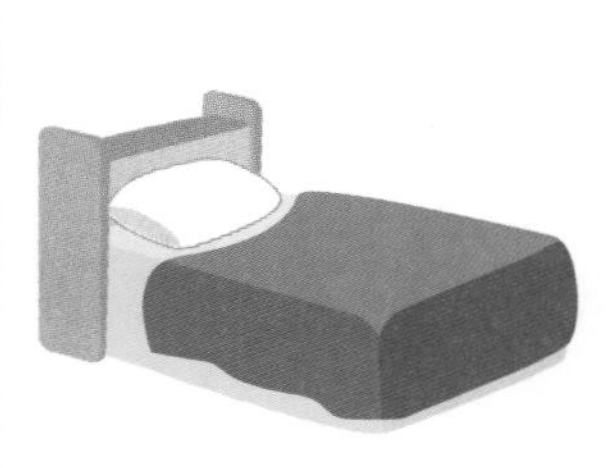

Which activity happens at about twelve o'clock?

Which activity happens after that?

Which happens before?

At what times would the other activities happen?

What time is showing on this clock? How do you know?

What hour is just before this hour?

What hour is just after this hour?
How do you know?

Step Up

1. Think about these four **morning** times.
Write them in order from the time that happens **first** to the time that happens **last**.

11 o'clock

3 o'clock

2 o'clock

7 o'clock

first

____

____

____

____

last

2. Look at the diary below.
Write these times in the story so that it makes sense.

3 o'clock	9 o'clock	5 o'clock	7 o'clock	11 o'clock

Monday

Today I woke up at ________________ and had breakfast. I rode my bike to school and got ready to start class at ________________. After our morning reading and sharing session, we started math at ________________. I left school about ________________ and rode straight home.

At ________________ I went to soccer training.

Step Ahead Write something that you do at 8 o'clock in the morning and something that you do at 8 o'clock at night.

At 8 o'clock in the morning ________________

____

At 8 o'clock at night ________________

____

4.1 Developing Subtraction Language

What is happening in this picture?

How many hens can you see?

How many hens are leaving the pen?

How many hens will be left in the pen? How do you know?

Step Up

1. Write the number of hens. **Cross out** the hens that run away. Write the number of hens that are left.

a.

8 hens in total. **3** run away. ____ hens are left.

b.

9 hens in total. **2** run away. ____ hens are left.

2. Write the number of hens. **Cross out** the hens that run away. Write the number of hens that are left.

a.

____ hens in total. **3** run away. ____ hens are left.

b.

____ hens in total. **4** run away. ____ hens are left.

Step Ahead a. Write some numbers to complete a subtraction story.

____ hens in total. ____ run away. ____ hens are left.

b. Draw a picture to match.

4.2 Using Subtraction Language

What is happening in this picture?

How many muffins can you see?

How many muffins did Little Fox take?

How many muffins are left on the tray?

Step Up

1. Write the number taken (X).
   Then write the number that are left.

a.

5 take ____ = ____

b.

6 take ____ = ____

c.

7 take ____ = ____

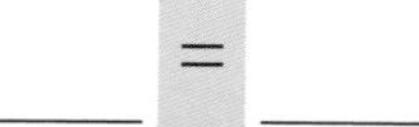

d.

9 take ____ = ____

2. Cross out muffins to match the sentence. Then write the number that are left.

a.

9 take 2 = ____

b.

10 take 4 = ____

c.

8 take 3 = ____

d.

12 take 5 = ____

Step Ahead

Look at the picture and the number sentence.

Loop the numbers that do not match the picture.

6 take 2 = 4

Working with the Subtraction Symbol (–)

Look at this subtraction sentence.

7 – 2 = 5

Read these stories.

7 birds in all.
2 **fly away**. 5 are left.

7 cakes **take away** 2 is 5.

There were 7 hens. 2 **run away**. There are 5 left.

How does each story match the subtraction sentence?

What is another story that matches the subtraction sentence?

What does "–" mean?

What does each number in the sentence show?

Step Up 1. Complete each subtraction sentence.

a.

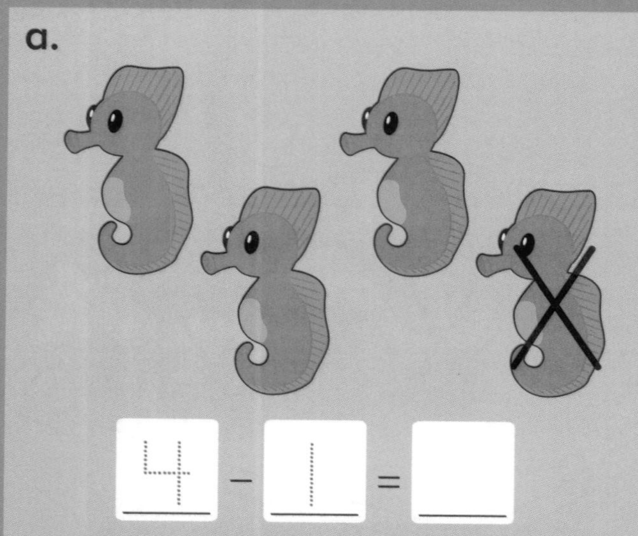

b.

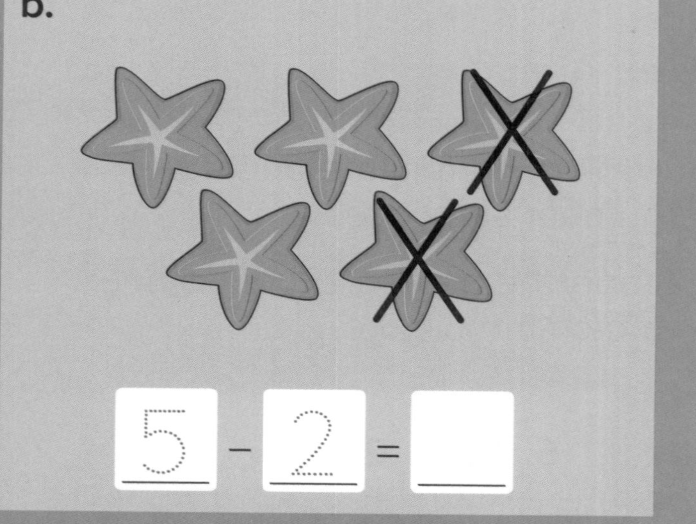

2. Write the subtraction sentence to match the picture.

a.

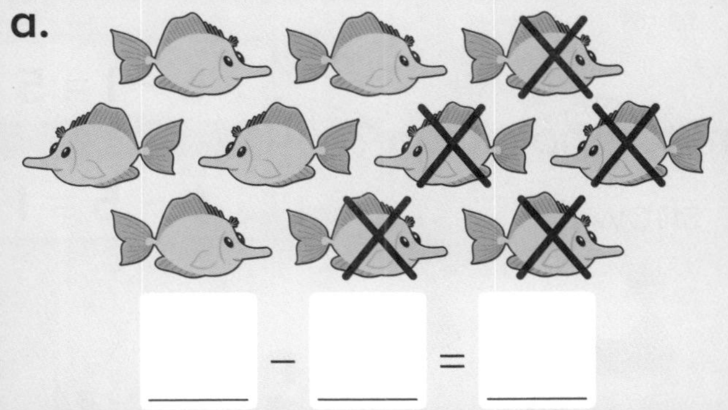

___ – ___ = ___

b.

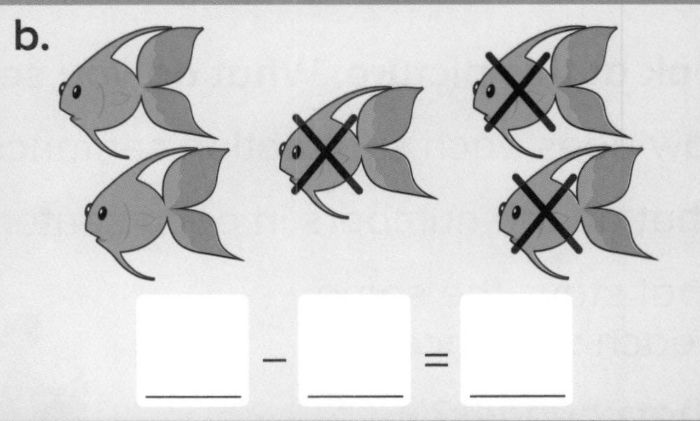

___ – ___ = ___

c.

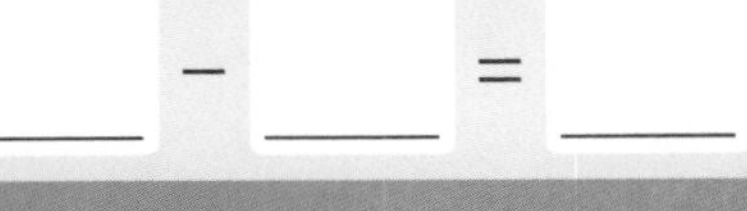

___ – ___ = ___

d.

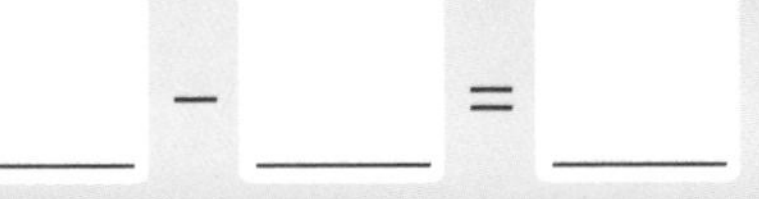

___ – ___ = ___

e.

___ – ___ = ___

f.

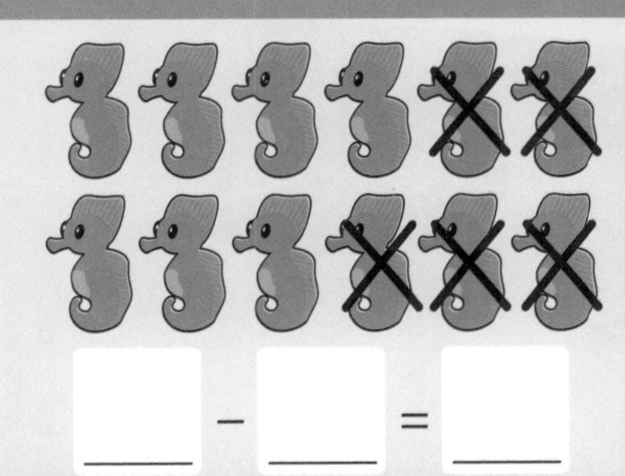

___ – ___ = ___

Step Ahead Look at these subtraction sentences.
Write numbers to show the possible solutions.

6 – ___ = ___   6 – ___ = ___   6 – ___ = ___   6 – ___ = ___

6 – ___ = ___   6 – ___ = ___   6 – ___ = ___

4.4 Writing Related Subtraction Sentences

Look at this picture. What do you see?

How does each subtraction sentence match the picture?

What do the numbers in each sentence show?

What stays the same in each sentence?

What changes?

6 – 1 = 5

6 – 5 = 1

Step Up 1. Write numbers to match each picture.

a.

___ frogs in total	___ frogs in total
___ frogs are out	___ frogs are in
___ frogs are in	___ frogs are out
7 – 2 = ___	7 – 5 = ___

b.

___ sheep in total	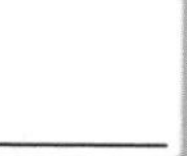 ___ sheep in total
___ sheep are out	___ sheep are in
 ___ sheep are in	 ___ sheep are out
9 – 4 = ___	9 – 5 = ___

2. Write the missing numbers.

a.

5 − 1 = ____

5 − 4 = ____

b.

8 − 5 = ____

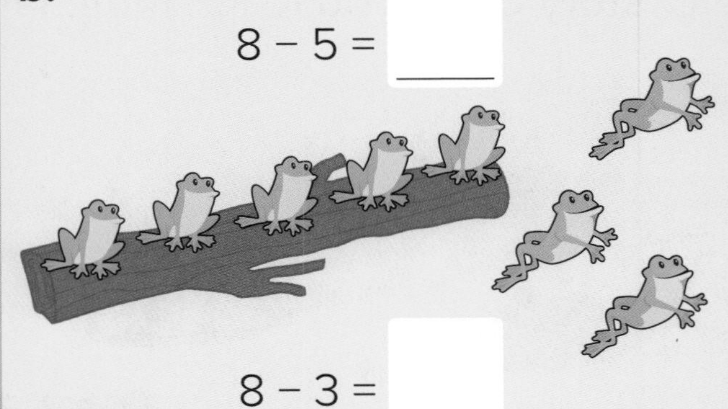

8 − 3 = ____

c.

12 − 9 = ____

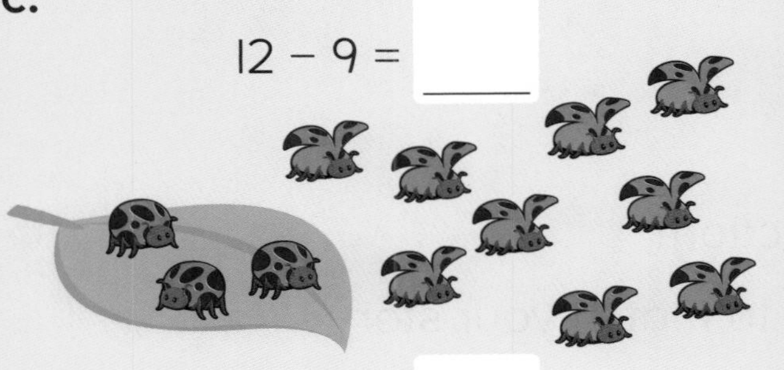

12 − 3 = ____

d.

11 − 4 = ____

11 − 7 = ____

Step Ahead Draw a subtraction picture.
Then write two subtraction sentences to match.

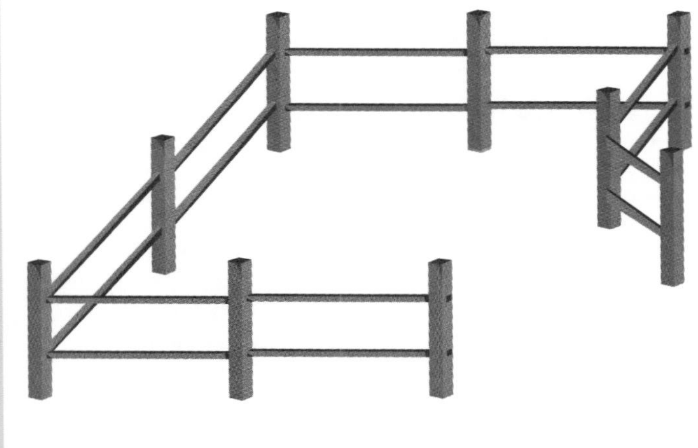

____ − ____ = ____

____ − ____ = ____

4.5 Solving Word Problems Involving Addition and Subtraction

What story could you tell to match this picture?

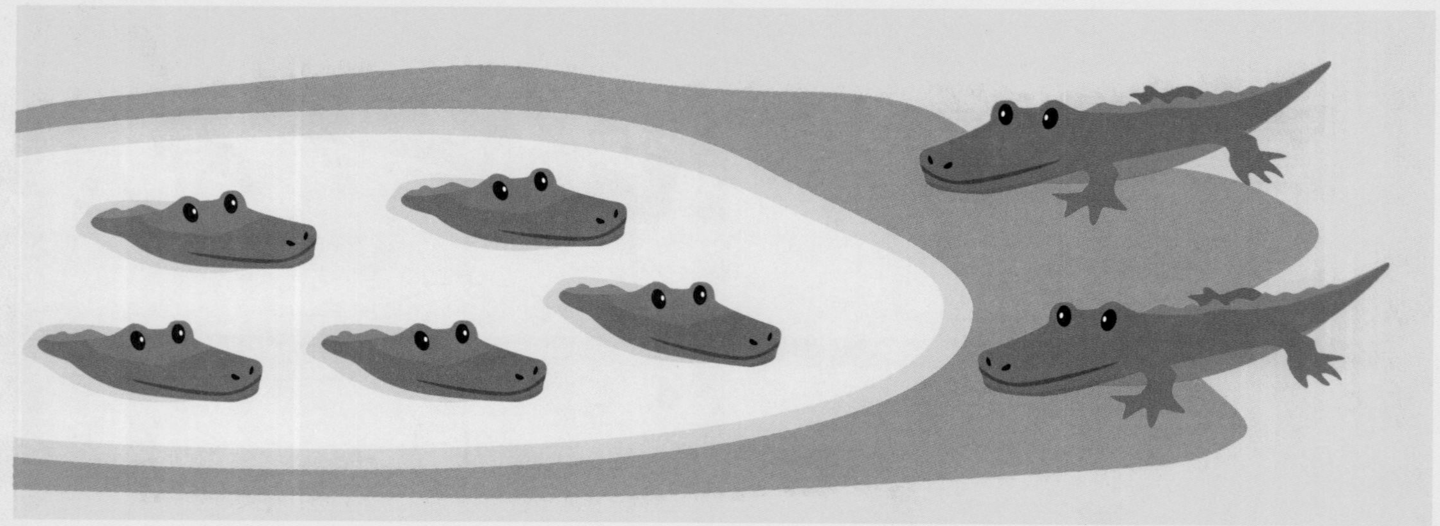

Does your story use addition or subtraction?

What number sentences can you write to match your story?

Step Up

1. Draw a picture to show the story. Then write a matching number sentence.

6 apples are on the tree.
4 apples are on the ground.
How many apples in all?

2. Draw a picture and write a number sentence to match the story.

a. There are 7 marbles in a bag.
2 of the marbles are blue.
The other marbles are red.
How many marbles are red?

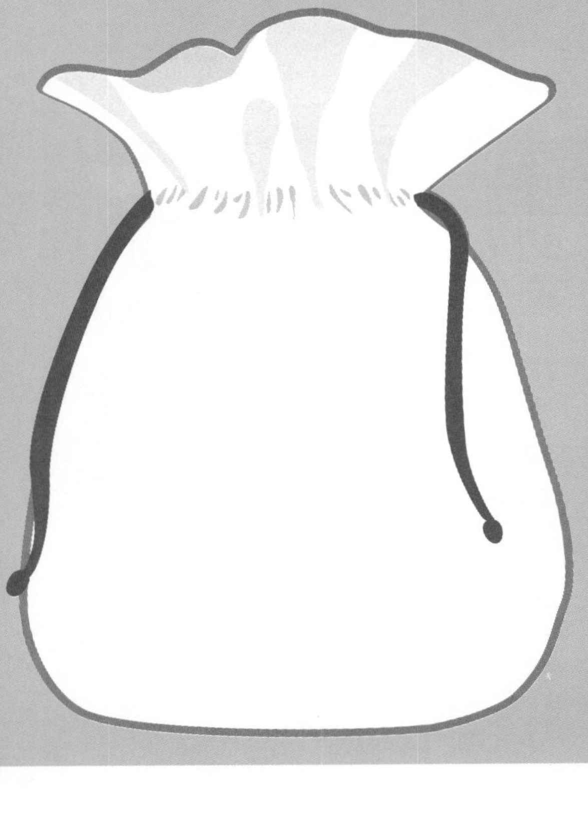

____

b. There are 11 fish in the tank.
4 fish are hiding.
How many fish can you see?

____

Step Ahead Color + or – to describe how you would solve each problem.

a.	There are 4 red balloons and 3 green balloons. How many in all?	+	–
b.	There were 7 berries. Someone ate 2 of them. How many berries are left?	+	–
c.	There were 11 spaceships in the sky. Then 3 landed. How many are still flying?	+	–
d.	Five friends are playing soccer. Four more friends join them. How many friends are now playing?	+	–

4.6 Writing Addition and Subtraction Number Sentences

Look at this picture.

What addition stories could you write?
What subtraction stories could you write?

Step Up

a. Write an addition story to match the picture on page 90.
Then write a number sentence to match.

b. Write a subtraction story to match the picture on page 90.
Then write a number sentence to match.

Step Ahead

Draw a picture that shows this fact.

7 – 6 = 1

4.7 Identifying Full and Empty

How would you describe the number of people in each car?

Which car is full? Which car is empty?

Which car is neither full nor empty? How do you know?

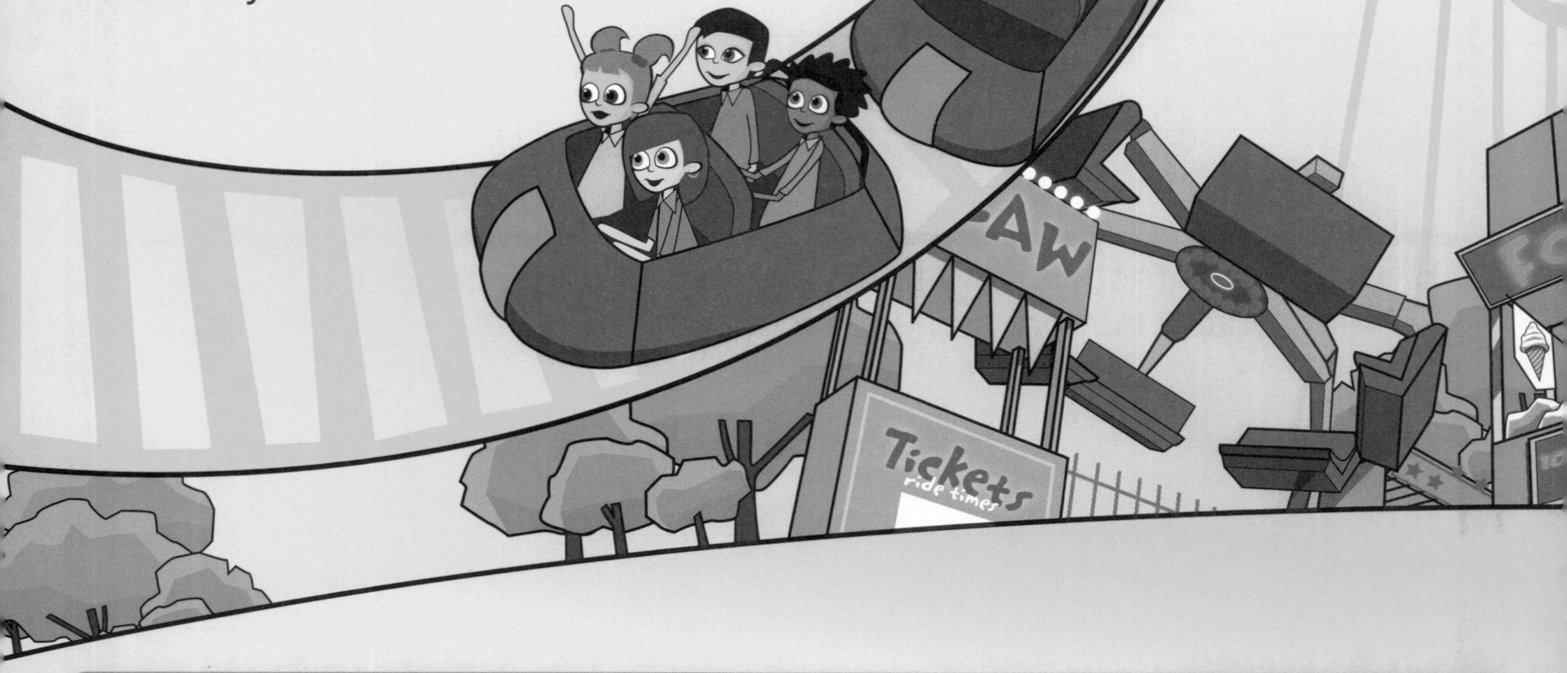

Step Up 1. Draw lines to connect each picture to a matching label.

full

empty

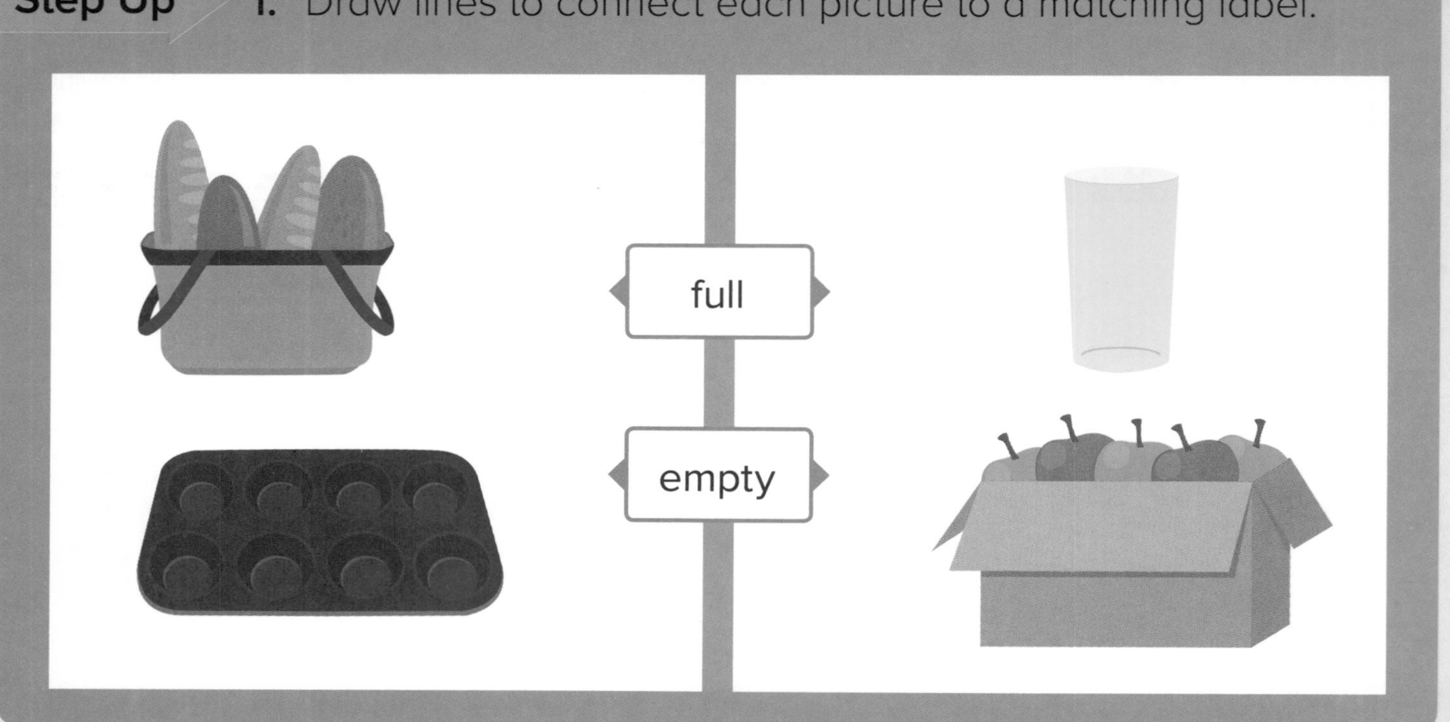

2. Write **full** or **empty** for each of these.

a.

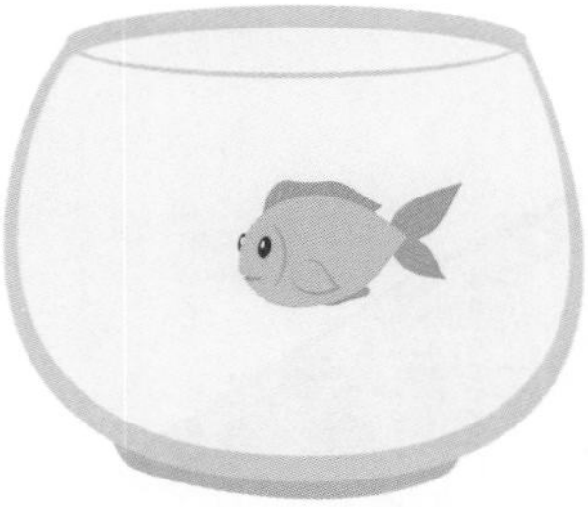

b.

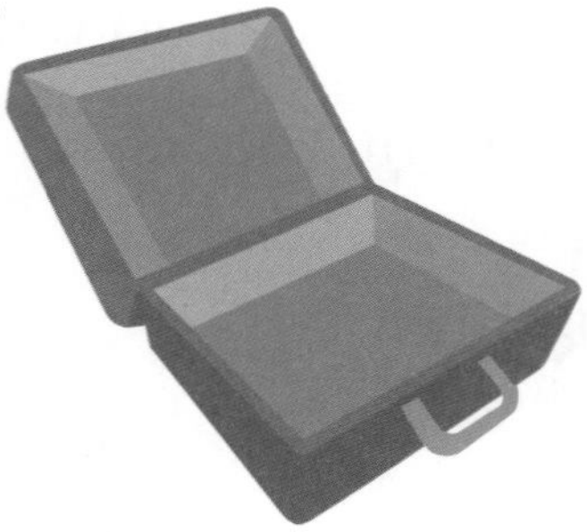

c.

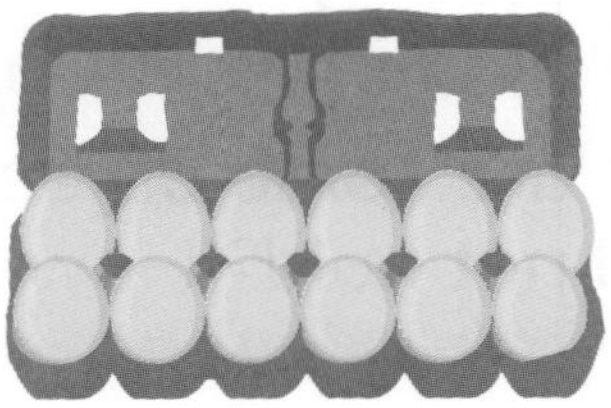

d.

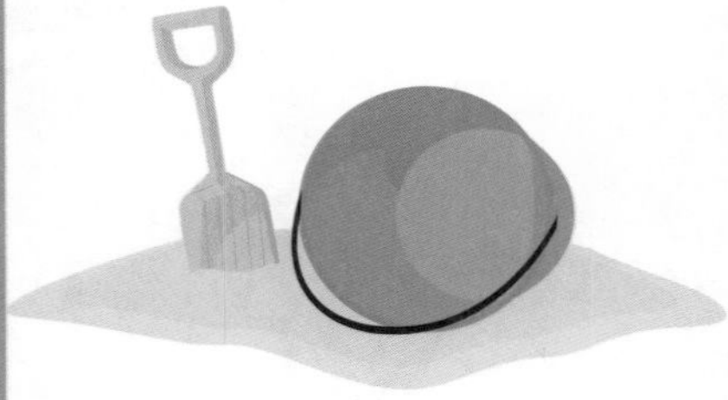

e.

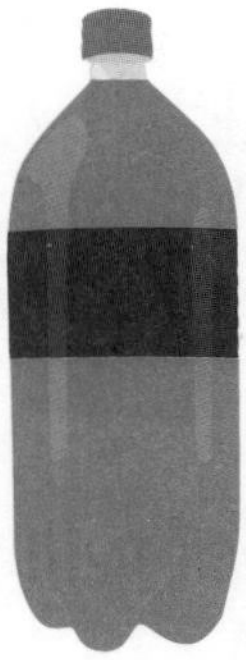

f.

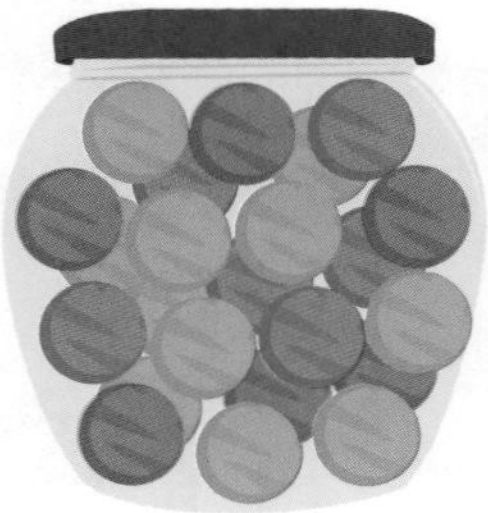

Step Ahead Color each container to match the label.

full

almost empty

half full

almost full

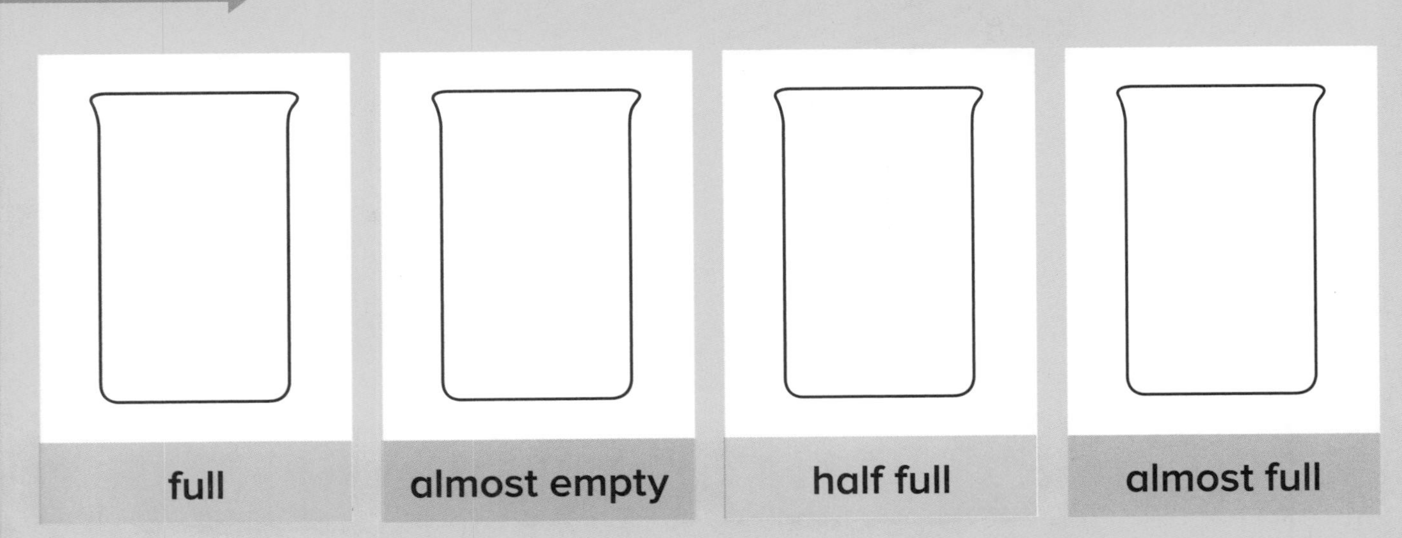

4.8 Exploring Capacity

A regular shoebox was found hidden in an old house.

What are some objects that it might hold?

What are some objects that it could **not** hold? How do you know?

Step Up 1. Loop the objects that **will not** fit in this box.

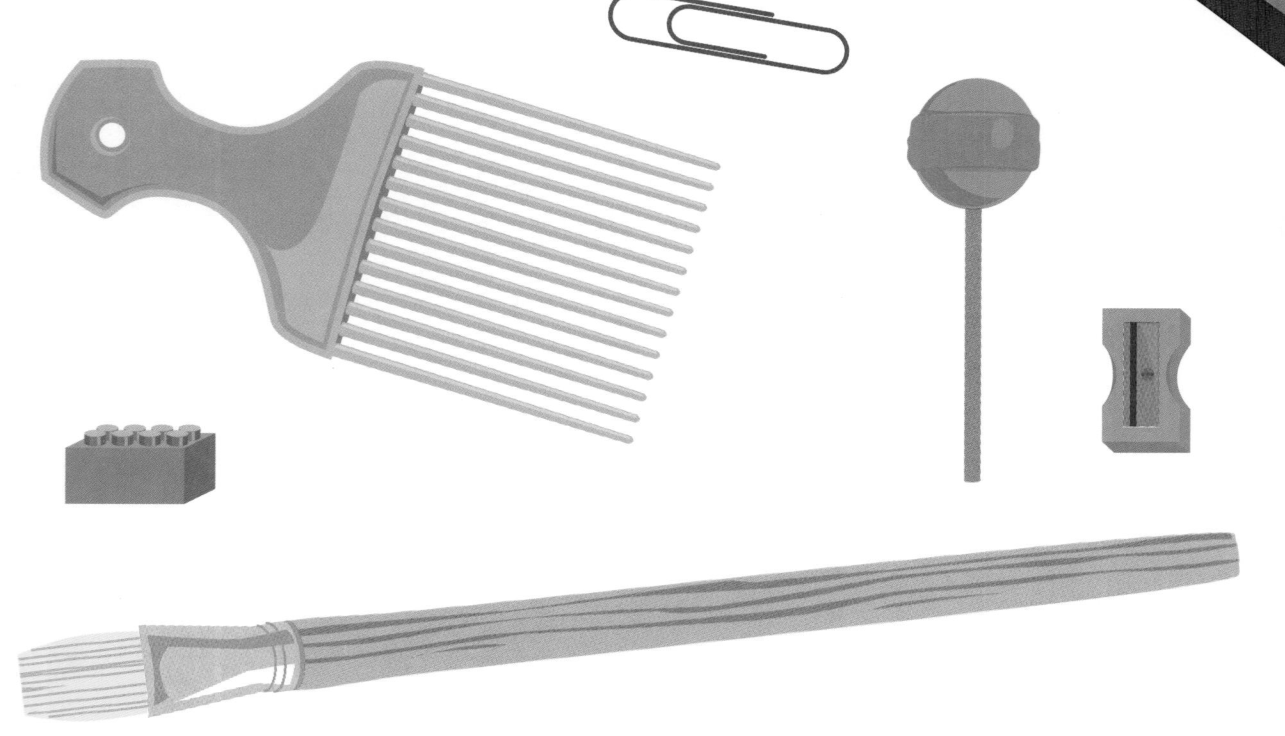

2. Loop the objects that **will** fit in the box on page 94.

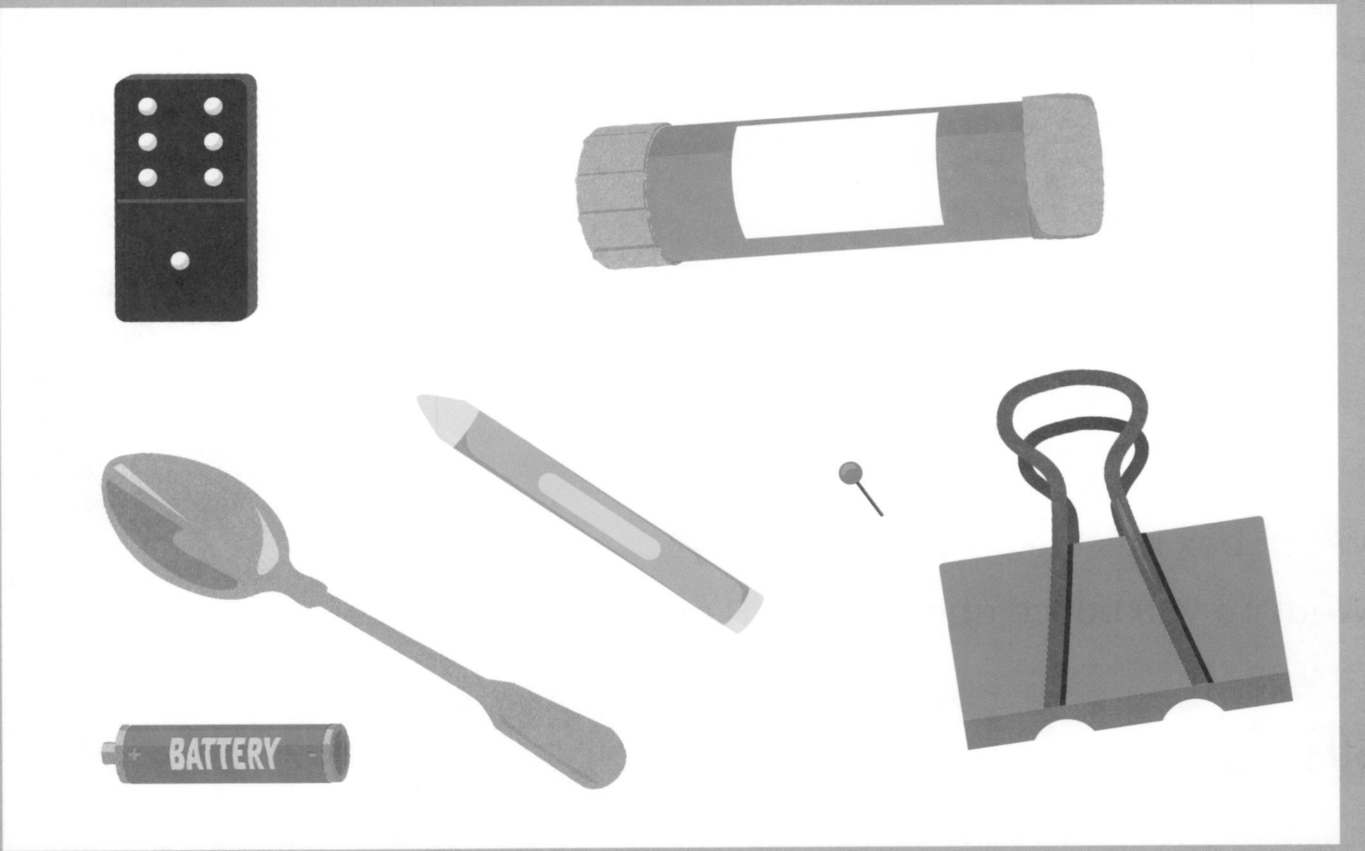

Step Ahead Draw an object that **will** fit in your school bag but **not** in a small cereal box.

4.9 Working with Capacity

Describe the capacity of each box.

Capacity is the amount that something can hold.

Which box has the greatest capacity?

What do you notice about Boxes B and C?

Step Up 1. Write the capacity of each box.

a.

_______ cans

b.

_______ cans

c.

_______ cans

d.

_______ cans

e.

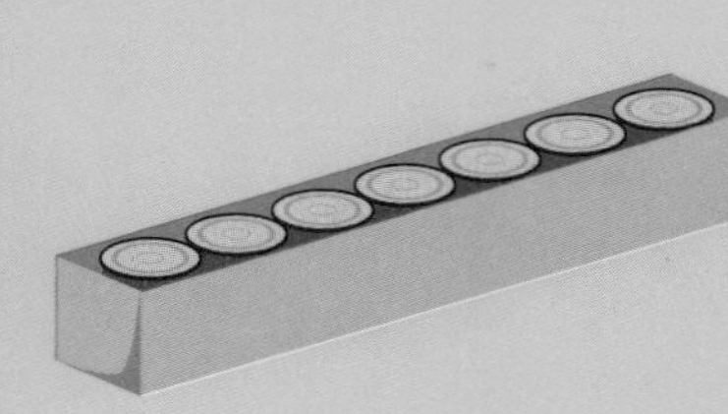

_______ cans

f.

_______ cans

2. For each pair, loop the box that has the **greater** capacity.

a.

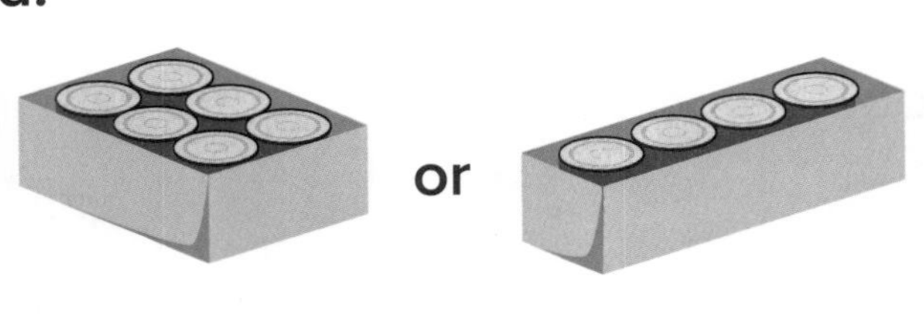

b.

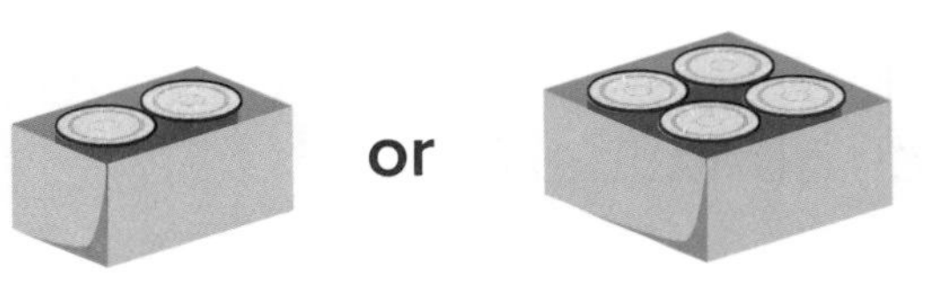

c.

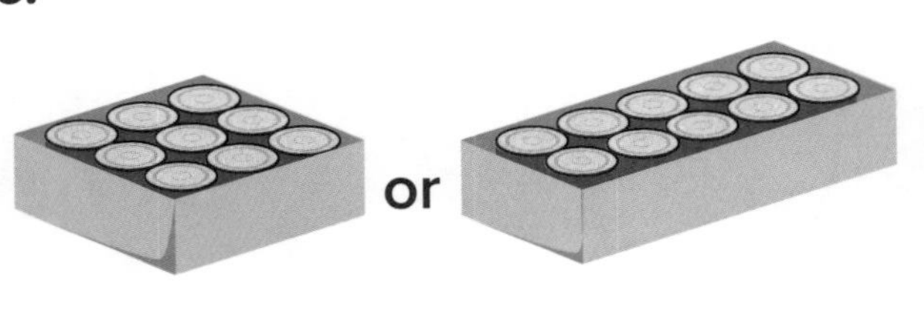

d.

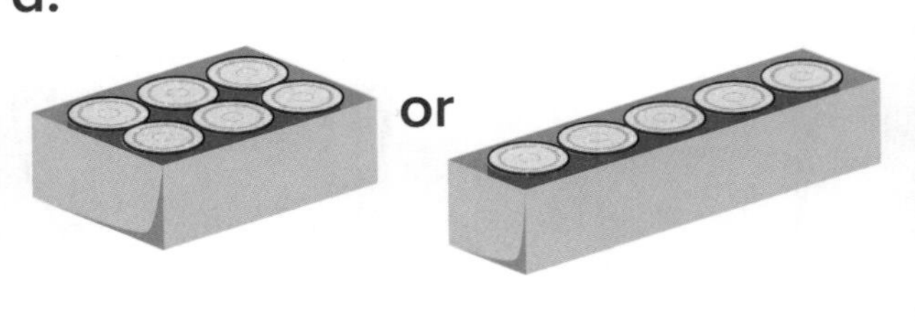

3. Write the boxes below in order from **least** capacity to **greatest** capacity.

__________ __________ __________ __________

Step Ahead List some other objects that you could use to measure the capacity of a shoebox.

____

____

____

____

4.10 Measuring Capacity with Non-Standard Units

Look at these containers.

How could you use the scoop to figure out the capacity of each container?

How could you record the results?

What else could you use to measure the capacity of each container?

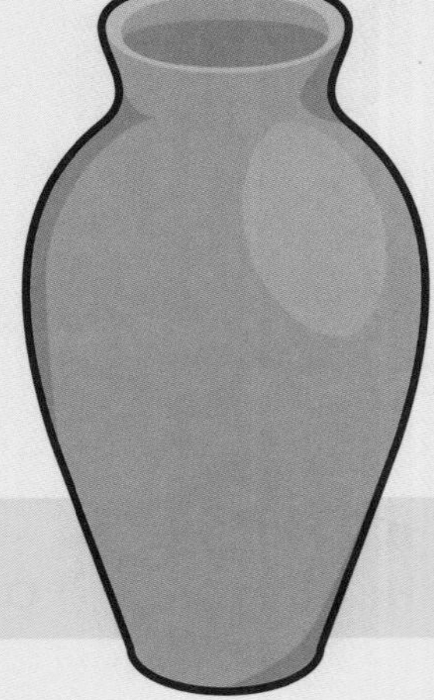

Step Up 1. Write the number of scoops for each container.

Container	Number of scoops of water
a.	_______ scoops
b.	_______ scoops
c.	_______ scoops
d.	_______ scoops

2. Write the number of scoops for these containers.

a. 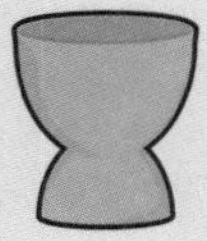 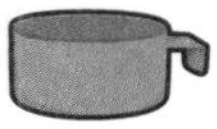 ________ scoop

b. 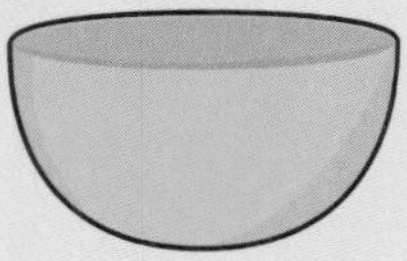 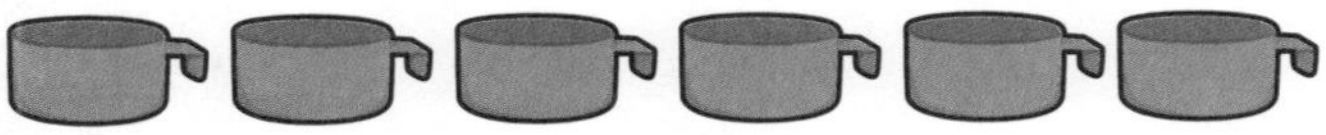 ________ scoops

c. 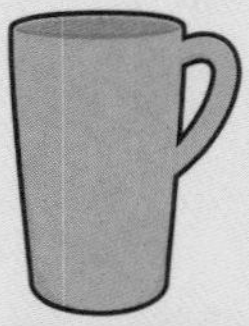 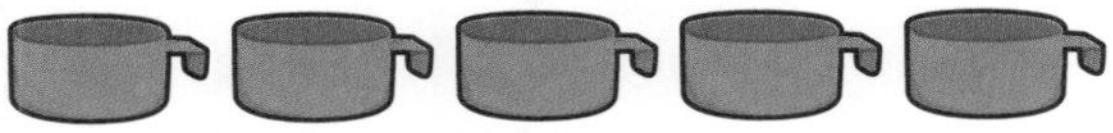 ________ scoops

3. Compare these containers from Questions 1 and 2. For each pair, loop the container that holds the most.

a. 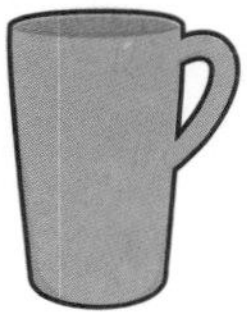 or

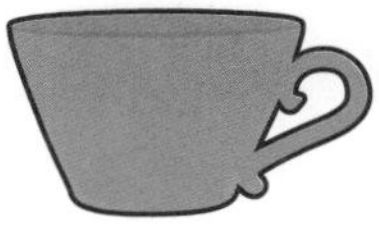

b. 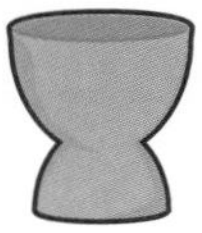 or

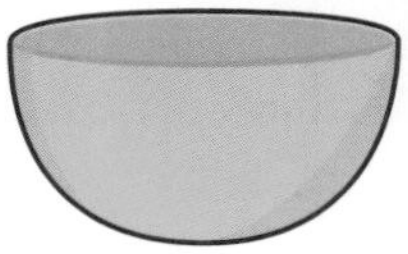

c. 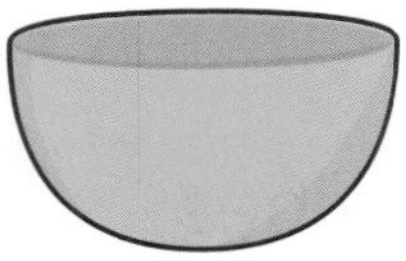 or

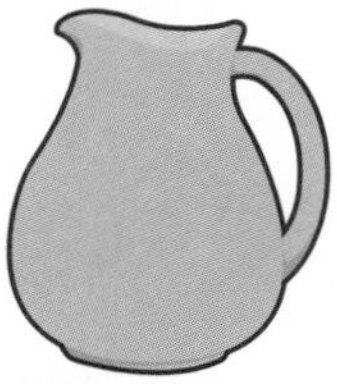

d. 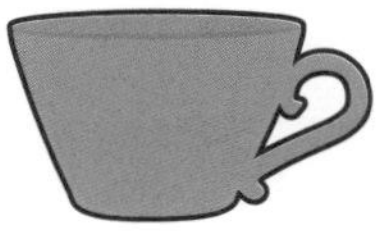 or

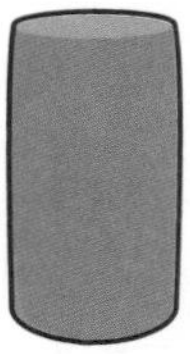

Step Ahead Look at the containers in Questions 1 and 2.

a. Shade the ⬭ beside the number of scoops it would take to fill two .

⬭ 5 ⬭ 8 ⬭ 6 ⬭ 10

b. Shade the ⬭ beside the number of scoops it would take to fill two .

⬭ 2 ⬭ 6 ⬭ 5 ⬭ 3

4.11 Using a Pan Balance to Compare Weight

Does the ball weigh more or less than the book? How do you know?

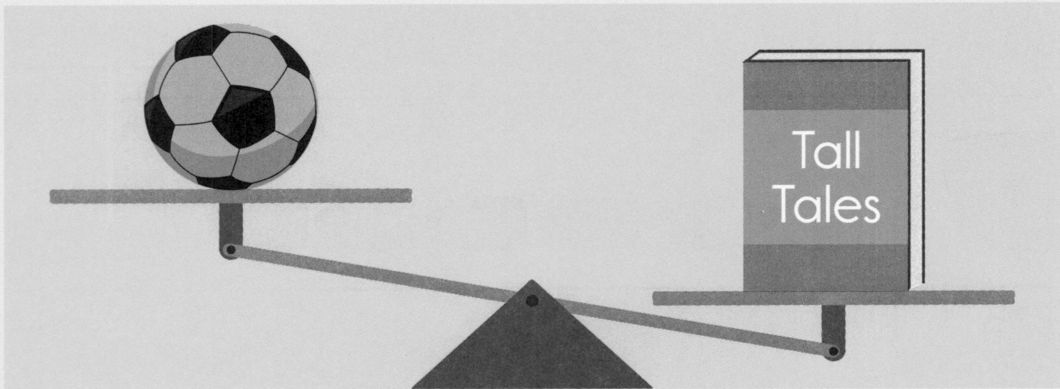

Imagine the ball and the book had the same weight.
What would the picture look like? How do you know?

Step Up

1. Look at the balance. Shade the ⬭ beside the words that best describe the weight of the toy.

a.

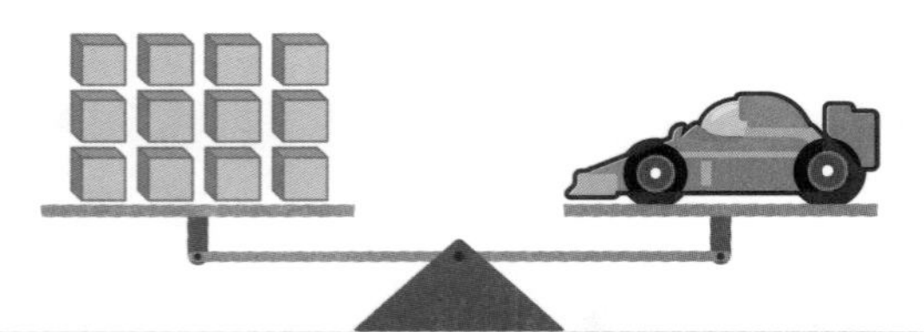

- ⬭ more than 12 cubes
- ⬭ less than 12 cubes
- ⬭ the same as 12 cubes

b.

- ⬭ more than 10 cubes
- ⬭ less than 10 cubes
- ⬭ the same as 10 cubes

c.

- ⬭ more than 16 cubes
- ⬭ less than 16 cubes
- ⬭ the same as 16 cubes

d.

- ⬭ more than 9 cubes
- ⬭ less than 9 cubes
- ⬭ the same as 9 cubes

2. Write the number of cubes. Then shade the ⬭ beside the words that best describe the weight of the toy.

a.

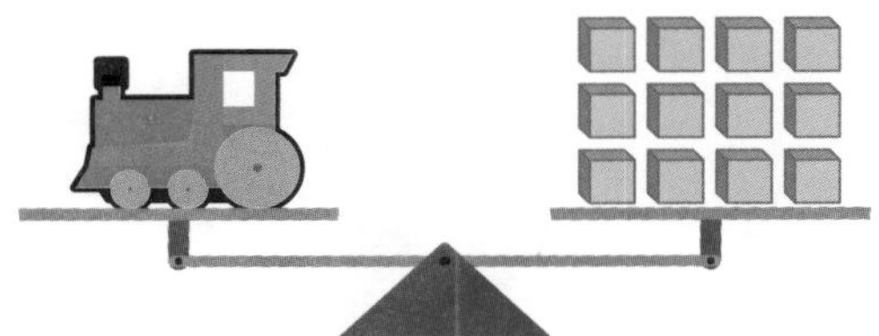

⬭ more than _____ cubes

⬭ less than _____ cubes

⬭ the same as _____ cubes

b.

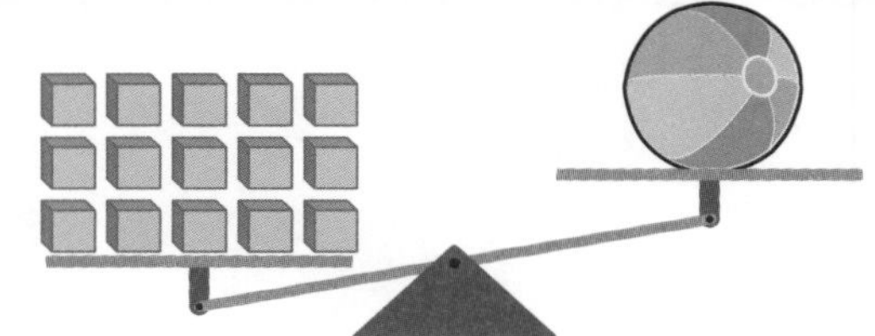

⬭ more than _____ cubes

⬭ less than _____ cubes

⬭ the same as _____ cubes

c.

⬭ more than _____ cubes

⬭ less than _____ cubes

⬭ the same as _____ cubes

d.

⬭ more than _____ cubes

⬭ less than _____ cubes

⬭ the same as _____ cubes

Step Ahead

How many cubes might this toy weigh? Write three possible answers.

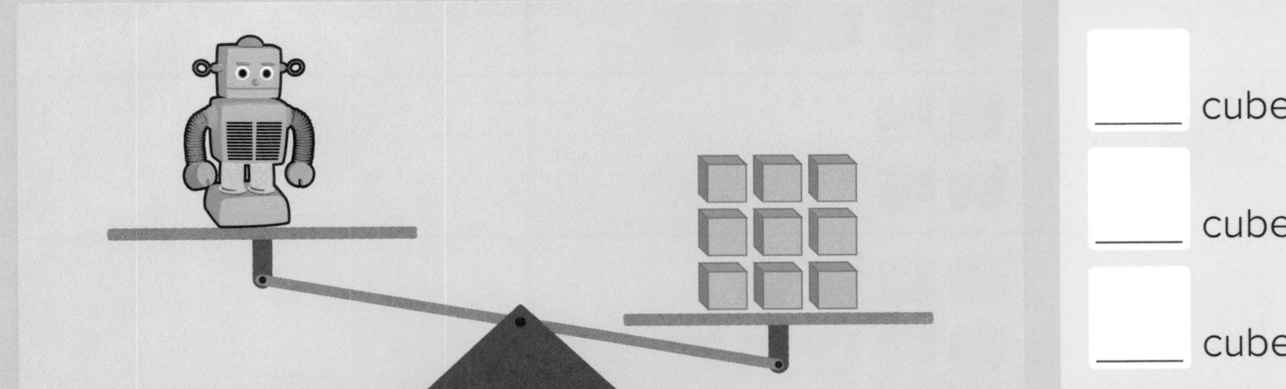

_____ cubes

_____ cubes

_____ cubes

4.12 Using Non-Standard Units to Compare Weight

What do you think is happening in this picture?

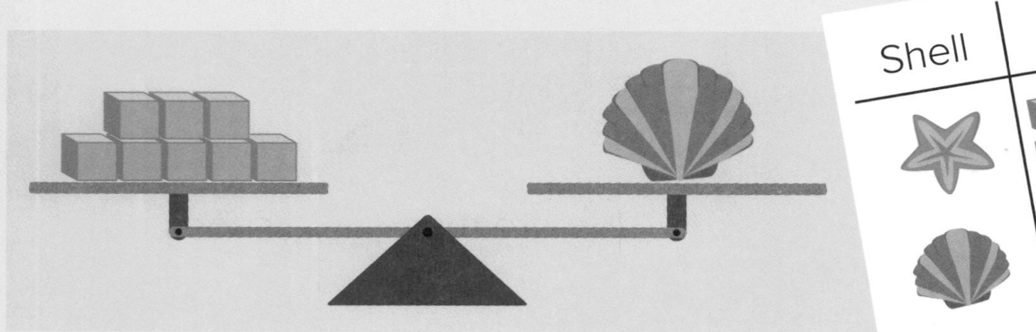

What do the cubes show?

How much does each shell weigh?

Which shell is heavier?
How do you know?

 or 

Step Up I. Write the total number of cubes that balances each shell.

Shell	Number of cubes	Total
		______
		______
		______
		______

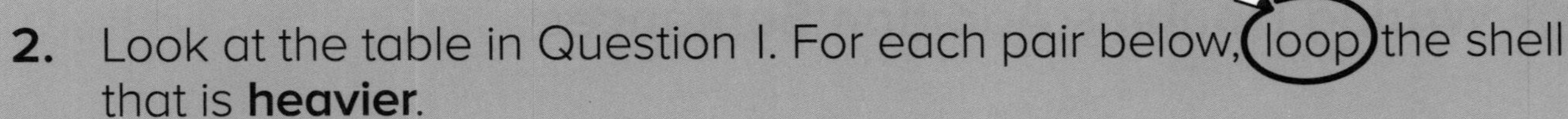

2. Look at the table in Question 1. For each pair below, loop the shell that is **heavier**.

a.  or 

b.  or 

c.  or 

d. 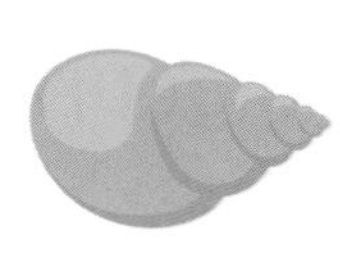 or 

3. What is the total weight of these shells?

a.  and 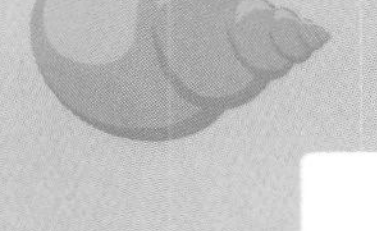

____ cubes

b.  and 

____ cubes

c.  and 

____ cubes

d.  and 

____ cubes

Step Ahead Look at the table in Question 1 on page 102. Then draw a shell on the left pan to make each balance picture true.

a.

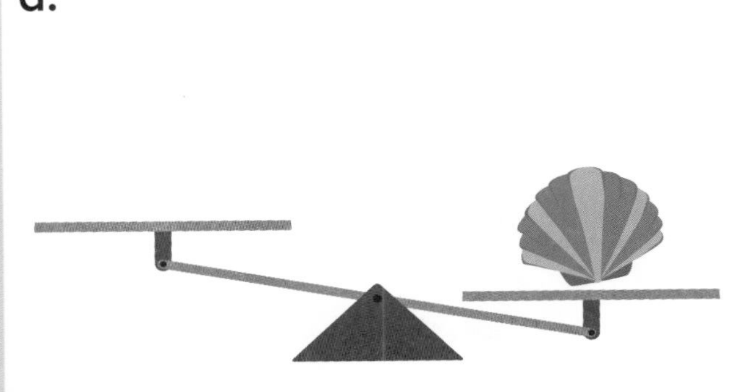

b.

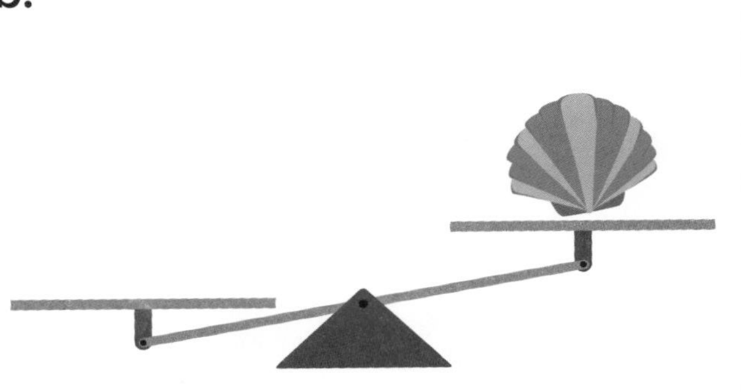

5.1 Writing Doubles Addition Sentences

One hand shows one group of five fingers.

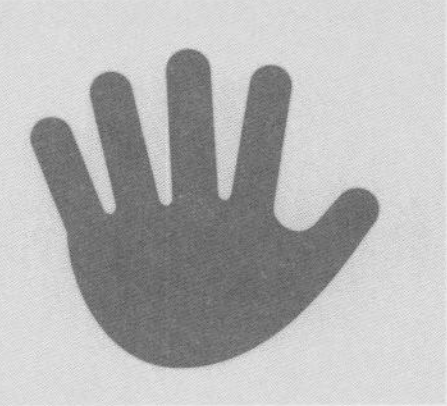

When you double five, you get two groups of five.

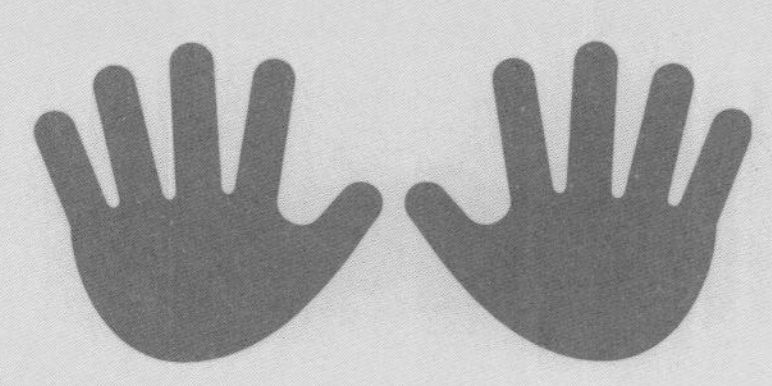

What addition sentence would you write to show the total number of fingers?

What doubles do these pictures show?

What other doubles have you seen?

Step Up 1. Write numbers to match the double.

a.

3 + 3 = ____

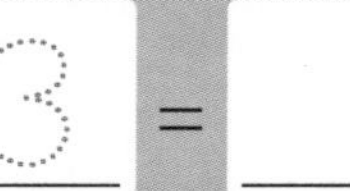

double 3 = ____

b.

____ + ____ = ____

double ____ = ____

2. Draw the same number of dots in the other wing.
Then write the numbers.

a.

___ + ___ = ___

double ___ = ___

b.

___ + ___ = ___

double ___ = ___

c.

___ + ___ = ___

double ___ = ___

d.

___ + ___ = ___

double ___ = ___

Step Ahead

Draw a butterfly showing dots for double 8.
Then write the matching facts below.

___ + ___ = ___

double ___ = ___

5.2 Introducing the Double-Plus-1 Strategy for Addition

What doubles fact do these cubes show?

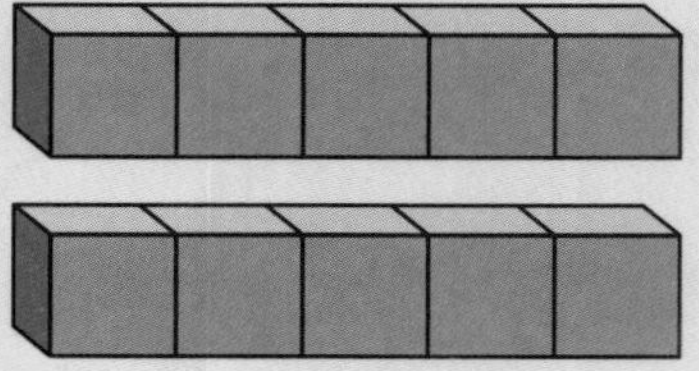

What number sentence can you write to show this double?

____ + ____ = ____

How can you use that doubles fact to figure out the total number of these cubes?

What number sentence can you write to match this fact?

5 plus 6 is the same as double 5 and 1 more. So 5 + 6 is 11.

Step Up 1. Write the answers.

a. Double 4 is ____.

b. Double 9 is ____.

c. Double 6 is ____.

d. Double 5 is ____.

e. Double 3 is ____.

f. Double 7 is ____.

g. Double 10 is ____.

h. Double 8 is ____.

2. Write the doubles fact. Draw **one more** dot on one side. Then write the **double-plus-1** fact and its turnaround.

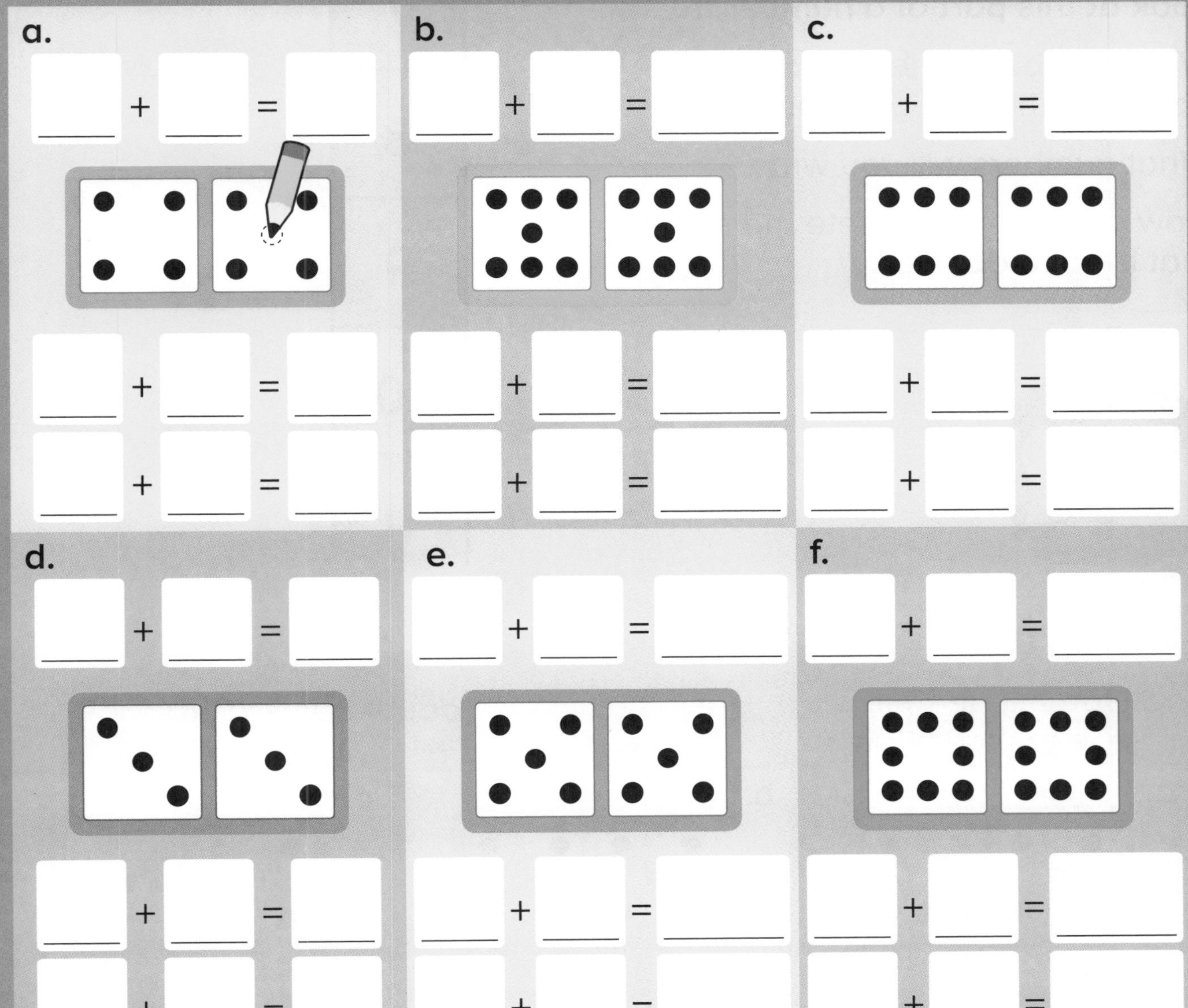

Step Ahead Write the double you could use to help figure out each answer. Then write the total.

a.

____ + ____ = ____

10 + 11 = ____

b.

____ + ____ = ____

12 + 13 = ____

5.3 Reinforcing the Double-Plus-1 Strategy for Addition

Look at this part of a number track.

What number sentences can you complete that are doubles facts?

What numbers will you write?

How could you complete the sentence that is not a double?

7
8 = ___ + ___
9 = ___ + ___
10 = ___ + ___
11

I would use a doubles fact to help me.

Step Up 1. Loop the dominos that show a **double-plus-1** fact.

a.

b.

c.

d.
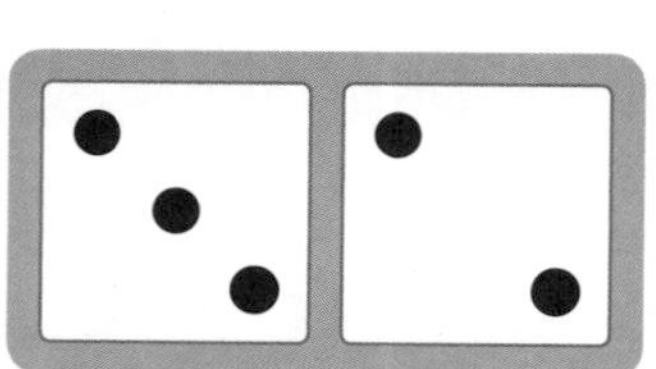

e.

f.

g.

h.
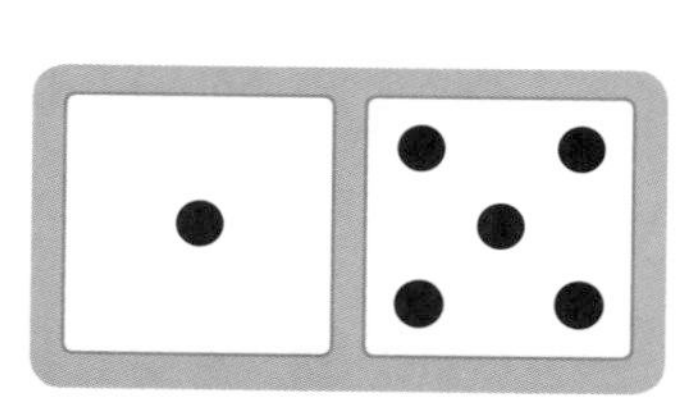

i.
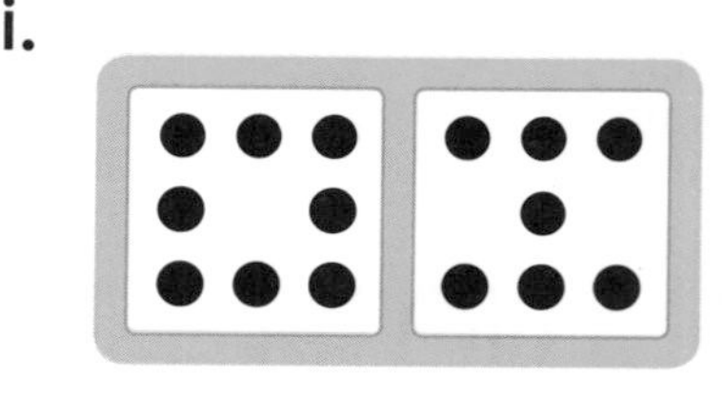

2. Write the doubles fact you can use to figure out the total on each domino. Then write the total for each **double-plus-1** fact.

a.

Double ____ is ____

so

$4 + 5 =$ ____

b.

Double ____ is ____

so

$2 + 3 =$ ____

c.

Double ____ is ____

so

$8 + 9 =$ ____

d.

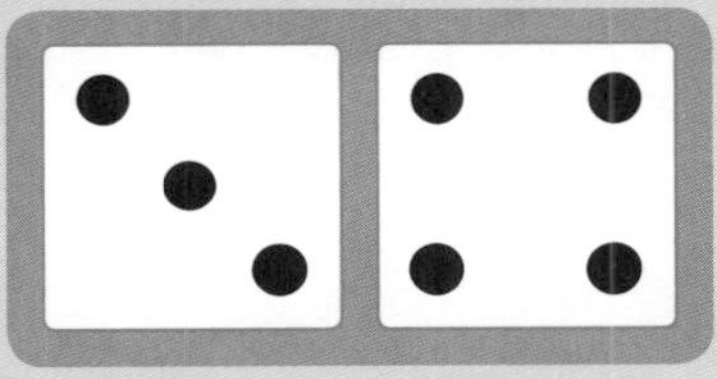

Double ____ is ____

so

$3 + 4 =$ ____

e.

Double ____ is ____

so

$7 + 6 =$ ____

f.

Double ____ is ____

so

$6 + 5 =$ ____

Step Ahead Write count-on facts that are also doubles facts or double-plus-1 facts.

____________________ ____________________

____________________ ____________________

____________________ ____________________

5.4 Introducing the Double-Plus-2 Strategy for Addition

What doubles fact do these cubes show?

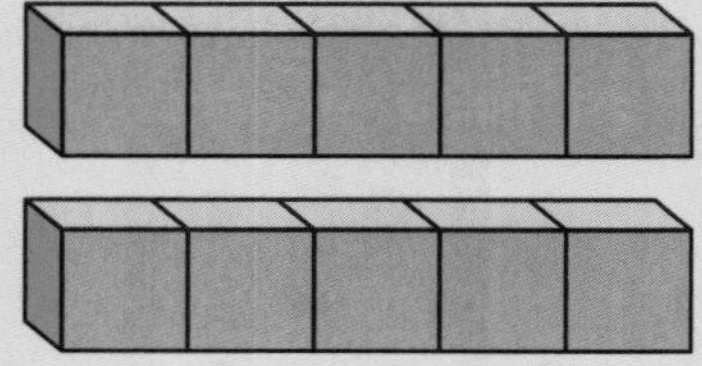

What number sentence can you write to show this double?

____ + ____ = ____

How can you use that doubles fact to figure out the total number of these cubes?

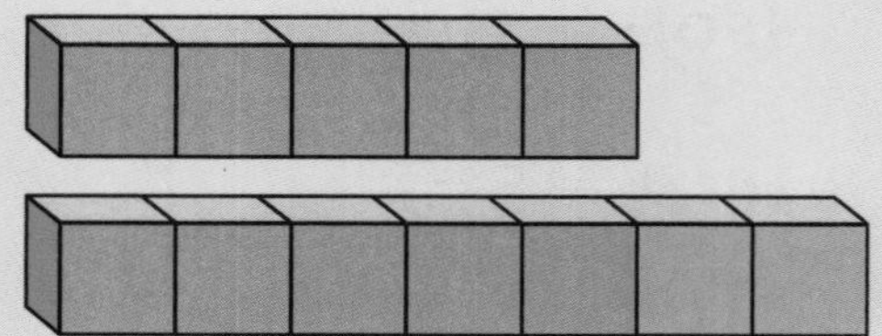

5 plus 7 is the same as double 5 and 2 more. So 5 + 7 is 12.

What number sentence can you write to match this fact?

Step Up I. Write the answers.

a. Double four is ____. Double four plus two more is ____.

b. Double seven is ____. Double seven plus two more is ____.

c. Double five is ____. Double five plus two more is ____.

d. Double nine is ____. Double nine plus two more is ____.

e. Double eight is ____. Double eight plus two more is ____.

2. Write the doubles fact. Draw **two more** dots on one side. Then write the **double-plus-2** fact and its turnaround.

a.

___ + ___ = ___

___ + ___ = ___

___ + ___ = ___

b.

___ + ___ = ___

___ + ___ = ___

___ + ___ = ___

c.

___ + ___ = ___

___ + ___ = ___

___ + ___ = ___

d.

___ + ___ = ___

___ + ___ = ___

___ + ___ = ___

e.

___ + ___ = ___

___ + ___ = ___

___ + ___ = ___

f.

___ + ___ = ___

___ + ___ = ___

___ + ___ = ___

Step Ahead Write the numbers.

a. If you double me and add 2, the answer is 18.

What number am I? ___

b. If you double me and add 2, the answer is 22.

What number am I? ___

5.5 Reinforcing the Double-Plus-2 Strategy for Addition

Look at these numbers.

5	8	14	11	6	15

Which number is equal to double 4?

Which number is the sum of 3 and 5?

What do you notice?

The **sum** is the total in an addition sentence. For example, 12 is the sum of 7 + 5.

Which numbers will you get if you use doubling? How do you know?

Which numbers will you get if you double and add 1?

Which numbers will you get if you double and add 2?

Step Up 1. Loop the dominos that show a **double-plus-2** fact.

a.

b.

c.

d.

e.

f.

g.

h.

i.

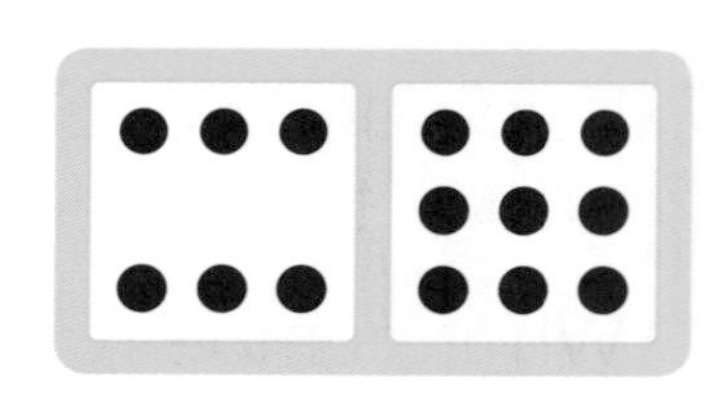

2. Write the doubles fact you can use to figure out the total on each domino. Then write the total for each **double-plus-2** fact.

a.

Double ____ is ____

so

5 + 3 = ____

b.

Double ____ is ____

so

6 + 4 = ____

c.

Double ____ is ____

so

7 + 9 = ____

d.

Double ____ is ____

so

5 + 7 = ____

e.

Double ____ is ____

so

8 + 6 = ____

Step Ahead Alyssa has $6. Her mom gives her $8 more to buy a toy. Loop all the toys that Alyssa could buy.

5.6 Comparing Addition Strategies

Look at these toys and prices.

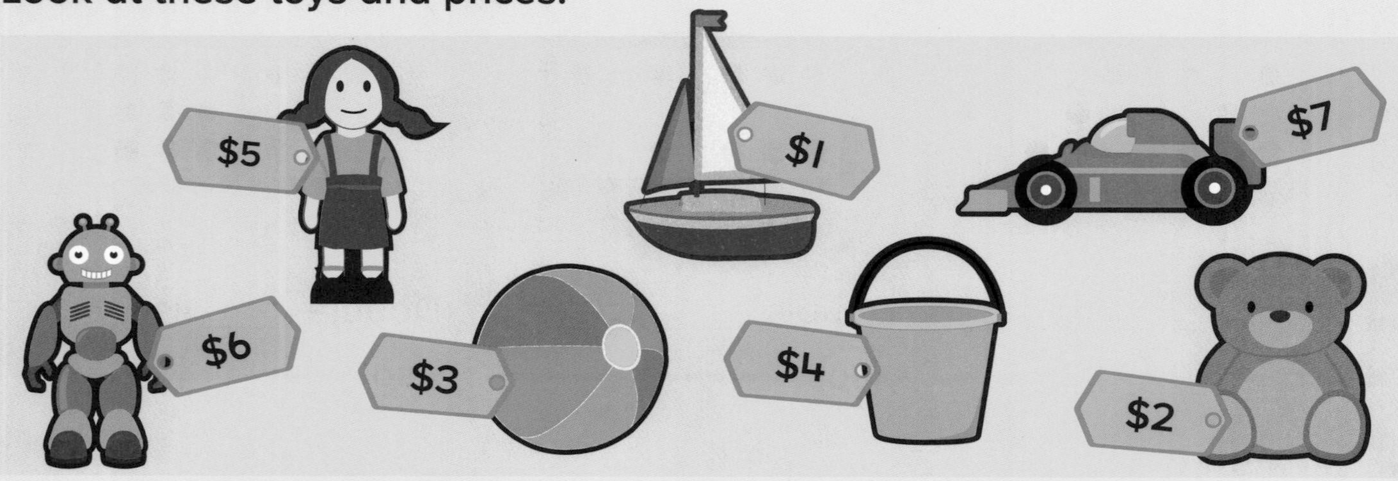

How can you figure out the total cost of the bucket and doll?

How can you figure out the total cost of the ball and bear?
What other way could you figure it out?

What other totals can you figure out using that strategy?

Step Up 1. Use the toys and prices above. Figure out the total cost.

a.

$ ____ + $ ____ = $ ______

b.

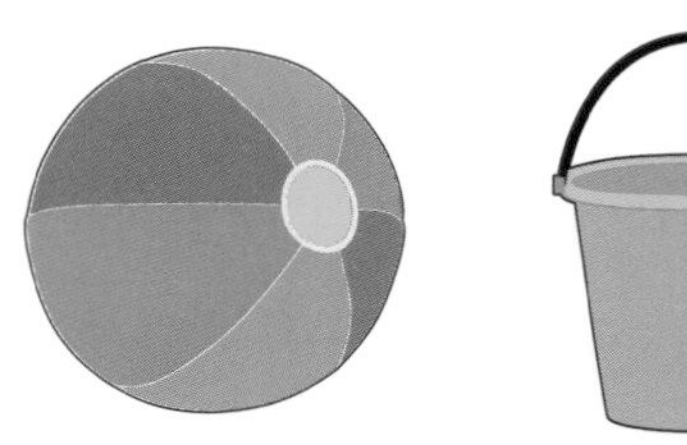

$ ____ + $ ____ = $ ______

c.

$ ____ + $ ____ = $ ______

d.

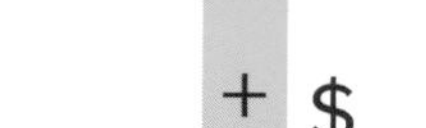

$ ____ + $ ____ = $ ______

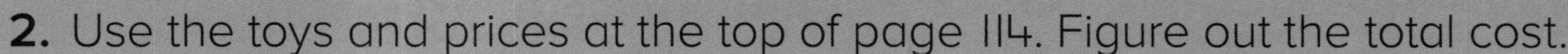

2. Use the toys and prices at the top of page 114. Figure out the total cost.

a.

$ ____ + $ ____ = $ ______

b.

$ ____ + $ ____ = $ ______

c.

$ ____ + $ ____ = $ ______

d.

$ ____ + $ ____ = $ ______

e.

$ ____ + $ ____ = $ ______

f.

$ ____ + $ ____ = $ ______

Step Ahead Write **true** or **false** for each sentence.

a. Counting on is one way to figure out the total cost for the **doll** and the **bear**. ______

b. You can double-add-1 to figure out the total cost of the **doll** and the **bucket**. ______

c. The price of the **robot** plus the price of the **ball** is a doubles fact. ______

5.7 Investigating Directions and Turns

Look at the dancing bears below.
Where is each bear's right hand?

What helped you figure out which hand was right?

Imagine you looked in a mirror. What would you notice about left and right?

Step Up I. Loop the left paws of each animal.

a.

b.

c.

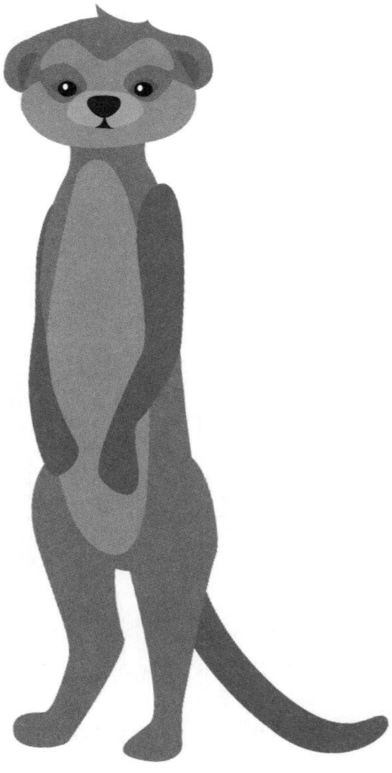

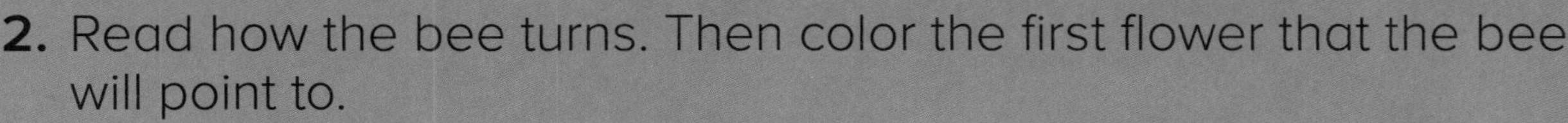

2. Read how the bee turns. Then color the first flower that the bee will point to.

a. Turn right.

b. Turn left.

c. Turn left.

d. Turn right.

e. Turn right.

f. Turn left.

Step Ahead Imagine each bee above makes one more turn in the same direction. Loop the next flower each bee will point to.

5.8 Identifying Features of Angles

Each corner of this shape has two sides.

The way the sides join together makes the corners look the way they do.

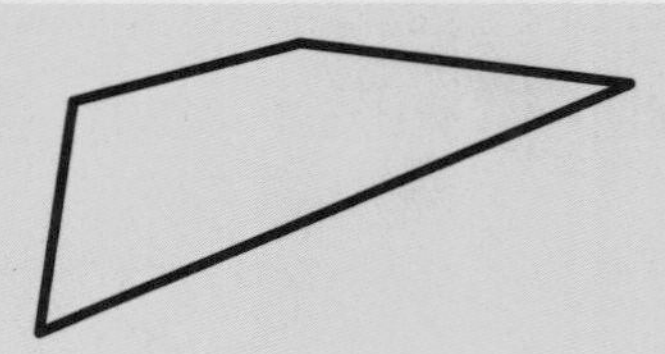

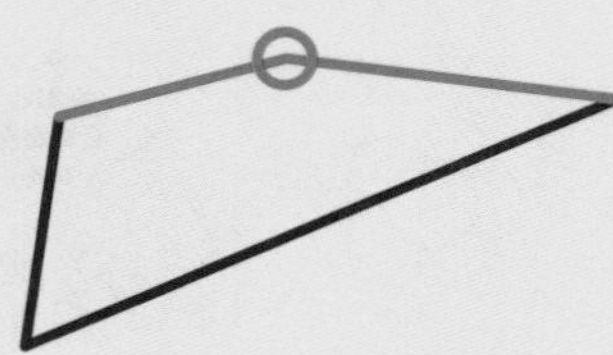

How would you describe the corner when the sides are close together?

How would you describe the corner when the sides are far apart?

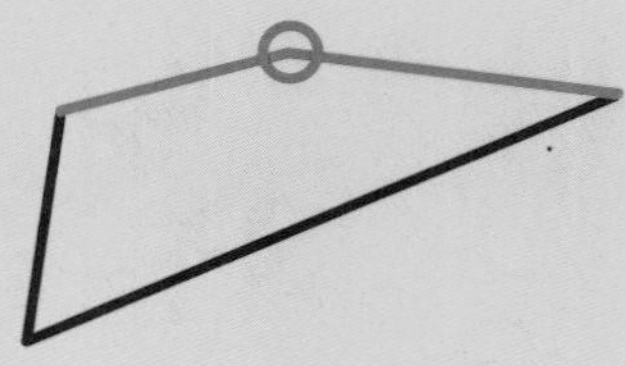

Step Up

1. Choose one corner on each shape. Color the two sides that make the corner. Loop the point where the two sides meet.

a.

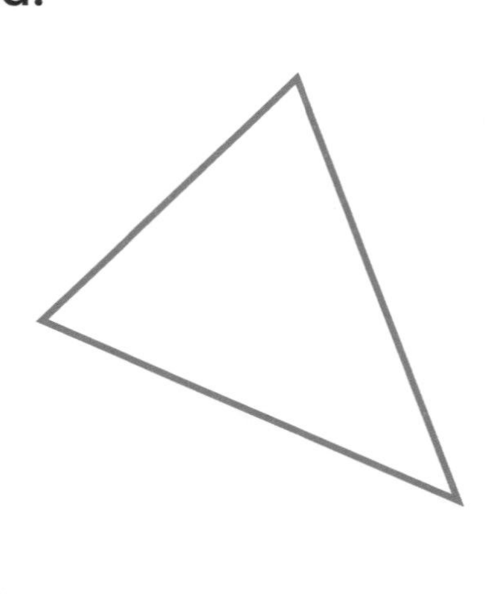

b.

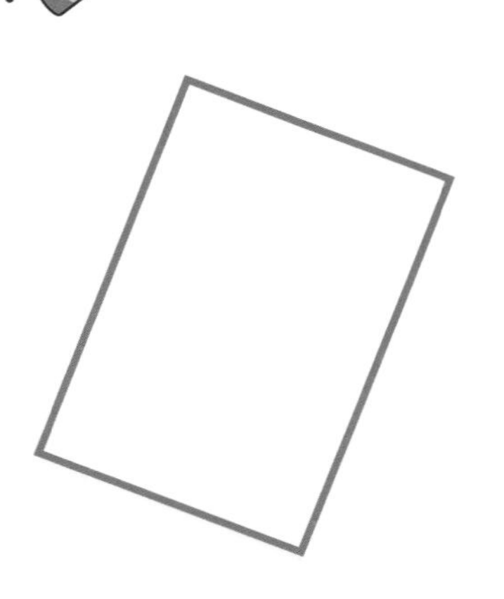

c.

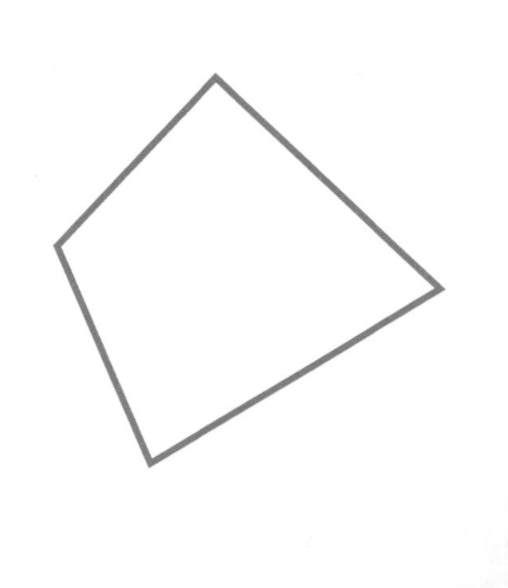

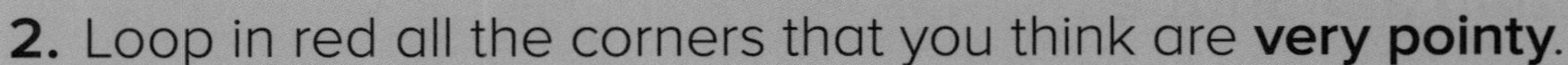

2. Loop in red all the corners that you think are **very pointy**.

a.

b.

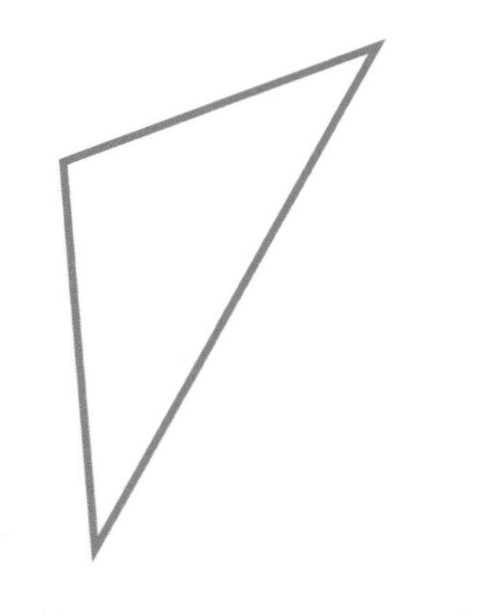

c.

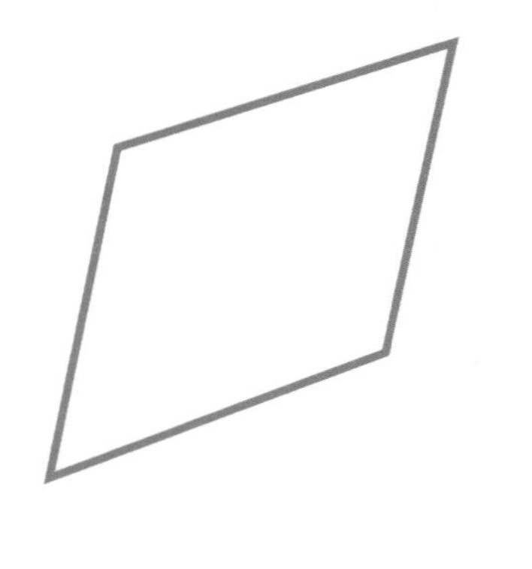

d.

e.

f.

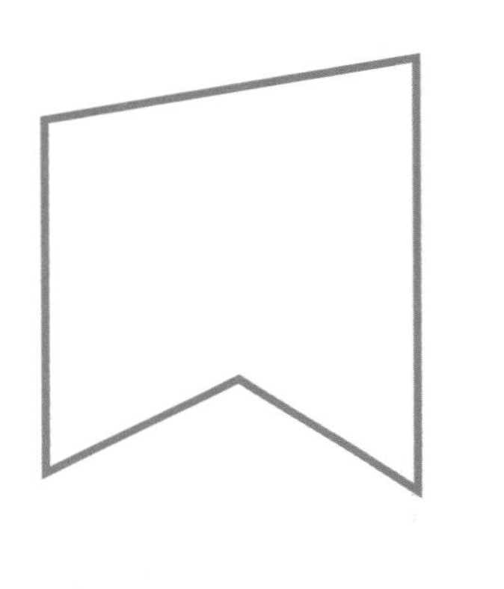

3. Look at the shapes above. Loop in blue all the corners that you think are **not as pointy**.

Step Ahead

Draw three different shapes that each have one corner that is **very pointy**.

5.9 Analyzing 2D Shapes

What words could you use to describe these vehicles?

We could use words like **big** and **small**, or **long** and **short**.
We could also describe the color or the number of wheels.

Look at the 2D shapes below.

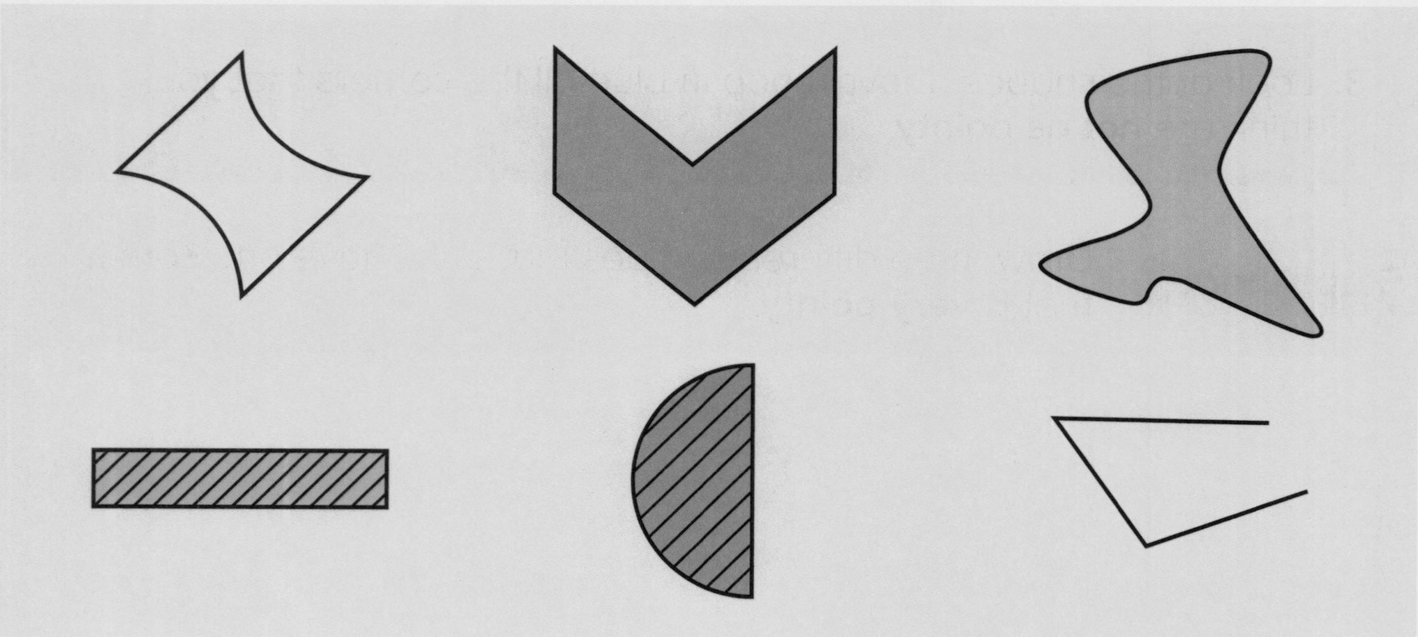

What facts do you know about each shape?

What words can you use to describe them?

Step Up **1.** Look at each shape. Write **true** or **false** for each fact.

Shape A 	• It has five sides. • All sides are the same length. • All sides are straight.	__________ __________ __________
Shape B 	• It is a triangle. • It is a closed shape. • One side is curved.	__________ __________ __________
Shape C 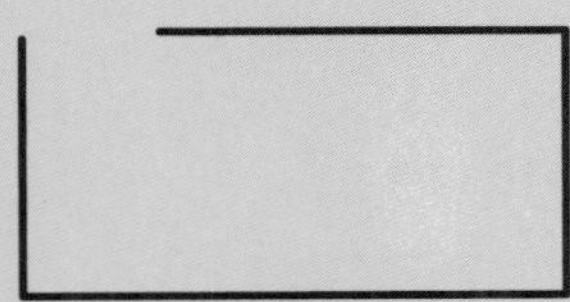	• It has four corners. • It has straight parts. • It is a rectangle.	__________ __________ __________

2. Draw two different shapes that match all the facts below.

- It has five sides.
- All sides are straight.
- One corner is very pointy.

Step Ahead Write one more true fact about these shapes in Question 1.

Shape A ______________________________

Shape B ______________________________

5.10 Sorting 2D Shapes

In his kitchen, Ethan sorts things into groups.

He puts the spoons in one part of the drawer.

He puts the forks in another part of the drawer.

What are some things that get sorted into groups in your house?

Sarah sorted these 2D shapes into two groups.
How did she figure out where they belong?

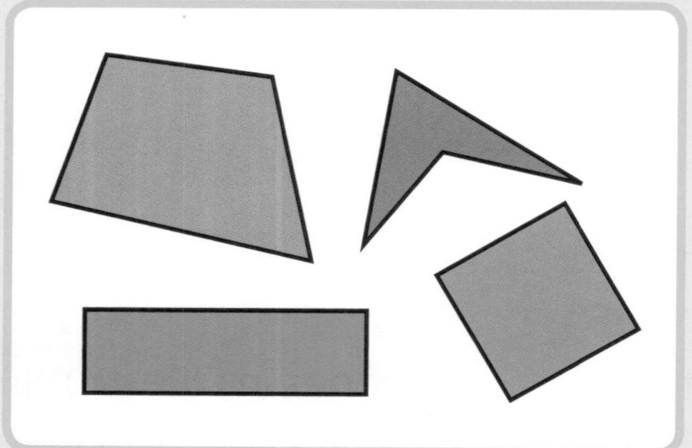

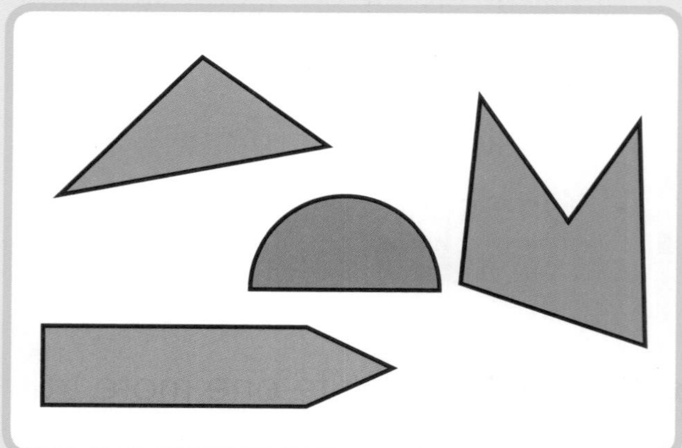

Step Up Your teacher will give you some cards. Sort the cards into two groups and paste them into the two boxes on page 123. Then write a name for each group.

Step Ahead Loop two of these shapes.
What is the same about them?

5.11 Identifying 2D Shapes

What type of shape is this?

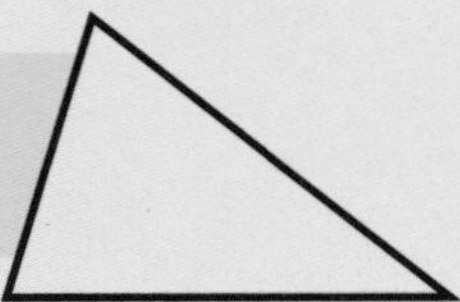

If we turn it around, does it become a different shape or stay the same shape?

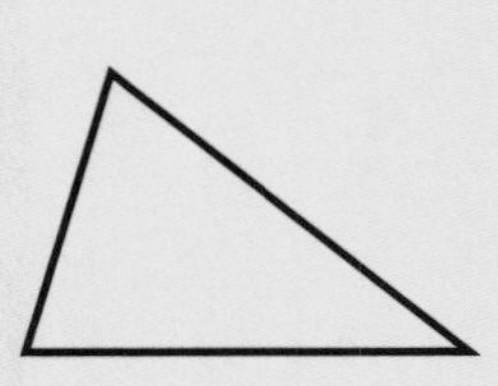

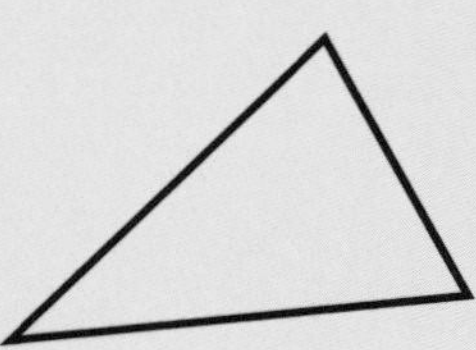
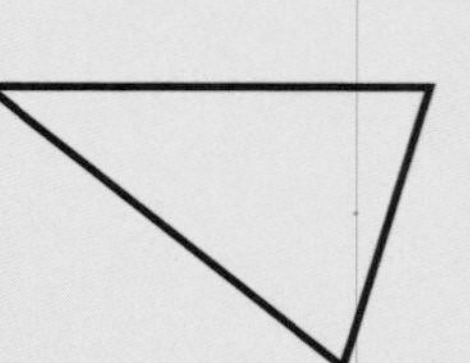

Step Up

1. Look at the shapes below. Write **T** inside each triangle. Write **S** inside each square rectangle. Write **N** inside each non-square rectangle. Some shapes will not have a letter inside them.

a. 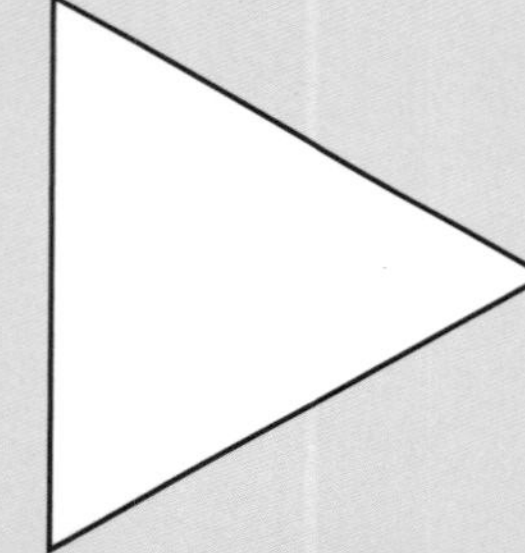

b. 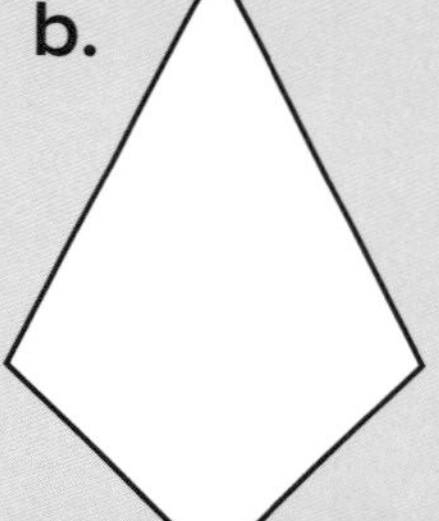

c. 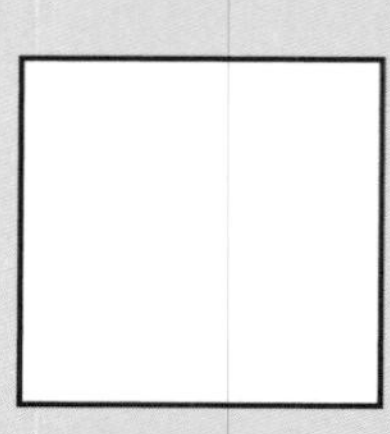

d. 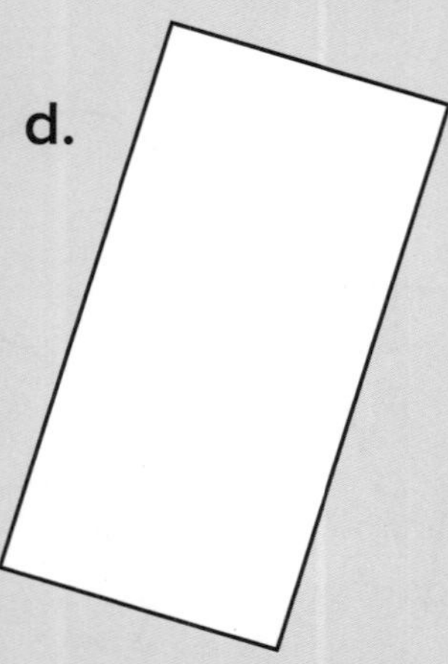

e. 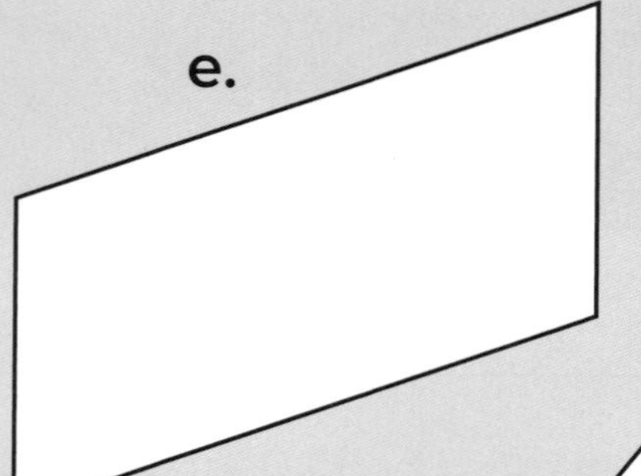

f. 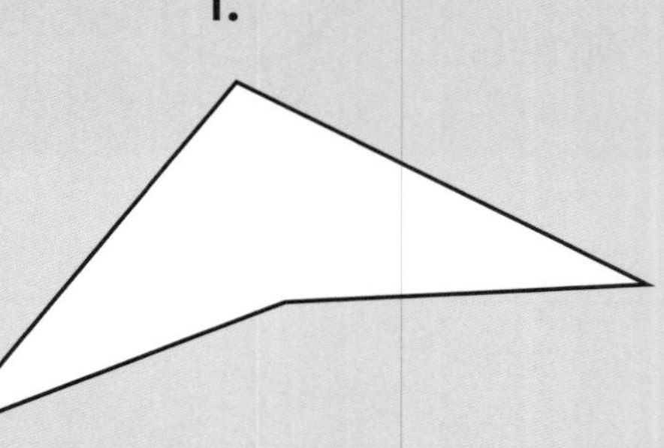

2. Read the label inside each shape. Then use your ruler to draw one or two straight sides to complete the shape.

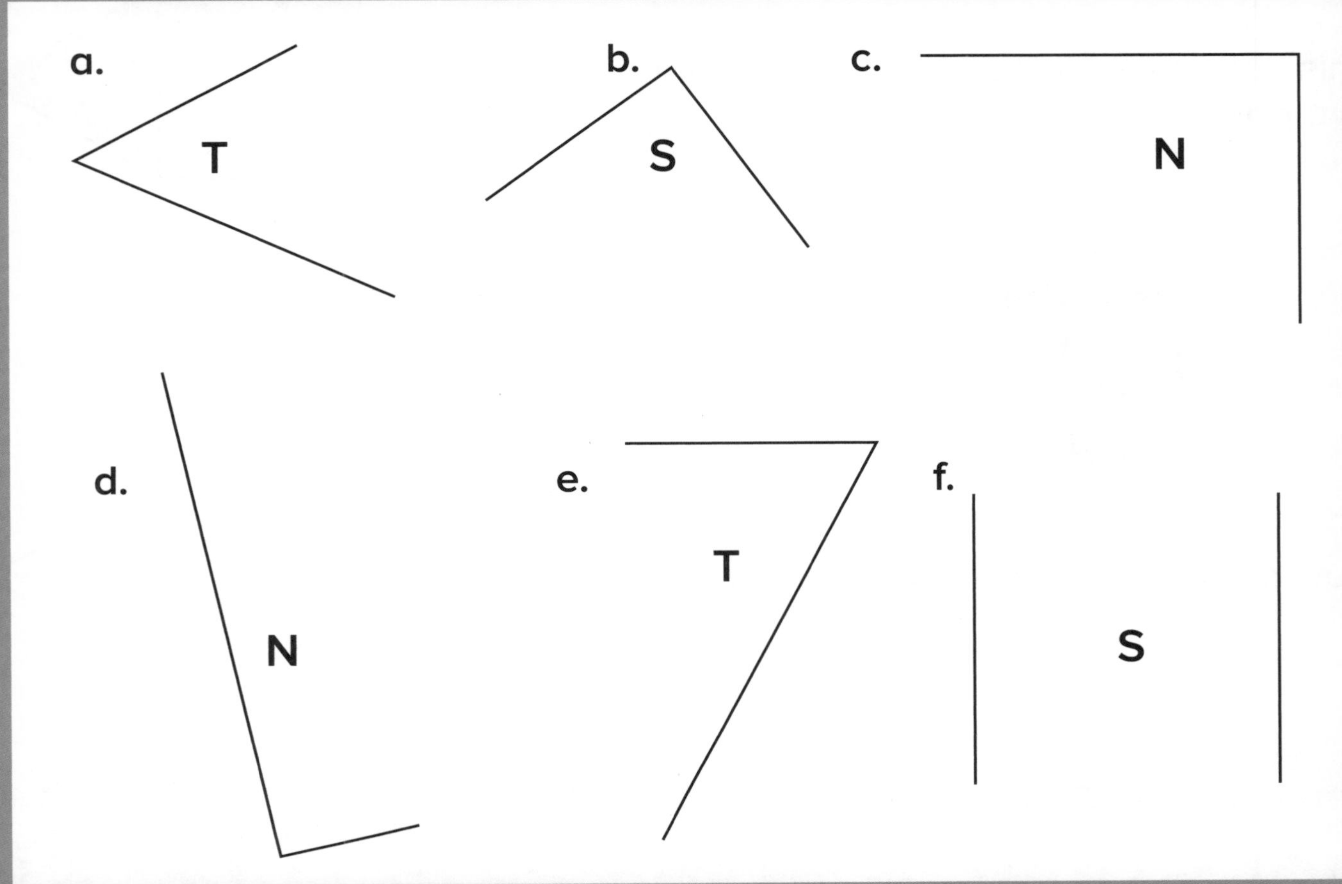

Step Ahead Draw five **different** triangles.

5.12 Joining 2D Shapes

This shape was made by tracing around two pattern blocks.

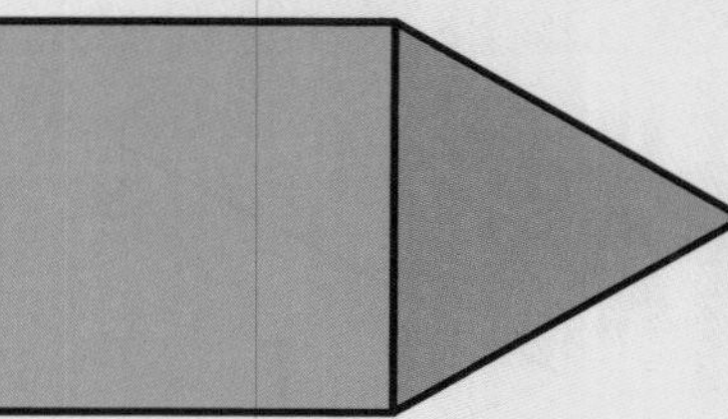

What two shapes do you see?

How many sides does the new shape have?

Step Up 1. Choose **two other** pattern blocks.

a. Join them together. Then trace around them below.

b. How many sides does your new shape have? 

2. Choose **three** different pattern blocks.

a. Join them together. Then trace around them.

b. How many sides does your new shape have? ____

3. Choose **three** different pattern blocks.

a. Join them together. Then trace around them.

b. How many sides does your new shape have? ____

Step Ahead Each shape below was made using **three** pattern blocks. Draw lines on the shapes to show which blocks were used.

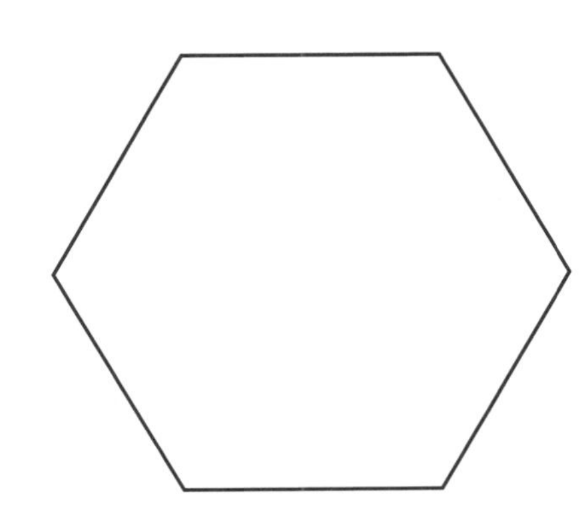

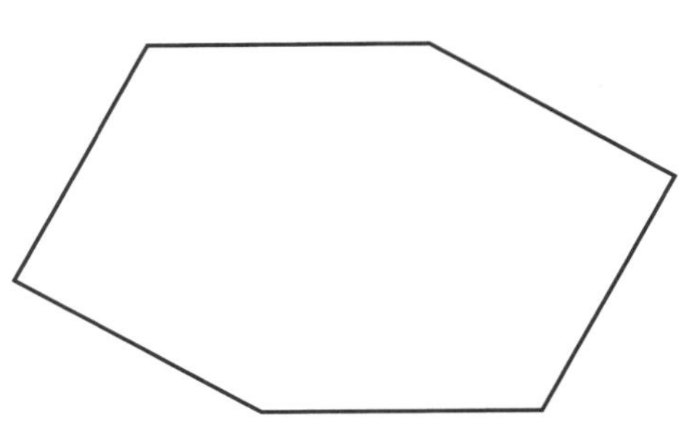

6.1 Working with Tens and Ones

Look at this picture.

How many groups of tens are raised?

How many extra fingers are raised?

Show the number on this expander and in the place-value chart below. Then write the numeral.

How many tens and ones are in this number?

How do you know?

45

Step Up

1. Write the number of tens and ones on the expander. Then write the numeral without the expander.

a.

b.

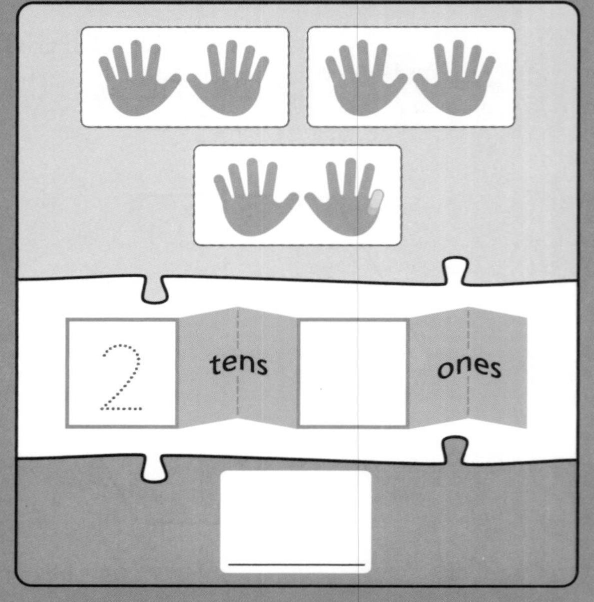

2. Write the number of tens and ones. Then write the numeral to match.

a.

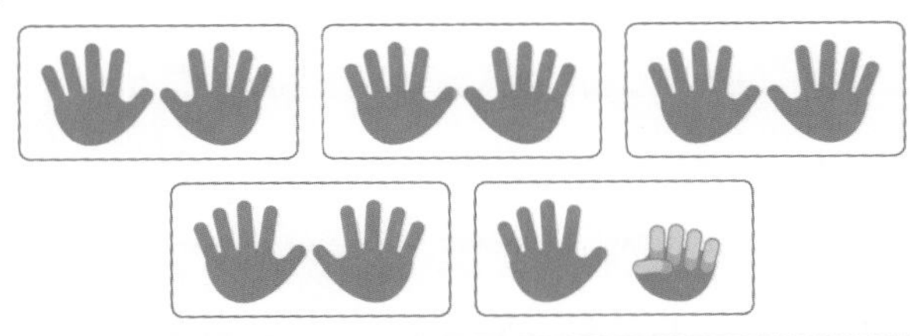

tens	ones
______	______

______

b.

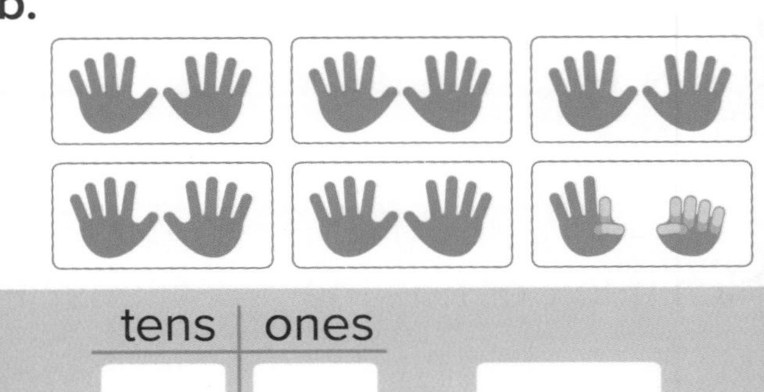

tens	ones
______	______

______

c.

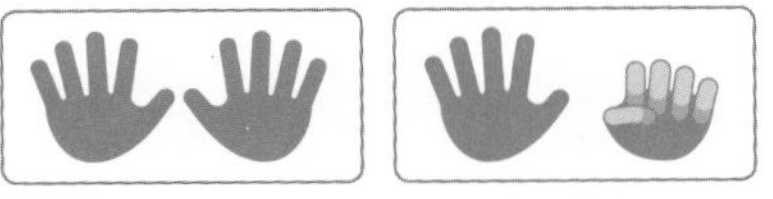

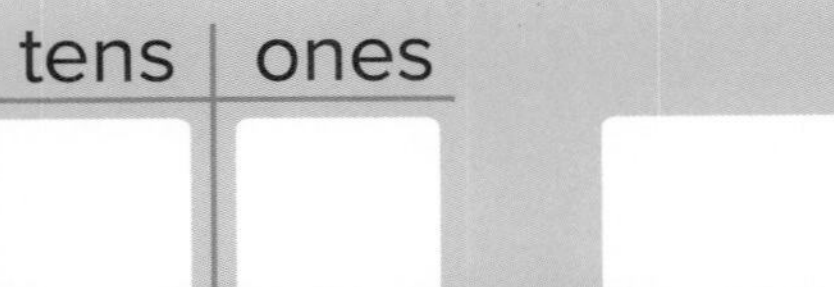

tens	ones
______	______

______

d.

tens	ones
______	______

______

e.

tens	ones
______	______

______

f.

tens	ones
______	______

______

Step Ahead Read the number of tens and ones.
Write the matching numerals.

a. two tens and seven ones ______

b. six ones and eight tens ______

c. three tens and four ones ______

d. five ones and nine tens ______

6.2 Representing Two-Digit Numbers

Look at these number names.

thirty-seven	nineteen	fifty-two

Which number has the most tens? How do you know?

Look at these numerals.

80	18	81

What does the 8 mean in each numeral? How do you know?

Step Up 

1. Color tens and ones to match each number name.

a. forty-seven

b. sixty-two

c. seventeen

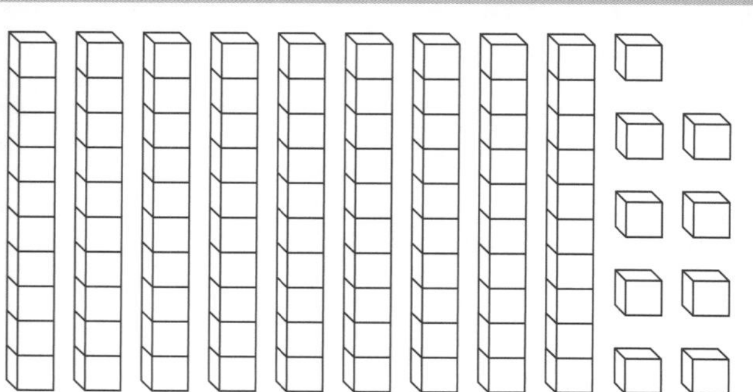

d. twenty-six

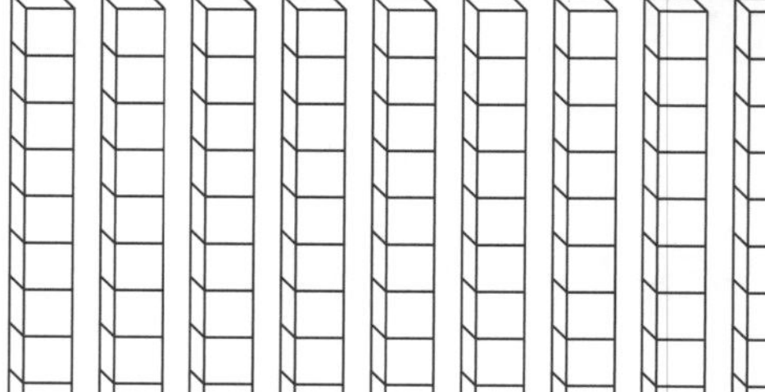

2. Color tens and ones to match each numeral.

a. 98 

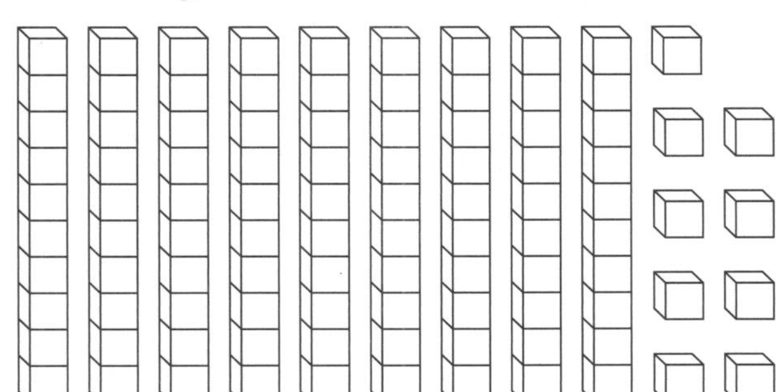

b. 61 

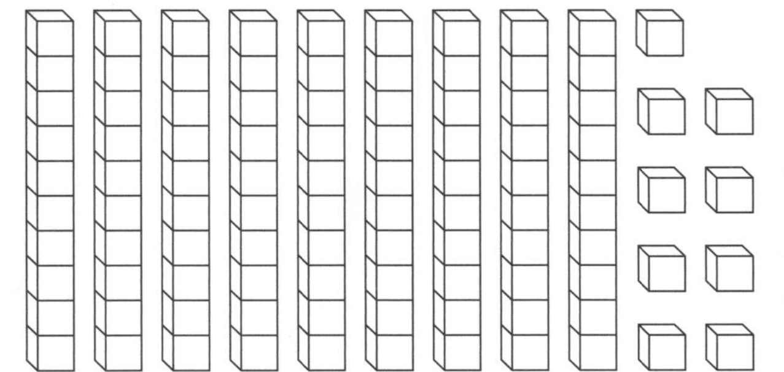

c. 56 

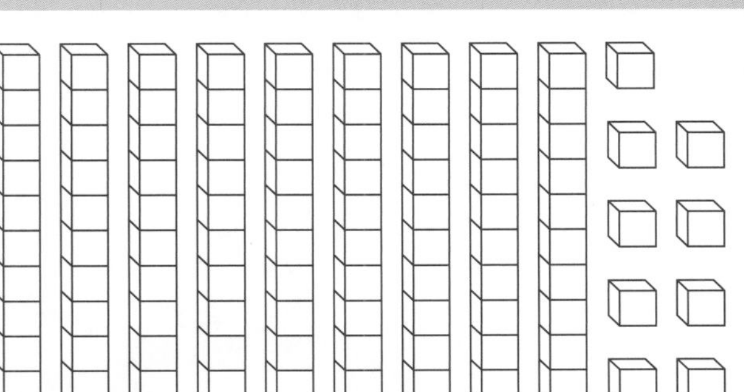

d. 11

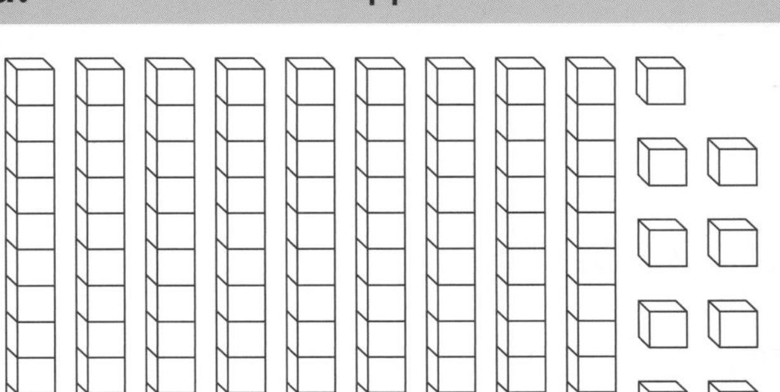

e. 75 

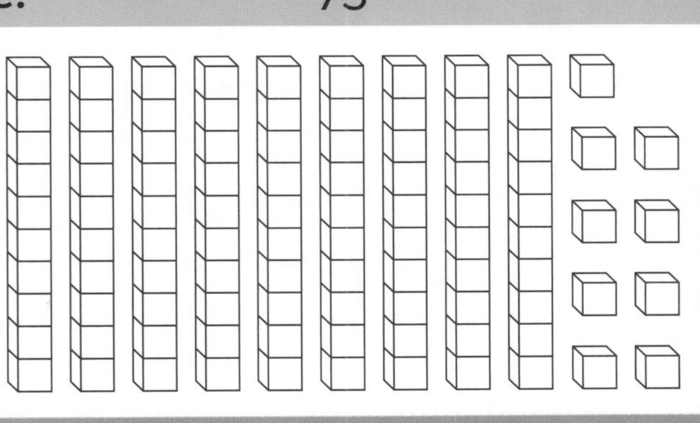

f. 40

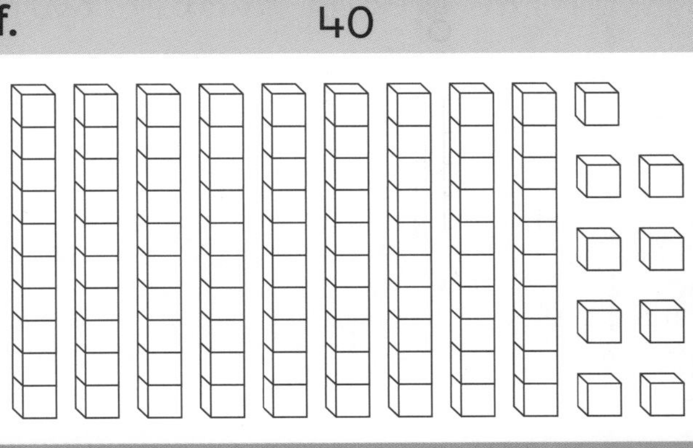

Step Ahead Write the number of tens and ones to match each number name.

a. thirty-two

tens	ones
____	____

b. twenty-one

tens	ones
____	____

c. fifteen

tens	ones
____	____

d. fifty

tens	ones
____	____

6.3 Using a Pan Balance to Compare Quantities

What two numbers are shown on this pan balance? How do you know?

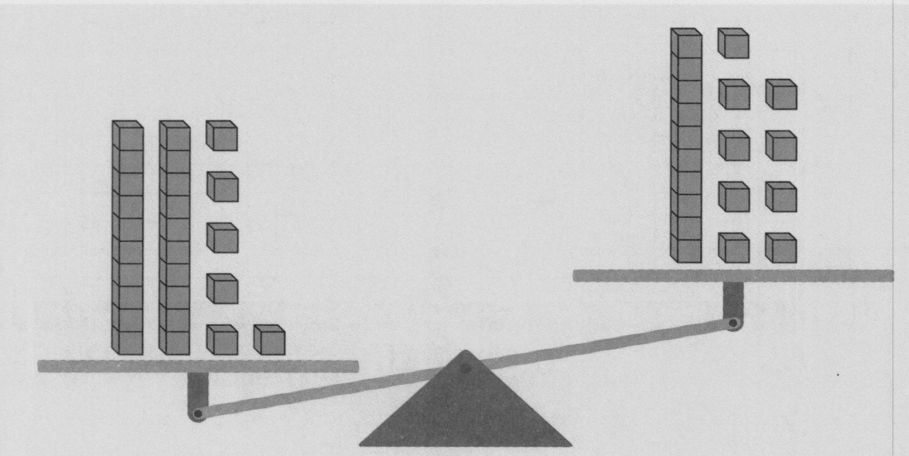

Which number is greater?
How do you know?

What is another way you can tell?

Step Up 1. Write numbers to match the blocks. Then loop the **greater** number.

a.

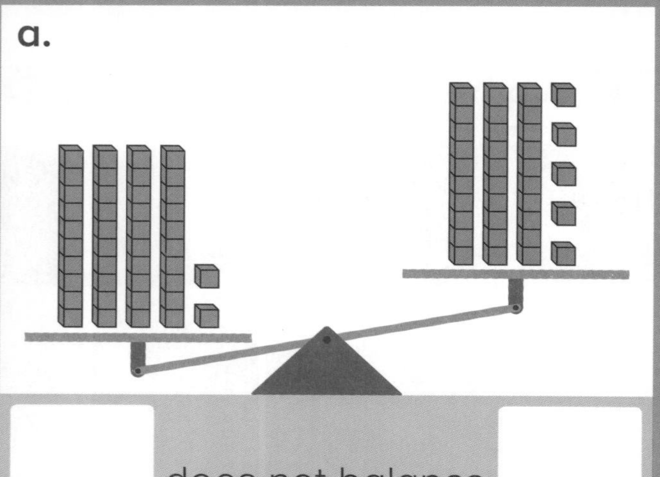

_____ does not balance _____

b.

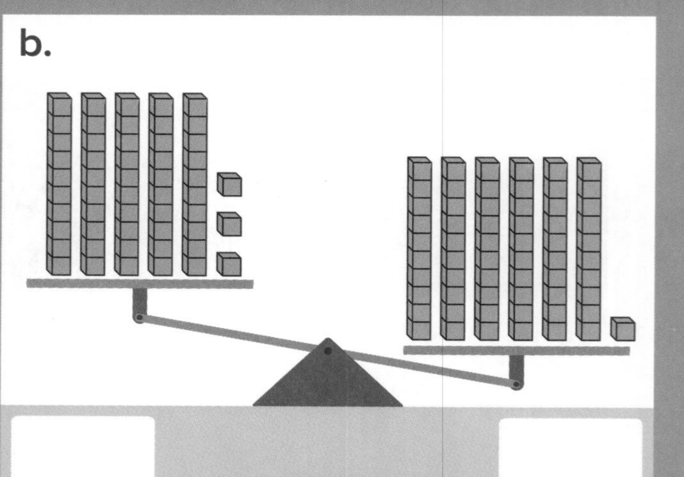

_____ does not balance _____

2. Write numerals to match the blocks. Then loop the numeral that is **less**.

a.

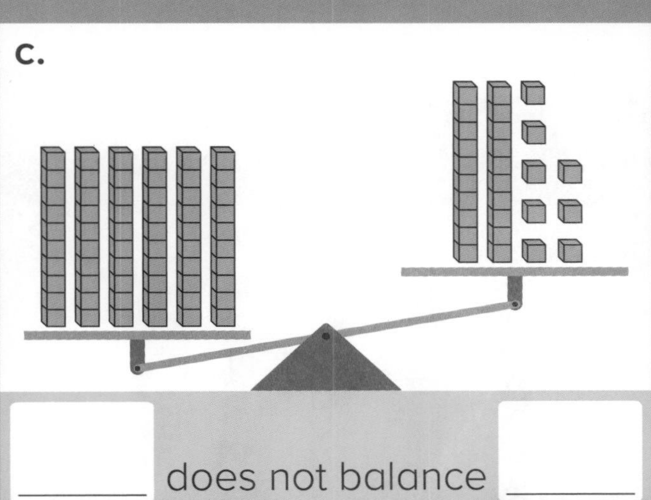

_______ does not balance _______

b.

_______ does not balance _______

c.

_______ does not balance _______

d.

_______ does not balance _______

Step Ahead Draw more blocks to make these balance pictures true. Then write the numbers.

a.

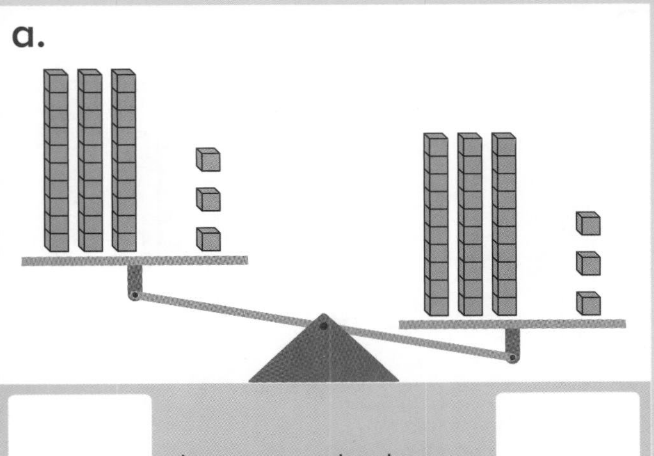

_______ does not balance _______

b.

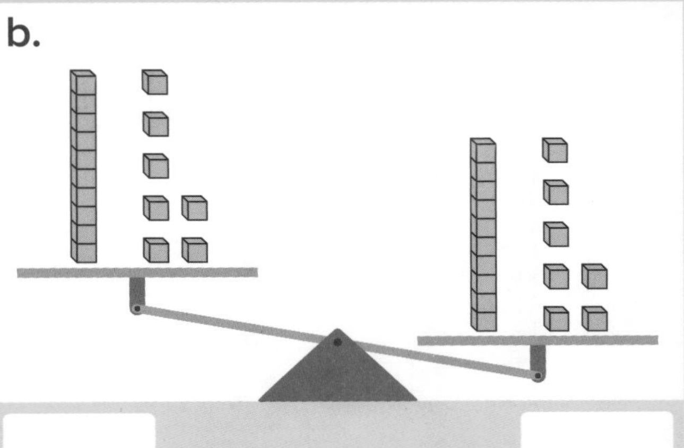

_______ does not balance _______

6.4 Comparing Quantities Less Than 100

How many tens blocks are purple?
How many ones blocks are purple?
How many tens and ones blocks are blue?

Which color shows the greater number?
How do you know?

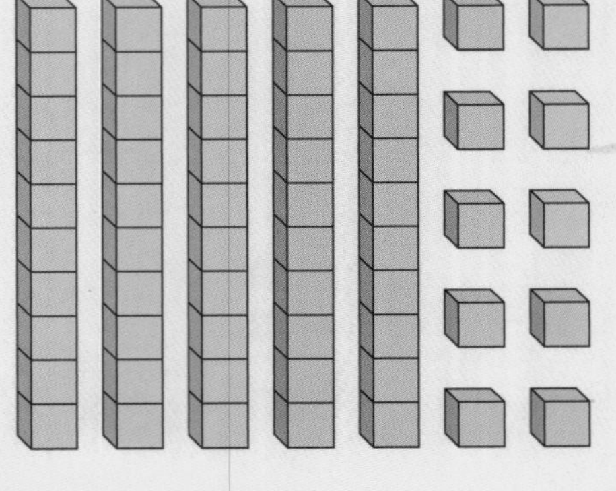

I looked at the tens first. There are 3 blue tens and only 2 purple tens.

Step Up 1. Color blocks to match each number name.
Then write the numerals to complete the statement.

a. twenty-four | thirty-seven

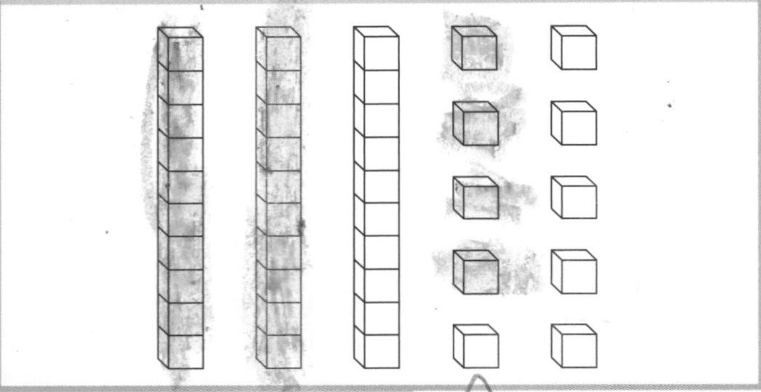

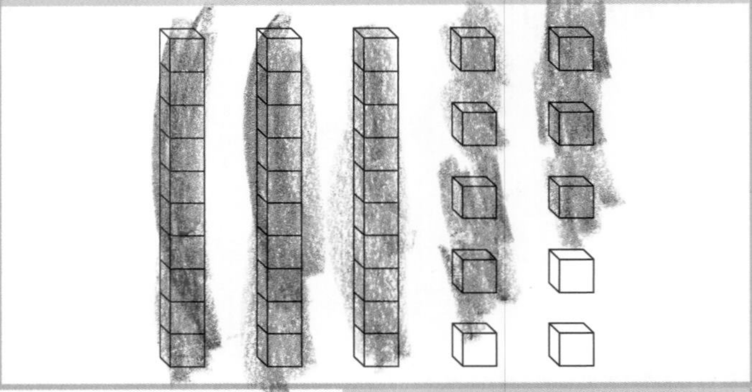

37 is greater than 24

b. fifty-one | forty-six

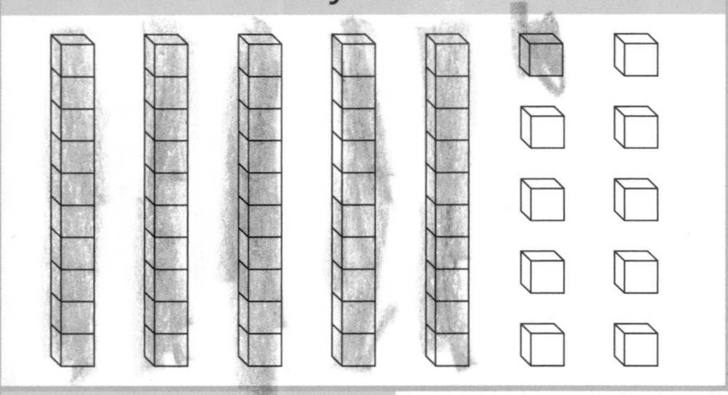

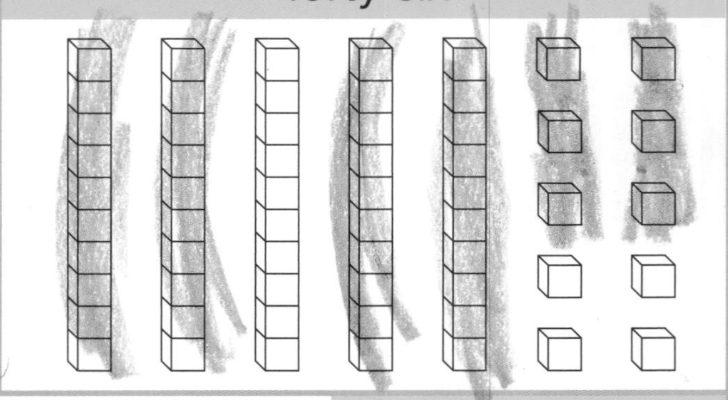

51 is greater than 46

2. Color blocks to match each number name.
Then write the numerals to complete the statement.

a. thirteen | thirty-three

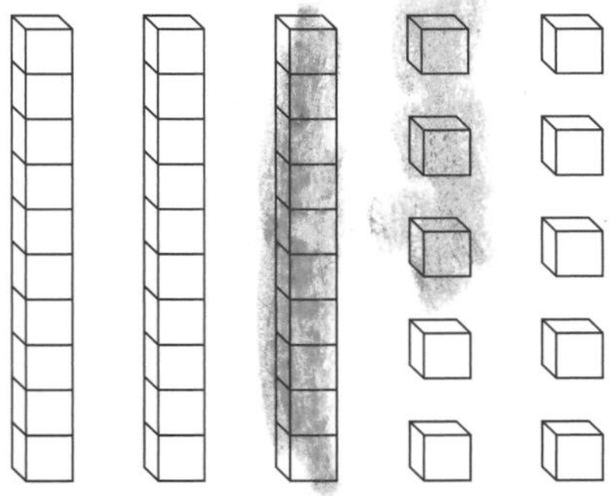

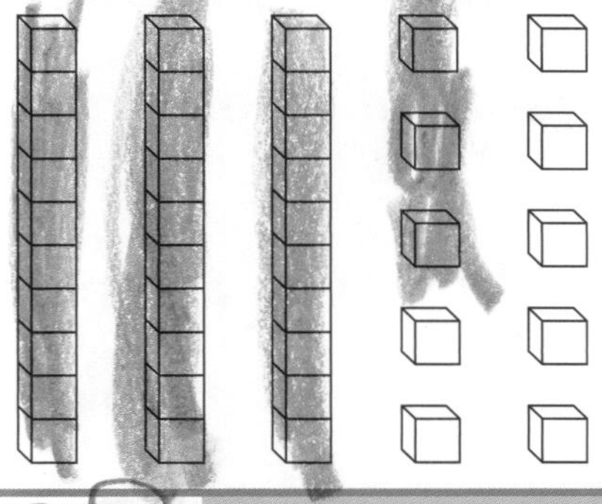

13 is less than 33

b. sixty | sixteen

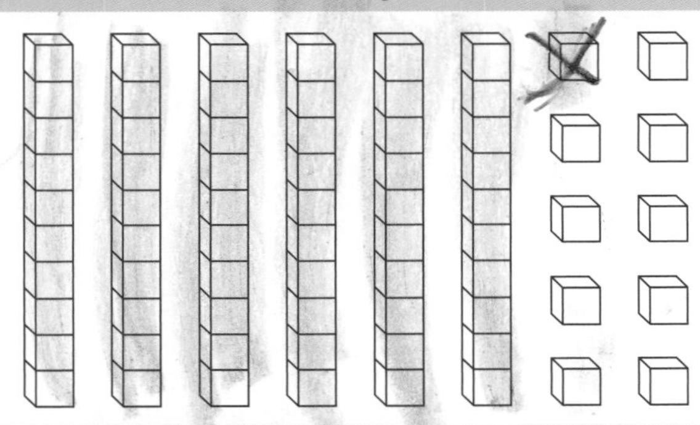

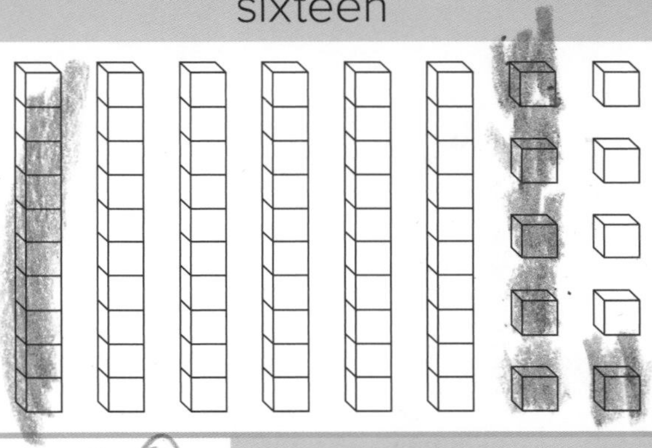

16 is less than 60

Step Ahead Which way is house number 58?
Draw an arrow on the street to show the direction.

6.5 Comparing Two-Digit Numbers (Place Value)

Compare the number of tens and ones in each place-value chart.

Is 51 **greater than** or **less than** 38?
How do you know?

tens	ones
5	1

tens	ones
3	8

When comparing two numbers which place do you look at first?

What would you do if the digits in the tens place were the same?

Step Up

1. Compare the numbers in the charts. Loop the words that are true.

a.

tens	ones
7	5

is greater than

is less than

tens	ones
5	2

b.

tens	ones
4	6

is greater than

is less than

tens	ones
5	0

c.

tens	ones
2	9

is greater than

is less than

tens	ones
2	2

d.

tens	ones
3	8

is greater than

is less than

tens	ones
6	8

2. Compare the numerals. Write **is greater than** or **is less than** to make true statements.

a. 88 ____________________ 90

b. 14 ____________________ 40

c. 67 ____________________ 29

d. 26 ____________________ 29

e. 33 ____________________ 19

3. Write other numerals to make true statements.

a. ______ is less than ______

b. ______ is greater than ______

c. ______ is greater than ______

d. ______ is less than ______

Step Ahead Write the digits in the boxes to make true statements. Use each digit only once.

0	1	2	3
4	5	6	7
8	8	9	9

__ __ is less than __ __

__ __ is greater than __ __

__ __ is less than __ __

6.6 Ordering Two-Digit Numbers

What does this picture show?

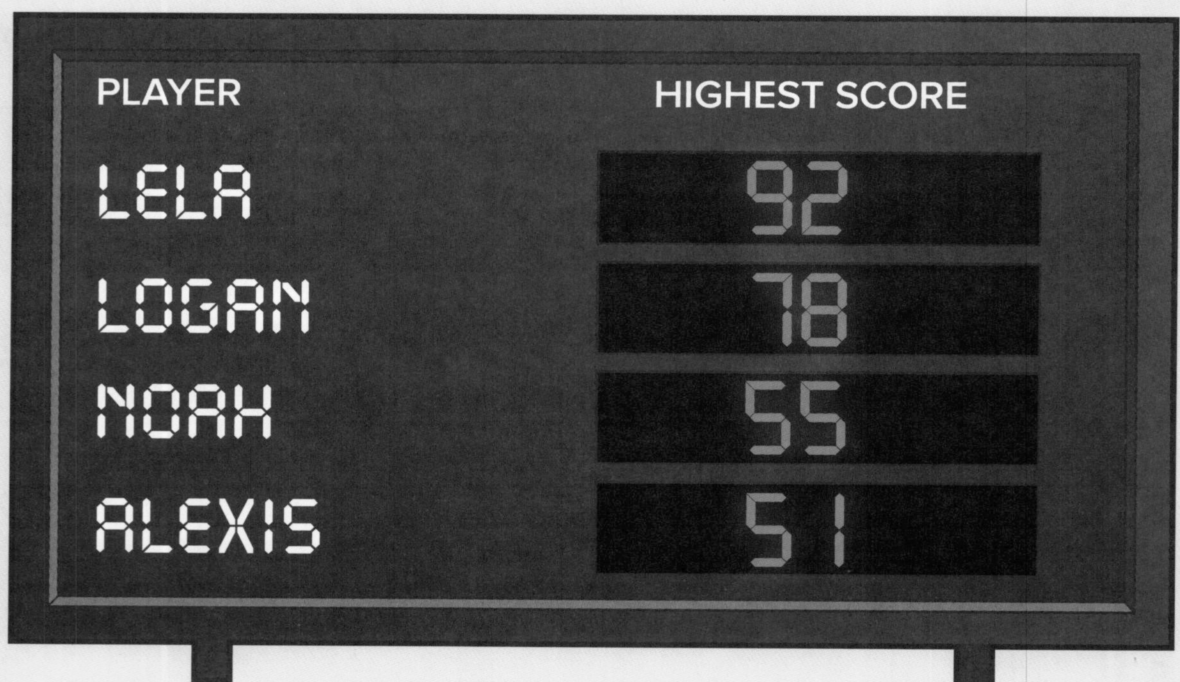

What do you notice about the scores?

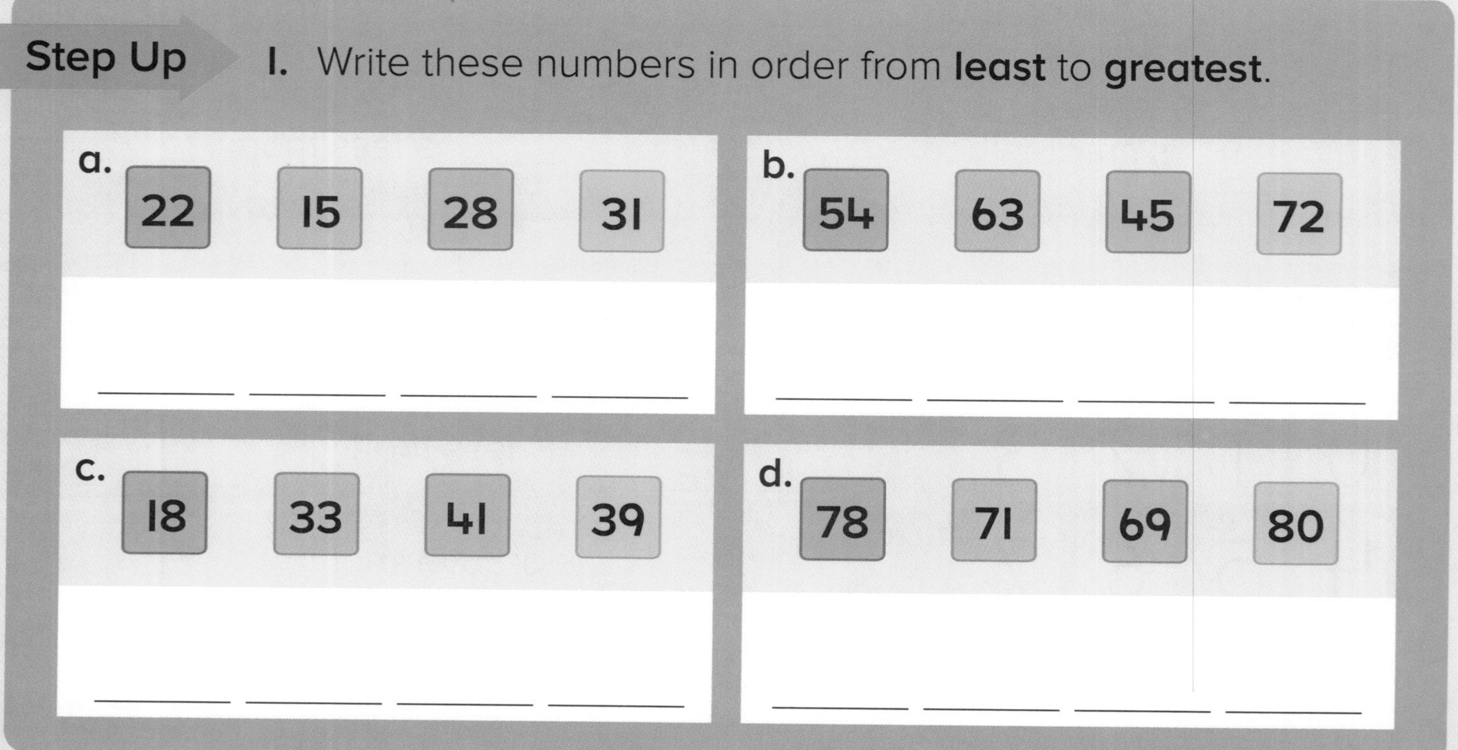

2. Write these numbers in order from **greatest** to **least**.

a. 29 31 24 19

____ ____ ____ ____

b. 48 42 46 55

____ ____ ____ ____

c. 65 70 73 61

____ ____ ____ ____

d. 90 82 88 18

____ ____ ____ ____

3. Write numbers to show **least** to **greatest**.

13, 17, 27, ____, ____, 52

4. Write numbers to show **greatest** to **least**.

88, ____, 61, 36, ____, 4

Step Ahead Read the story. Then write each name above the score that matches.

a. **John's** score was greater than **Peta's** score. **Emily's** score was less than **Peta's**.

____	____	____
13	22	34

b. **Anton's** score was greater than **Sofia's** but less than **Dixon's**.

____	____	____
35	42	57

6.7 Working with Place Value on a Hundred Chart

Look at the hundred chart below.
Run your finger along all the numbers that have 6 in the ones place.

Run your finger along the numbers that have 6 in the tens place.

What do you notice?

1	2	3	4	5	6	7	8	9	10
11	12	13	14	15	16	17	18	19	20
21	22	23	24	25	26	27	28	29	30
31	32	33	34	35	36	37	38	39	40
41	42	43	44	45	46	47	48	49	50
51	52	53	54	55	56	57	58	59	60
61	62	63	64	65	66	67	68	69	70
71	72	73	74	75	76	77	78	79	80
81	82	83	84	85	86	87	88	89	90
91	92	93	94	95	96	97	98	99	100

Color any two numbers on the hundred chart.

What digits are written in the tens and ones places?

Which of your numbers is greater?

Is either number greater than 50? How do you know?

Step Up Use the hundred chart on page 140 to help you answer these questions.

1. Read the clue then write the number.

a. I have 2 in the tens place and 5 in the ones place.

b. I have four ones and three tens.

c. I have 9 in the ones place and 2 in the tens place.

2. a. Write all the numbers less than 100 that have an 8 in the **tens** place.

____, ____, ____, ____, ____, ____, ____, ____, ____, ____

b. What do you notice about these numbers?

3. a. Write all the numbers less than 100 that have an 8 in the **ones** place.

____, ____, ____, ____, ____, ____, ____, ____, ____, ____

b. What do you notice about these numbers?

Step Ahead a. Look at the hundred chart on page 140. Write all the **two-digit** numbers that have the same digit in the tens and ones places.

____, ____, ____, ____, ____, ____, ____, ____, ____

b. What pattern do you see?

6.8 Skip Counting by 5 and 10

Look at the number track below.

How many fives can you find? Which numbers have a five?
How many zeros can you find? Which numbers have a zero?

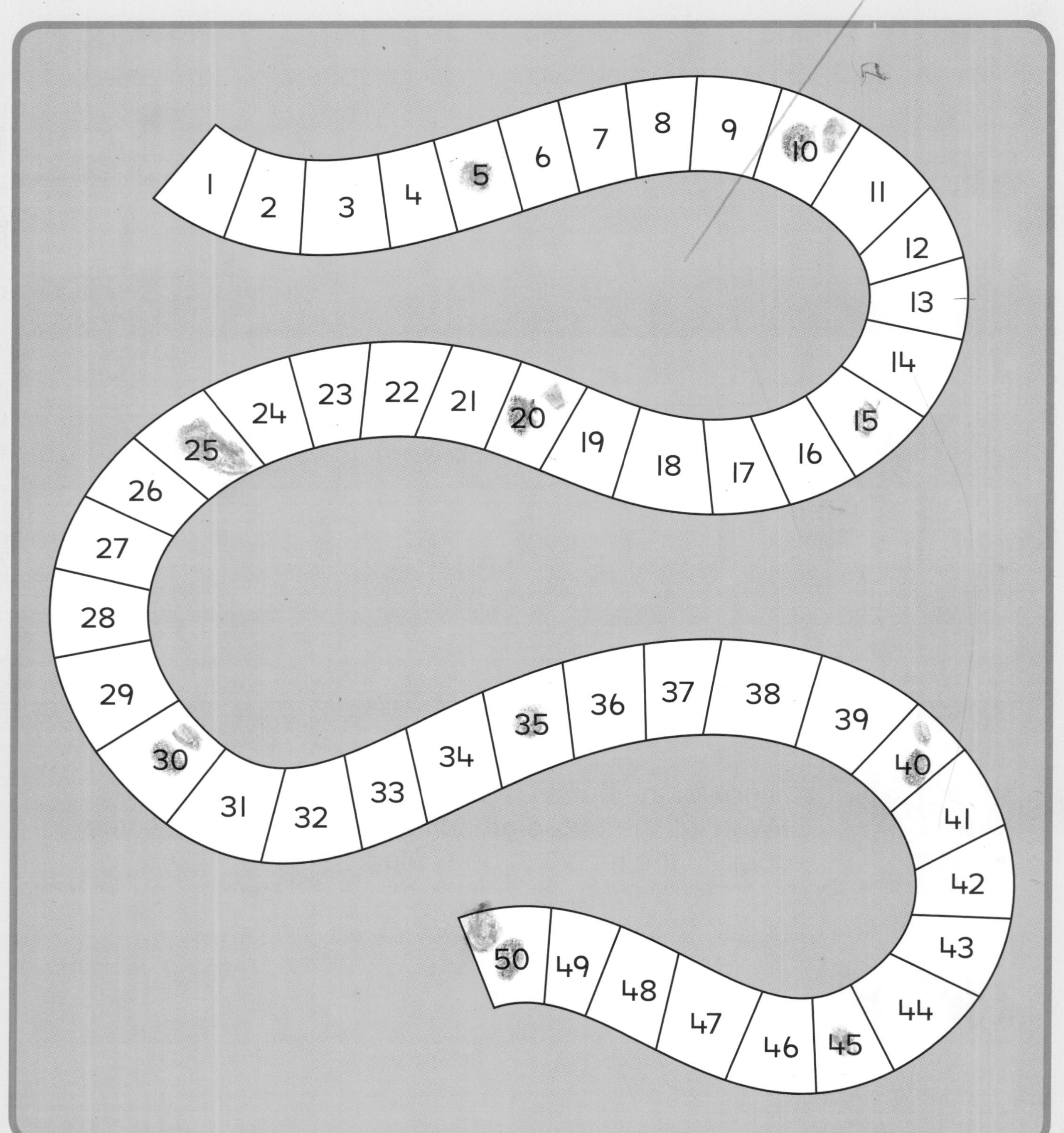

Step Up Use the number track on page 142 to help you answer these questions.

1. a. Start at 10. Draw ○ on the numbers you say when you count by 10.

   b. Write the numbers you say when you count by 10.

   10, 20, 30, 40, 50

   c. Look at the numbers you wrote. Write about a pattern you see.

   the numders all end with a Zero.

2. a. Start at 5. Draw ○ on the numbers you say when you count by 5.

   b. Write the numbers you say when you count by 5.

   5, 10, 15, 20, 25, 30, 35, 40, 45, 50

   c. Look at the numbers you wrote. Write about a pattern you see.

   they all end in a Zero or a five.

Step Ahead Imagine the number track on page 142 went to 100.

a. Write the numbers you would say if you kept counting by 10.

50, ___, ___, ___, ___, ___

b. Write the numbers you would say if you kept counting by 5.

50, ___, ___, ___, ___, ___, ___, ___, ___, ___, ___

6.9 Skip Counting by 2

Look at the number track below.

How many twos can you find? Which numbers have a two?

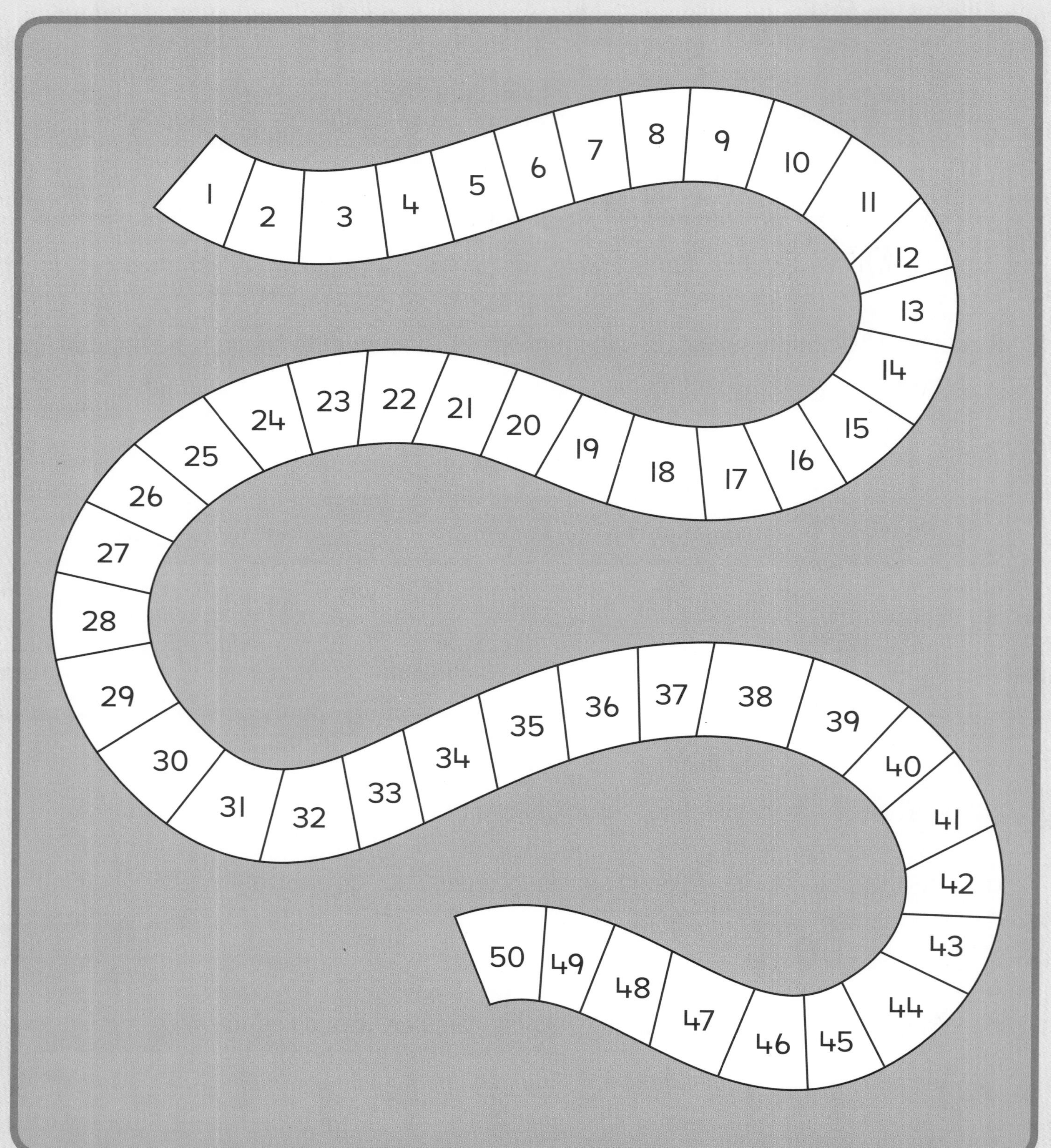

Step Up Use the number track on page 144 to help you answer these questions.

1. Start at 2. Draw ◯ on the numbers you say when you count by 2.

2. a. **Look at the numbers with orange dots.**
   Write the numbers that are between 12 and 40.

____, ____, ____, ____, ____, ____, 40

   b. Look at the numbers you wrote. Write about a pattern you see.

____

____

3. Imagine the number track on page 144 went to 100.
   Loop the numbers you say if you keep counting by 2.

53	62	56	79	90	81	68
99	74	60	88	57	75	

Step Ahead Use the number track on page 144.

a. Start at 3. Draw ● on the numbers you say when you count by 2.

b. **Look at the numbers with blue dots.**
   Write about what you notice.

____

____

6.10 Solving Number Puzzles on a Hundred Chart

Color three numbers greater than 10 on this hundred chart.

Each number should be in a different row.

1	2	3	4	5	6	7	8	9	10
11	12	13	14	15	16	17	18	19	20
21	22	23	24	25	26	27	28	29	30
31	32	33	34	35	36	37	38	39	40
41	42	43	44	45	46	47	48	49	50
51	52	53	54	55	56	57	58	59	60
61	62	63	64	65	66	67	68	69	70
71	72	73	74	75	76	77	78	79	80
81	82	83	84	85	86	87	88	89	90
91	92	93	94	95	96	97	98	99	100

What things do you know about your numbers?

Which number has the greatest number of ones?

Which number has the greatest number of tens?

Which number is the greatest?

Which number is the least?

How do you know?

Step Up Use the hundred chart on page 146 to help answer these questions.

1. Read the clue. Write the numeral that matches.

a. I have 7 in the tens place and 3 in the ones place.

______

b. I am greater than 44 but less than 46.

______

c. I am between 33 and 39. You say me when you start at 5 and count by 5.

______

d. I am in the same row as 56. You say me when you start at 10 and count by 10.

______

2. Write all the numerals that match these clues.

a. I am less than 43 and I have 4 tens.

______ ______ ______

b. I am greater than 69 and have 8 in the ones place.

______ ______ ______

c. I am greater than 86. You say me when you start at 50 and count by 5.

______ ______ ______

d. I am greater than 27 and less than 31.

______ ______ ______

Step Ahead Choose and write one numeral greater than 10. Write clues about your number.

______

____

____

____

6.11 Exploring Repeating Patterns

In repeating patterns there is a part that repeats over and over again.

What is the part that repeats in this pattern?

Loop the part. Then draw the next two shapes in the pattern.

Step Up 1. Loop the part that repeats in each of these patterns.

a.

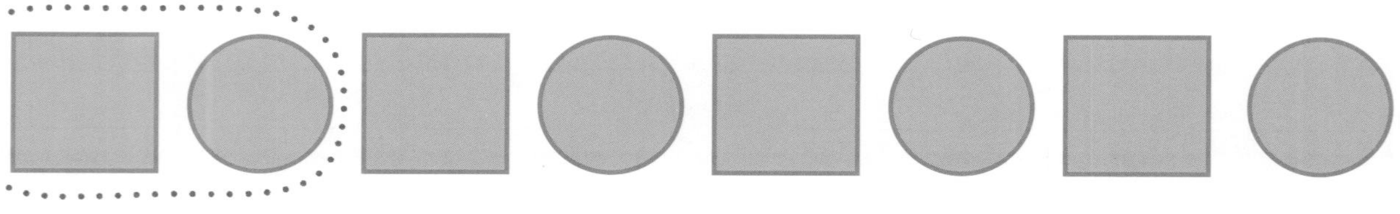

b.

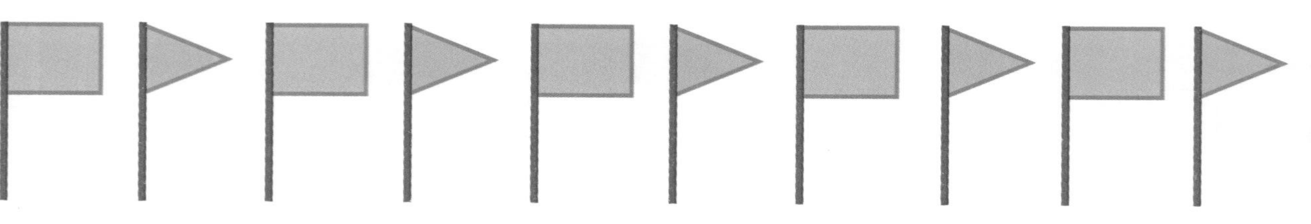

c.

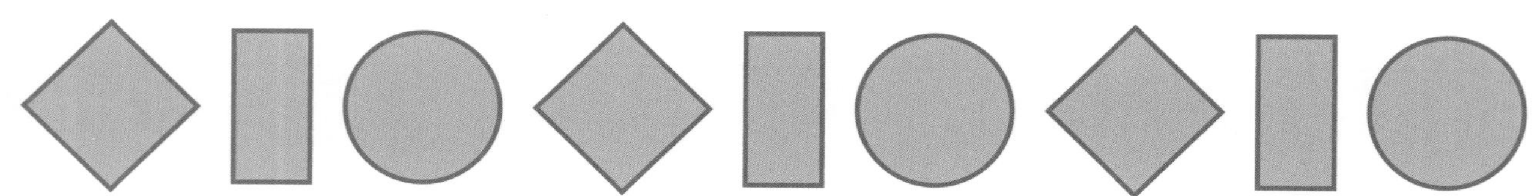

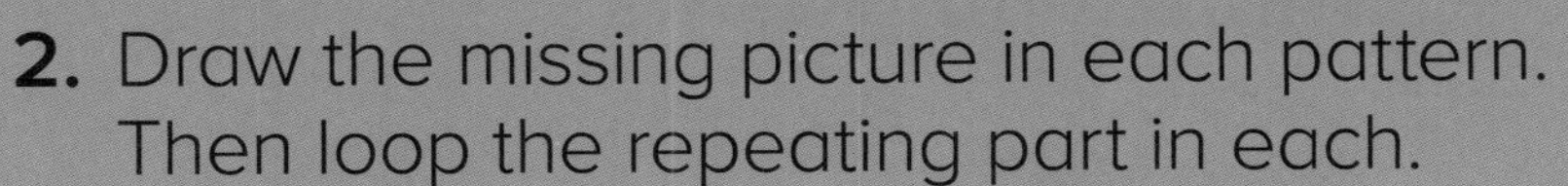

2. Draw the missing picture in each pattern.
Then loop the repeating part in each.

a.

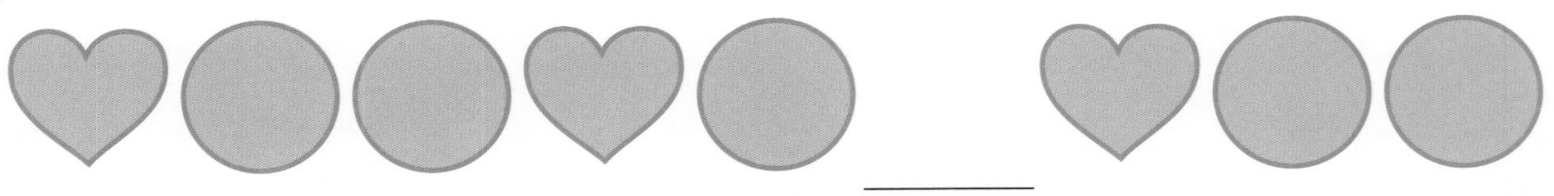

b.

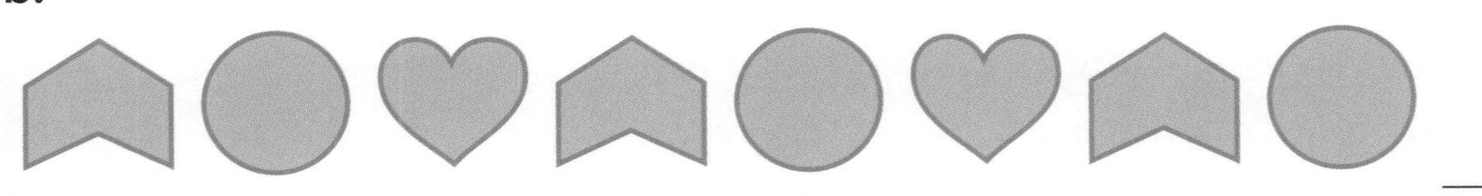

3. Draw two **different** repeating patterns using 2 or 3 shapes.
Loop the part that repeats in each.

Step Ahead Draw ♡ and △ to show the same repeating pattern.
Loop the part that repeats in each pattern.

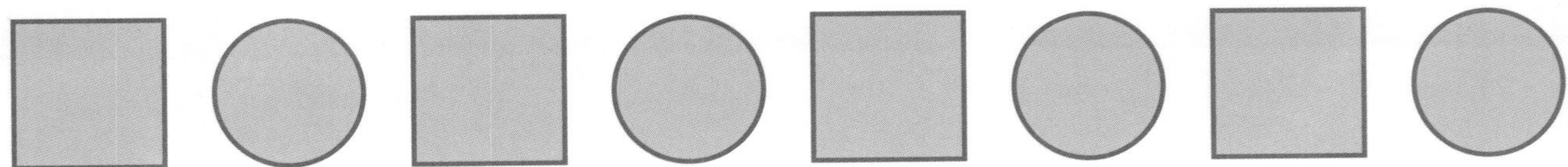

6.12 Exploring Growing and Shrinking Patterns

This is a **growing pattern**. Draw the next picture.

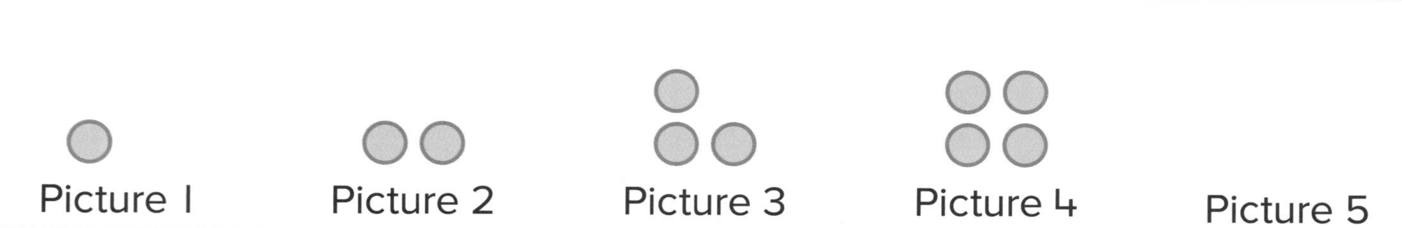

How would you describe this pattern to a friend?

This is a **shrinking pattern**. Draw the next picture.

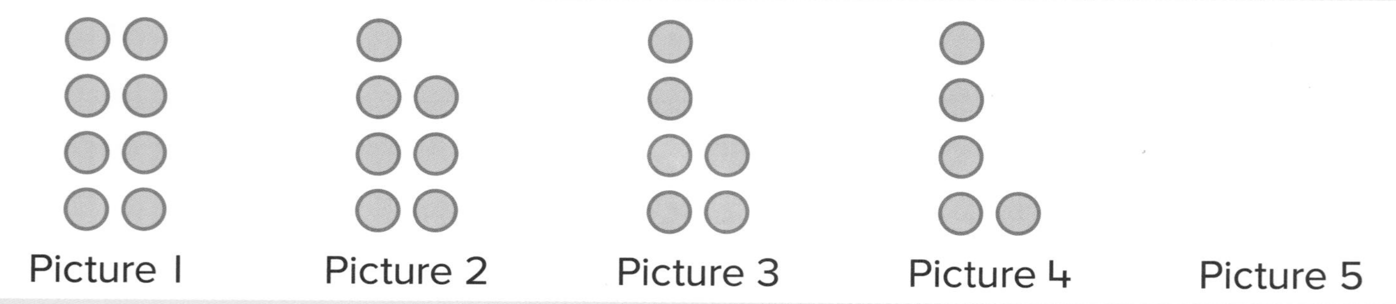

What will the next picture look like? How do you know?

Look at this number pattern. Is this a growing or shrinking pattern?
How do you know?

What is a shrinking pattern that uses numbers?

Step Up **1.** Draw the next picture in this pattern.

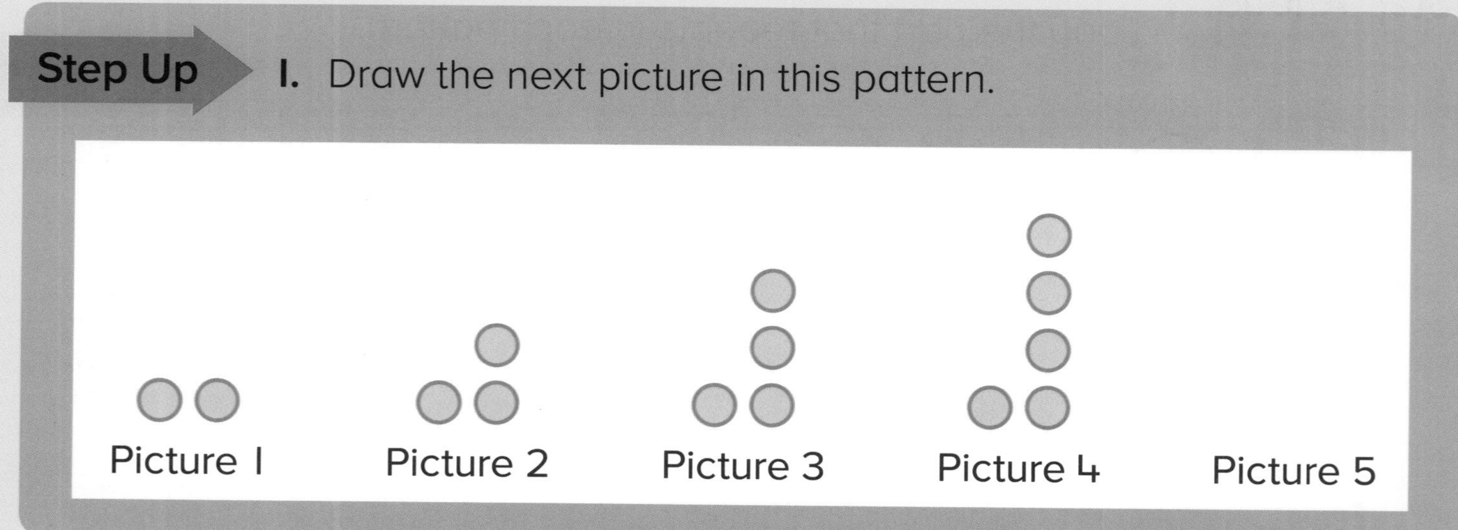

2. Draw the missing picture in each pattern.

a.

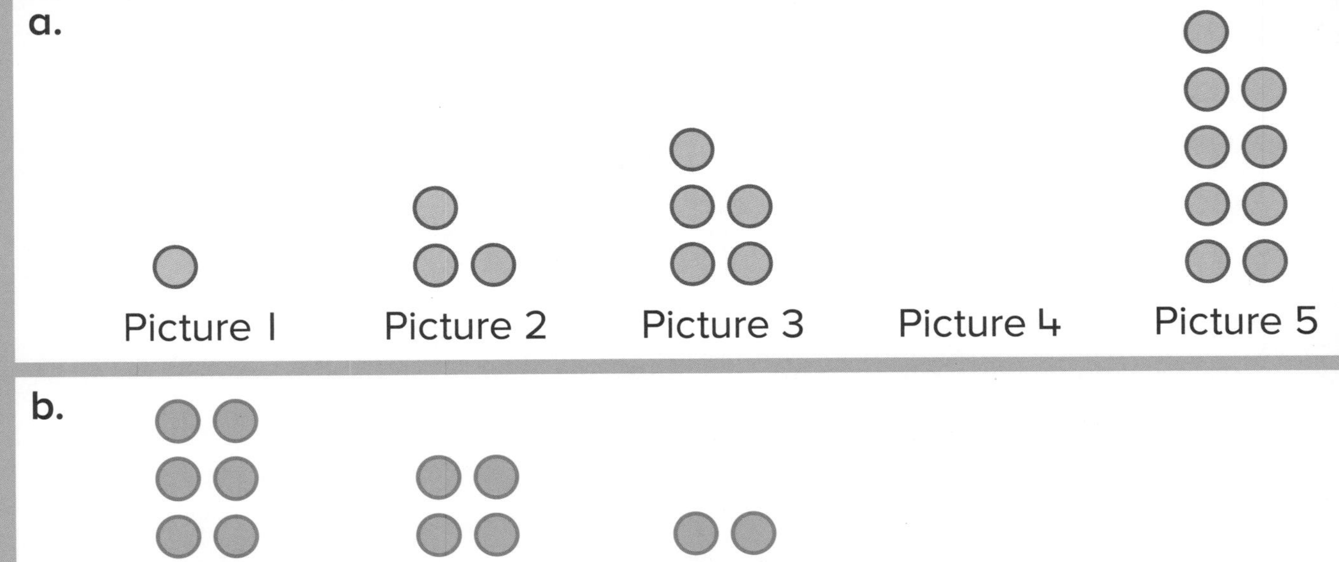

b.

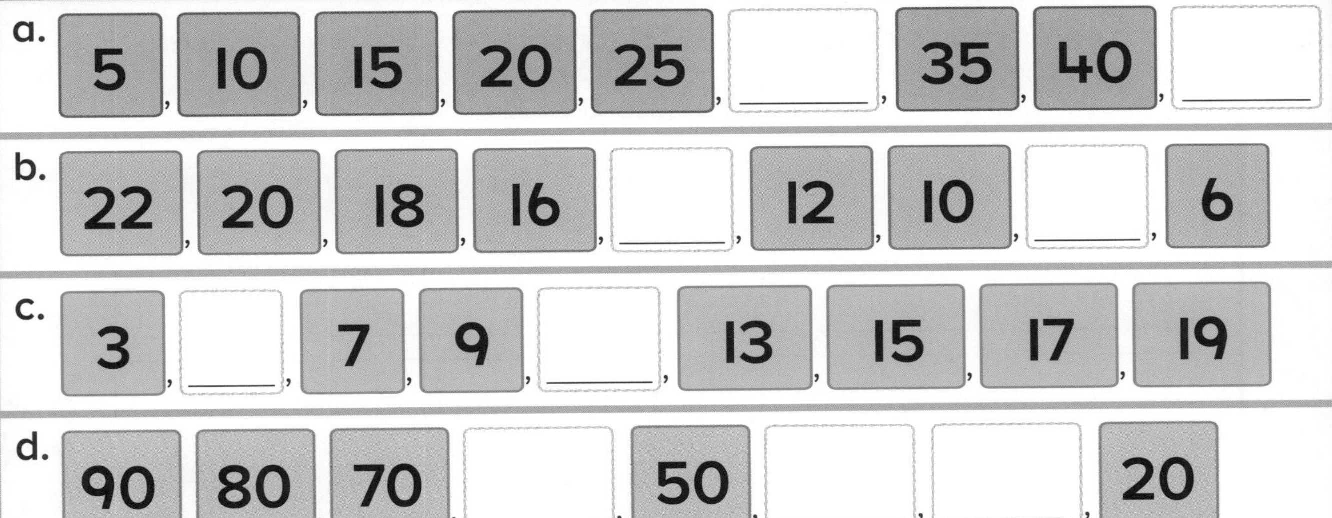

3. Write the missing numbers in each pattern.

a. 5, 10, 15, 20, 25, ____, 35, 40, ____

b. 22, 20, 18, 16, ____, 12, 10, ____, 6

c. 3, ____, 7, 9, ____, 13, 15, 17, 19

d. 90, 80, 70, ____, 50, ____, ____, 20

Step Ahead Write numbers to show another **growing** number pattern.

____, ____, ____, ____, ____, ____, ____, ____

7.1 Exploring Combinations of Ten

Look at these cubes.

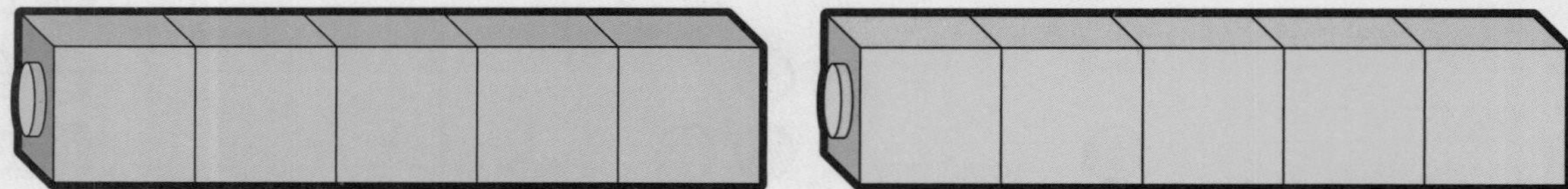

What addition sentence matches the picture?

How else could you break up the cubes?

What other addition sentences could you write?

Step Up

1. Color some of the cubes.
   Then write a matching addition sentence.

a. ___ + ___ = 10

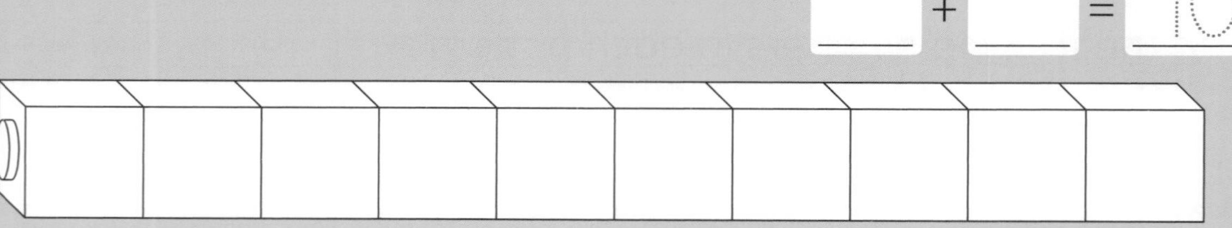

b. ___ + ___ = 10

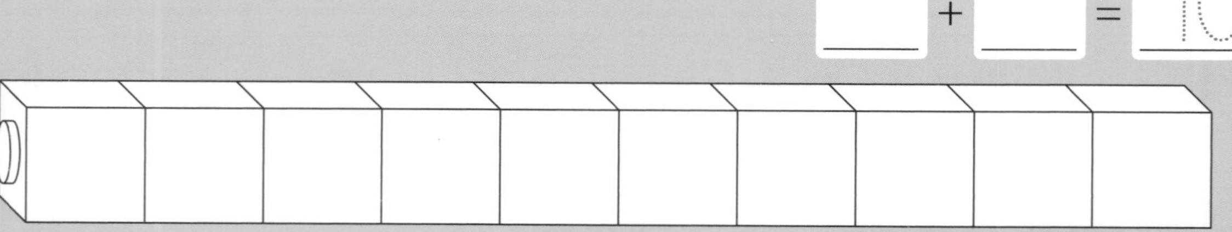

c. ___ + ___ = 10

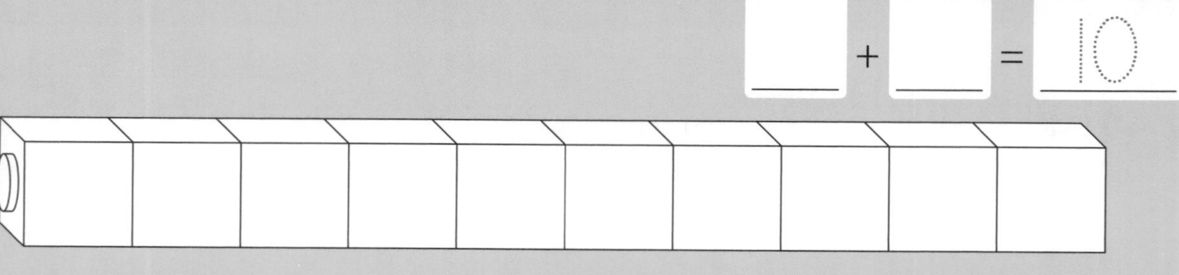

2. Color some of the cubes to make three parts.
Then write a matching sentence.

a. ___ + ___ + ___ = 10

b. ___ + ___ + ___ = ___

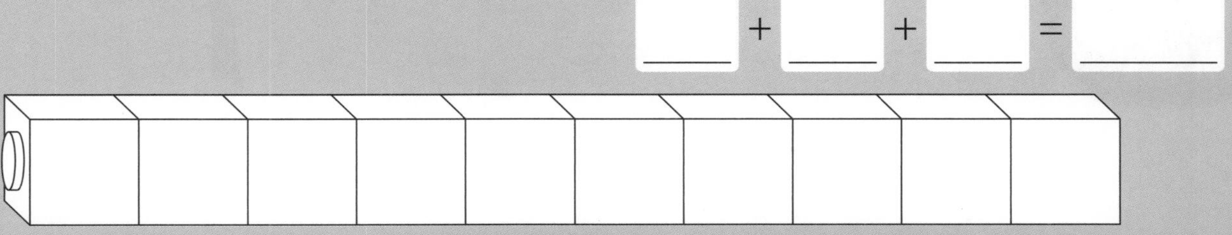

c. ___ + ___ + ___ = ___

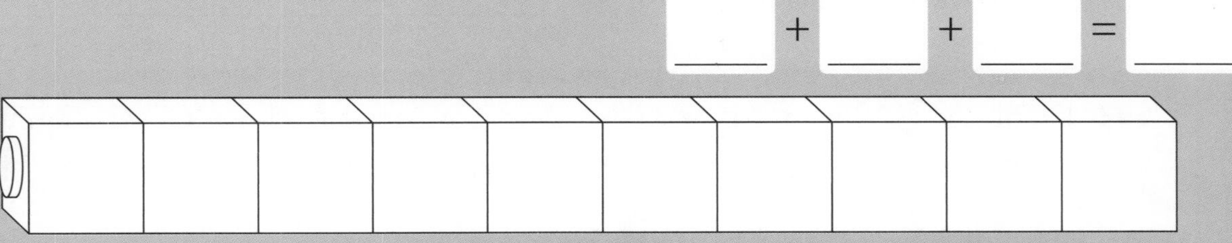

d. ___ + ___ + ___ = ___

Step Ahead Think of some different ways to break up **11** cubes.
Then complete these addition sentences to match.

___ + ___ = 11

11 = ___ + ___

___ + ___ + ___ = 11

11 = ___ + ___ + ___

7.2 Using the Associative Property of Addition with Three Whole Numbers

How many bugs are there in total?

How do you know?

I know there are 12 because 6 + 4 is 10 and 2 more are 12.

What addition sentence could you write to show how you added?

6 + 2 + 4 = 12

Step Up

1. Draw ⟷ to show two groups that make 10. Write an addition sentence to show how you add to find the total.

a.

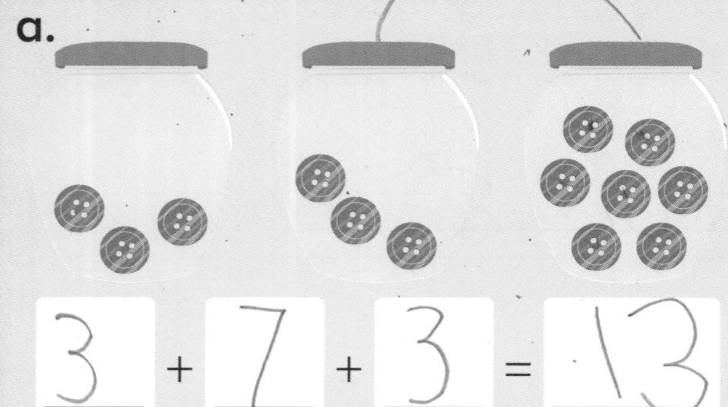

3 + 7 + 3 = 13

b.

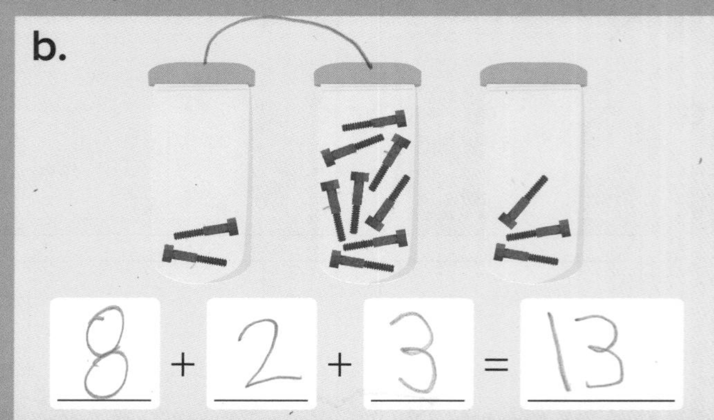

8 + 2 + 3 = 13

c.

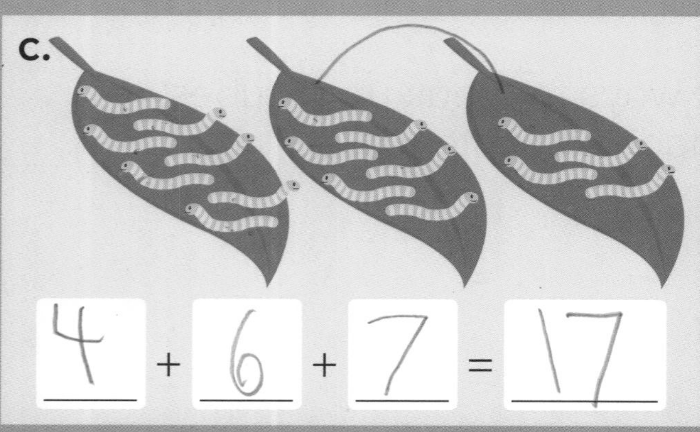

4 + 6 + 7 = 17

d.

5 + 5 + 4 = 14

2. Figure out the total. Write an addition sentence to show how you added.

a.

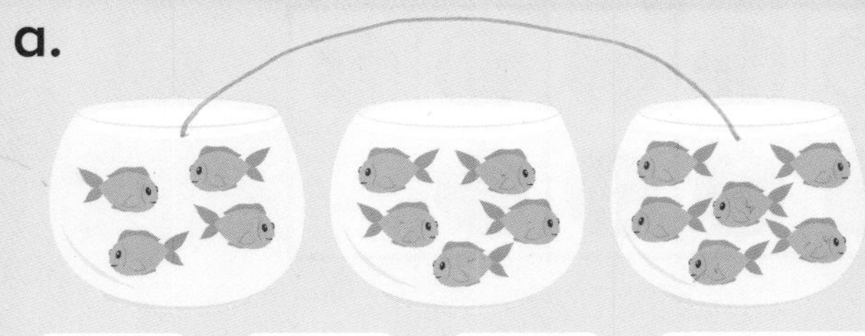

4 + 6 + 5 = 15

b.

9 + 1 + 5 = 15

c.

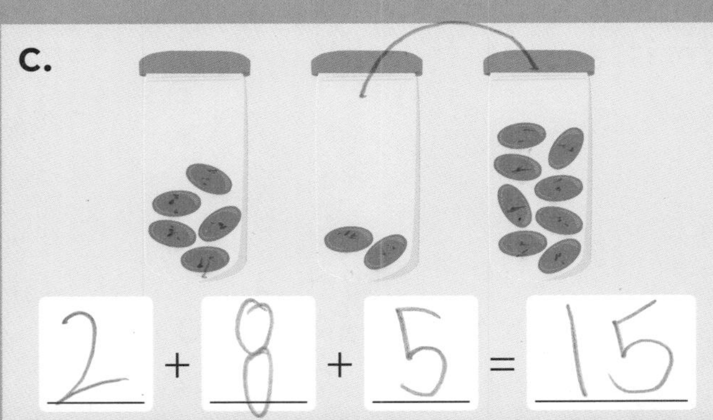

2 + 8 + 5 = 15

d.

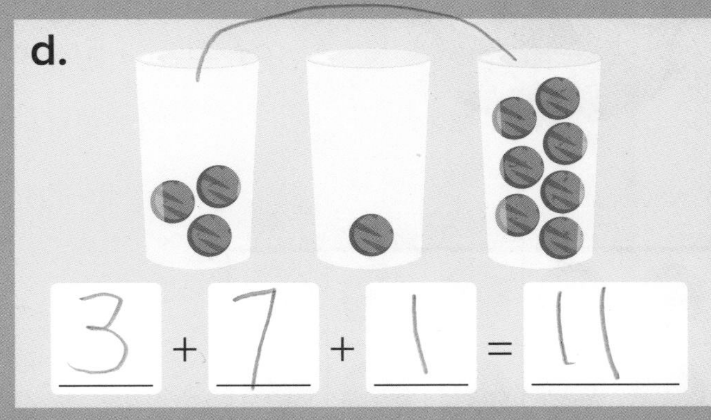

3 + 7 + 1 = 11

e.

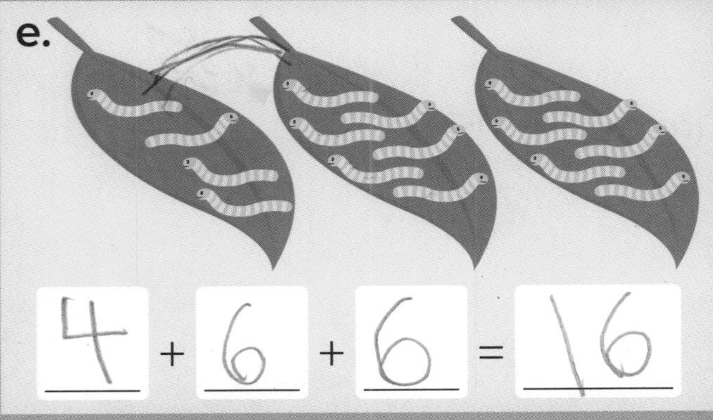

4 + 6 + 6 = 16

f.

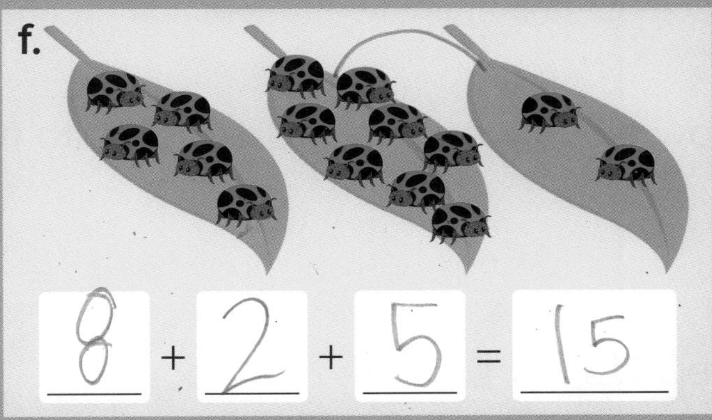

8 + 2 + 5 = 15

Step Ahead Write three different addition sentences to match this picture.

4 + 5 + 3 = 12

5 + 4 + 3 = 12

4 + 3 + 5 = 12

7.3 Introducing the Make-Ten Strategy for Addition

Look at this picture of counters.

How can you figure out the total?

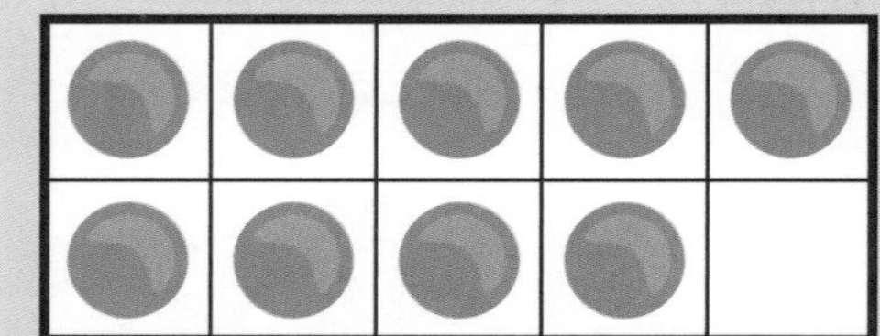

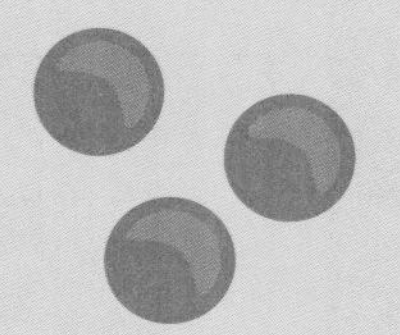

I moved one counter to make a group of 10. This made it easier to add.

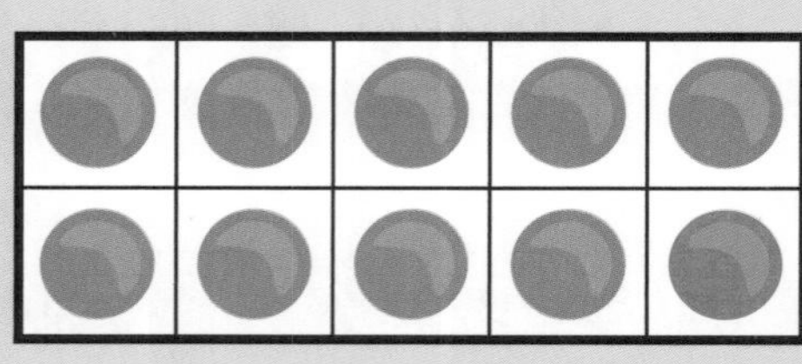

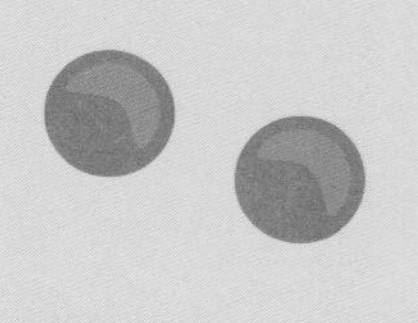

9 + 3
is the same as 10 + 2.
10 + 2 is 12.

How would you use this strategy to figure out 9 + 6?

Step Up **1.** Draw more counters. Then write the numbers to match.

a. Draw 5 more.

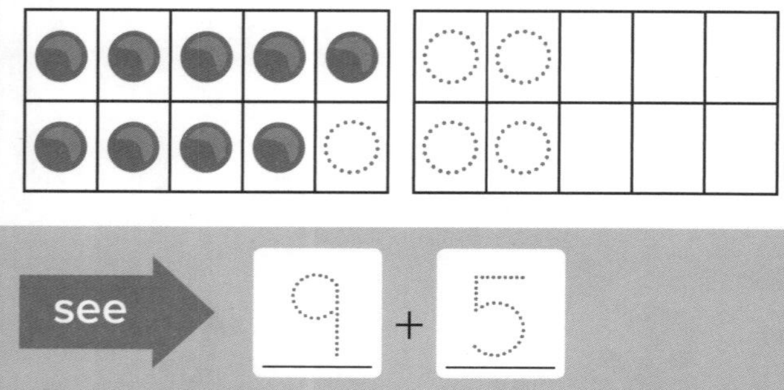

see 9 + 5

think 10 + 4

b. Draw 3 more.

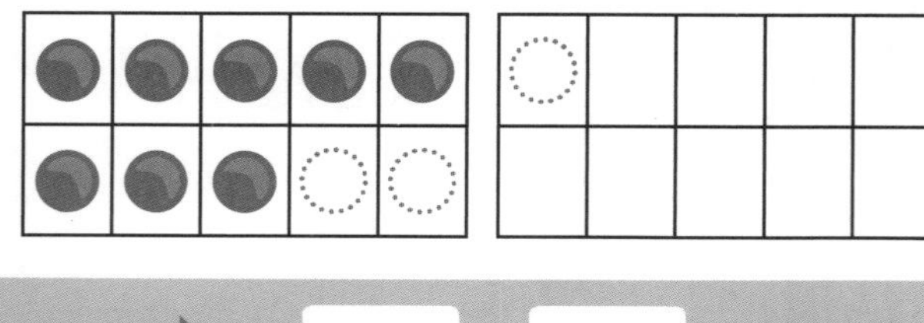

see ___ + ___

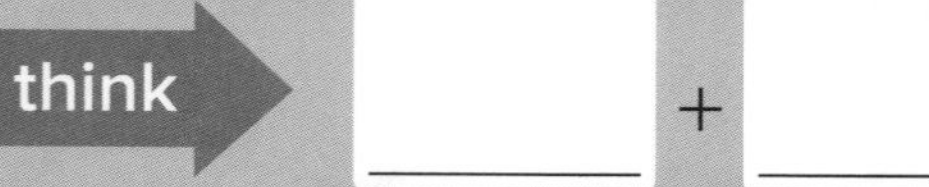

think ___ + ___

2. Draw more counters. Then write the numbers to match.

a. Draw 6 more.

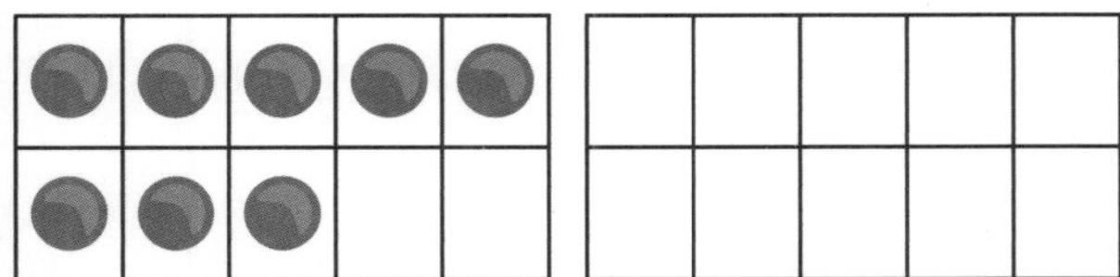

b. Draw 7 more.

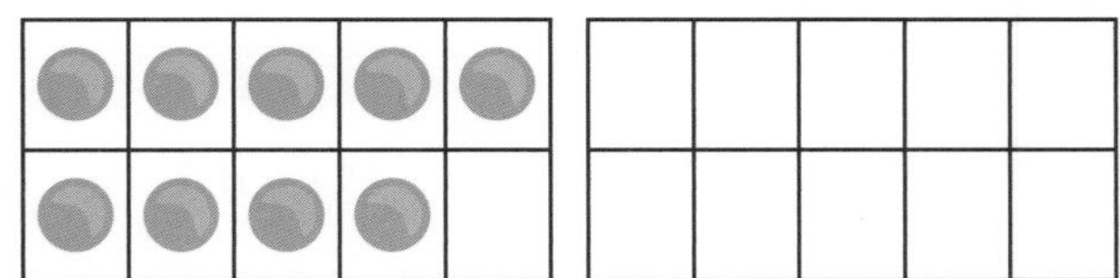

c. Draw 4 more.

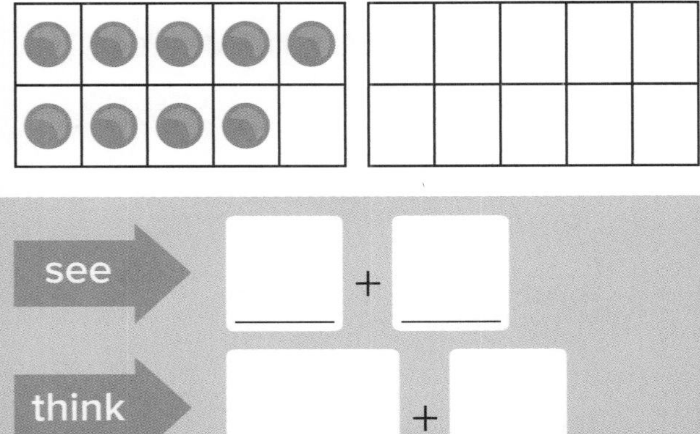

d. Draw 5 more.

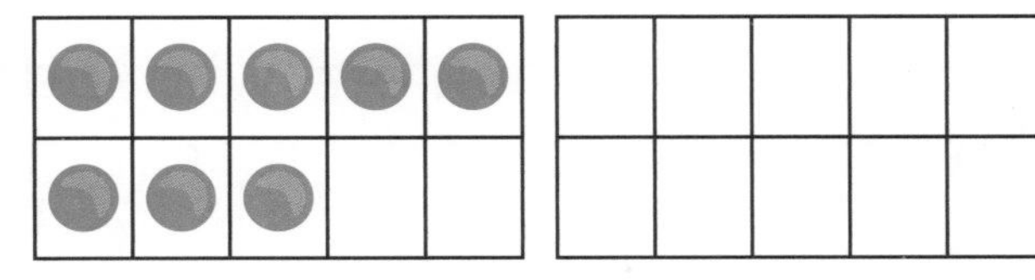

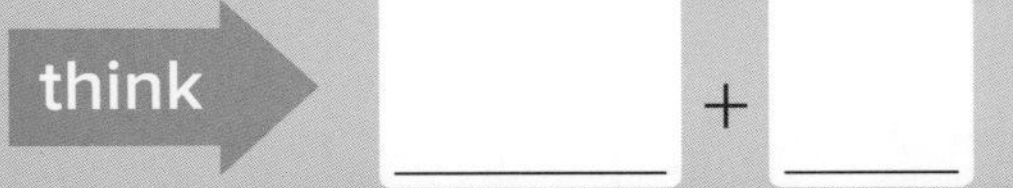

Step Ahead Think of **six** different ways this cube train could be broken into two groups. Complete the addition sentences to match.

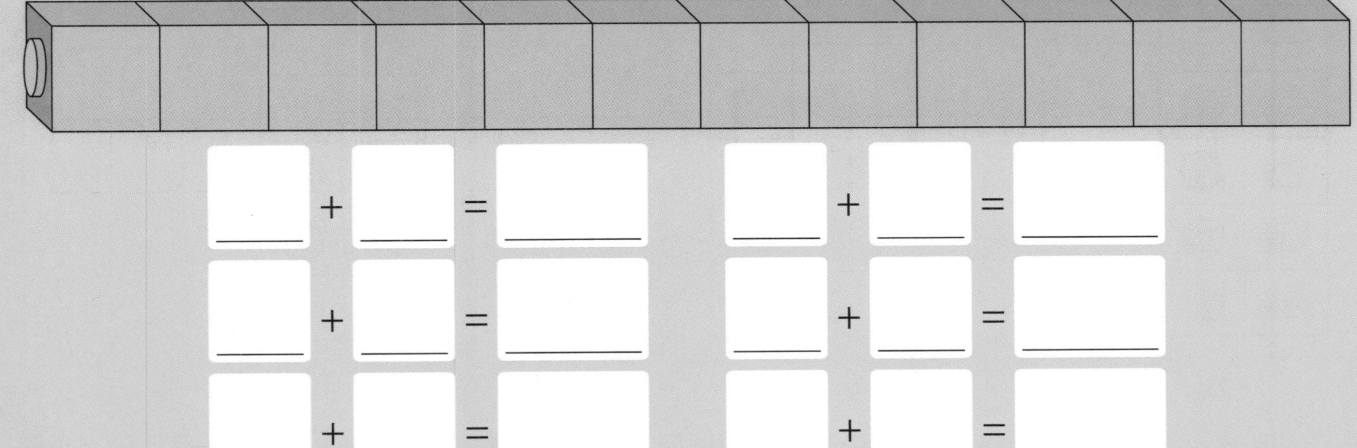

7.4 Using the Make-Ten Strategy for Addition

What do you notice about the counters in this picture?

How can you easily figure out the total?

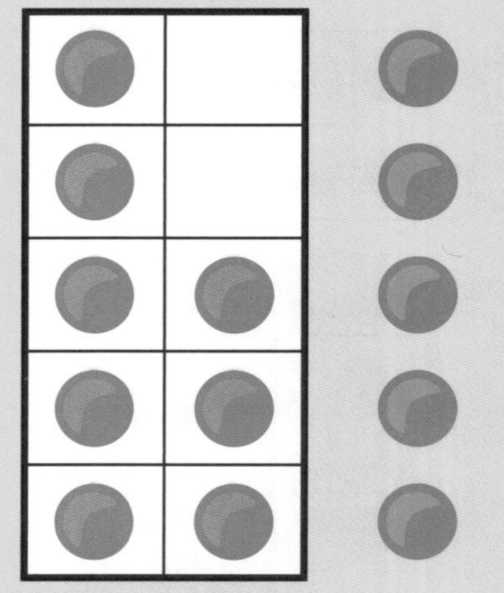

I would move two counters to fill the frame then figure out the total.

If you moved two counters, what addition sentence could you write to show the number of counters that would be on and off the frame?

______

Step Up

1. Draw more counters to figure out the total. Fill the ten-frame first. Then write the tens fact to match the picture.

a. 9 + 3 = ____

10 + ____ = ____

b. 9 + 6 = ____

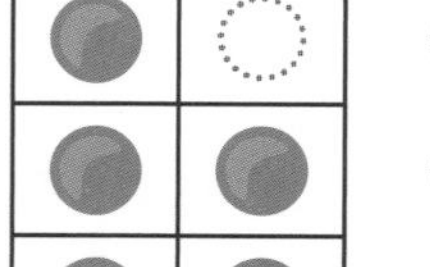
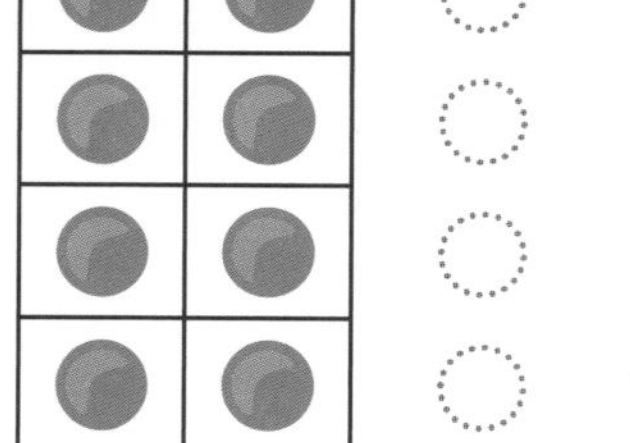

10 + ____ = ____

c. 8 + 4 = ____

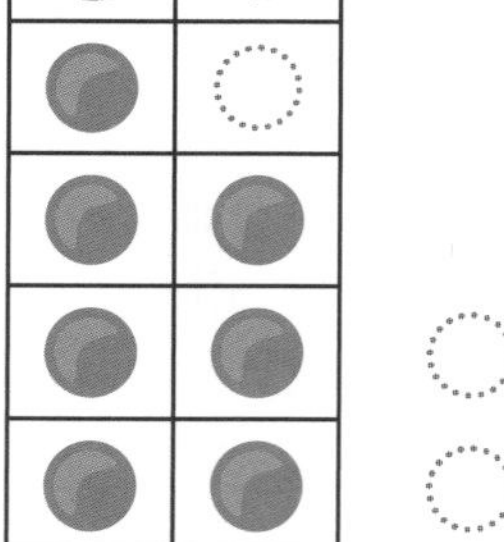

10 + ____ = ____

2. Draw more counters to figure out the total. Fill the ten-frame first. Then write the tens fact to match the picture.

a. 9 + 5 = ____

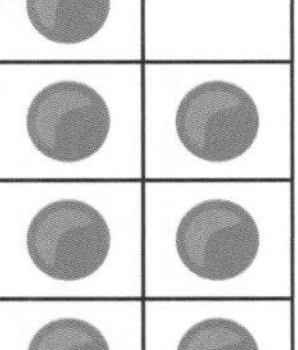

____ + ____ = ____

b. 8 + 5 = ____

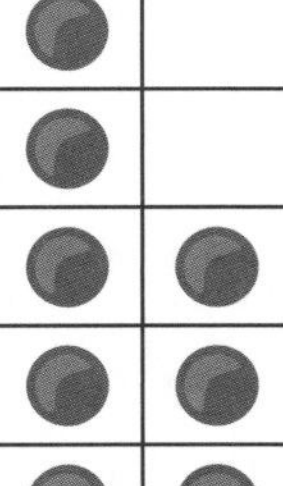

____ + ____ = ____

c. 9 + 7 = ____

____ + ____ = ____

d. 8 + 7 = ____

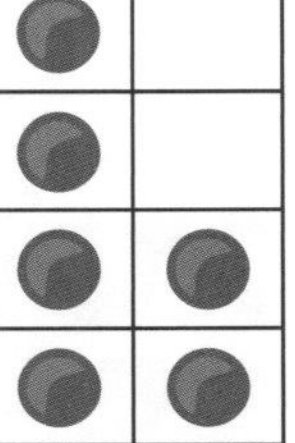

____ + ____ = ____

e. 9 + 8 = ____

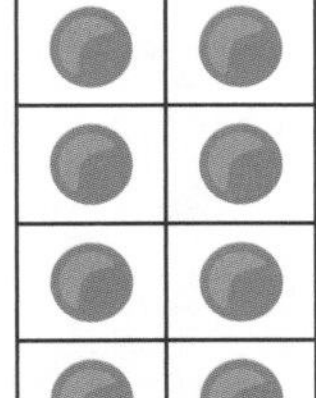

____ + ____ = ____

f. 8 + 3 = ____

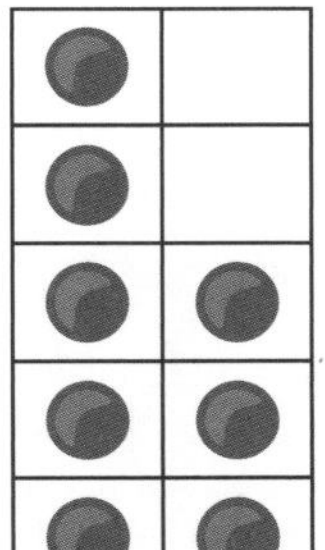

____ + ____ = ____

Step Ahead Loop the facts that have the same total as the counters in this picture.

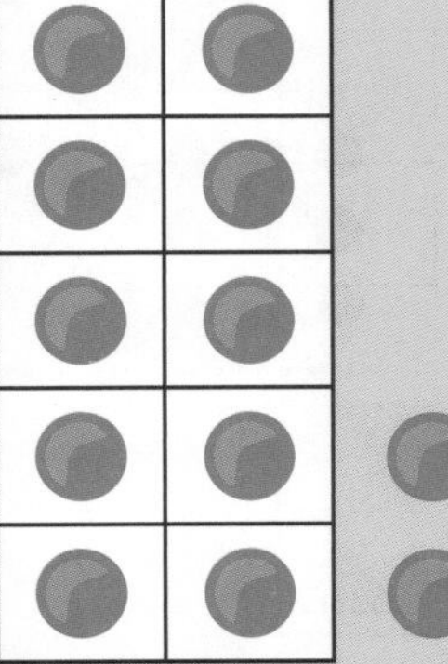

9 + 3   8 + 5   7 + 5

8 + 4   8 + 3

Using the Commutative Property of Addition with Make-Ten Facts

What two addition facts match this picture?

Which fact do you think is easier to figure out? Why?

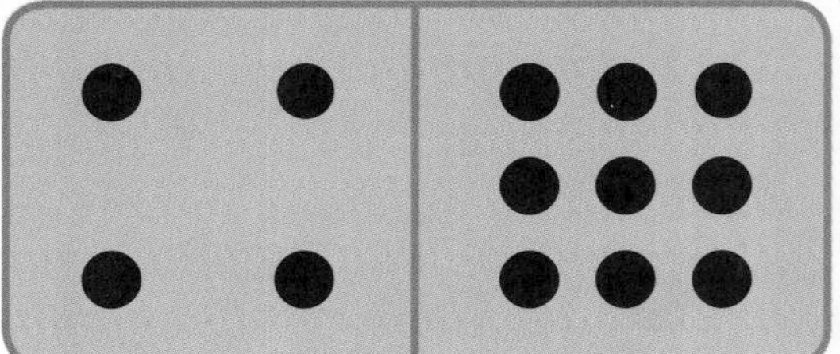

I find it easier to figure out 9 + 4 then write the turnaround.

Step Up

1. Write an addition fact to match each picture. Then write the turnaround fact.

a.

___ + ___ = ___

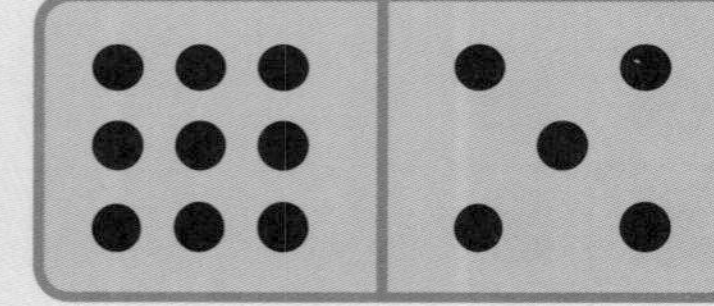

___ + ___ = ___

b.

___ + ___ = ___

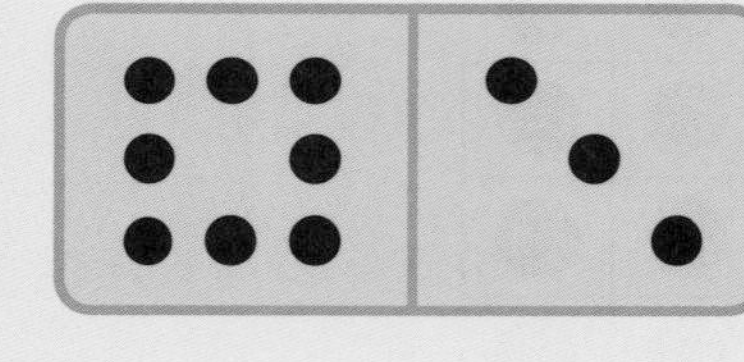

___ + ___ = ___

c.

___ + ___ = ___

___ + ___ = ___

d.

___ + ___ = ___

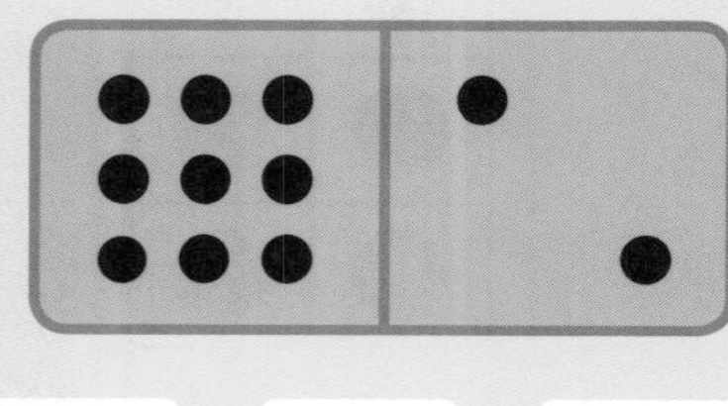

___ + ___ = ___

e.

___ + ___ = ___

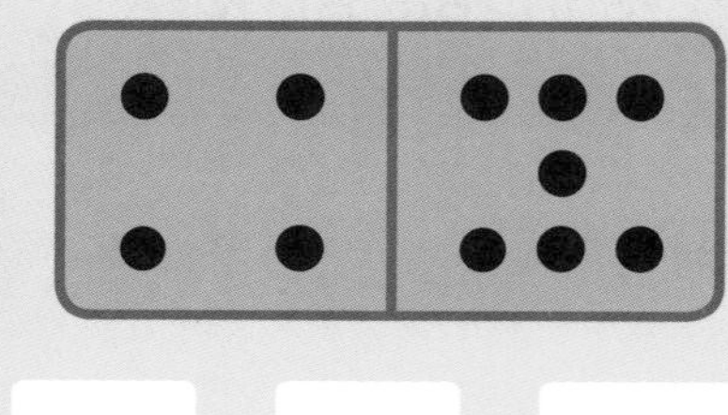

___ + ___ = ___

f.

___ + ___ = ___

___ + ___ = ___

2. Write an addition fact to match each picture. Then write the turnaround fact.

a.

___ + ___ = ___

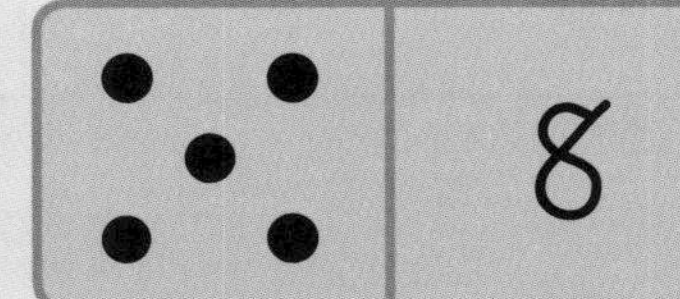

8

___ + ___ = ___

b.

___ + ___ = ___

9

___ + ___ = ___

c.

___ + ___ = ___

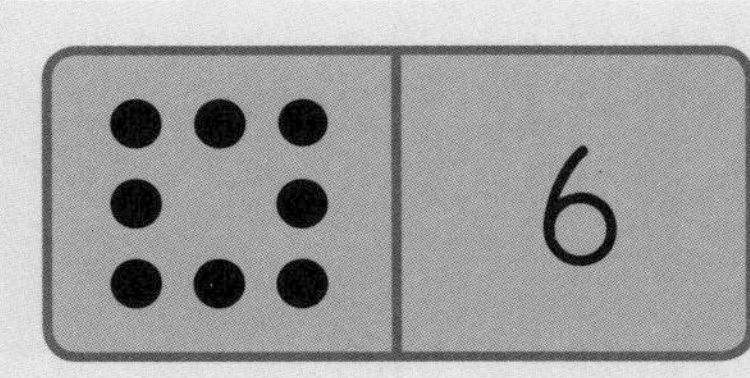

6

___ + ___ = ___

d.

___ + ___ = ___

3

___ + ___ = ___

e.

___ + ___ = ___

7

___ + ___ = ___

f.

___ + ___ = ___

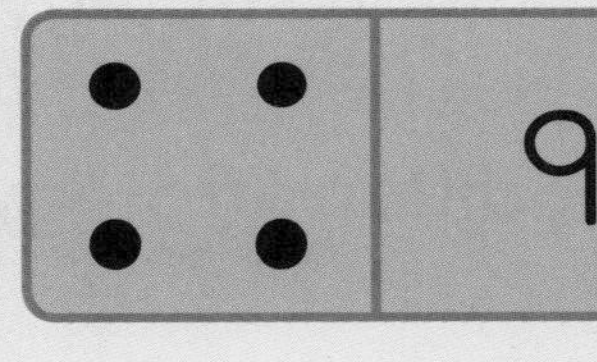

9

___ + ___ = ___

Step Ahead Add the numbers in each row. Then add the numbers in each column. Write what you notice.

8	1	6	___
3	5	7	___
4	9	2	___
___	___	___	

____

____

____

____

7.6 Consolidating Addition Strategies

Look at these pictures.

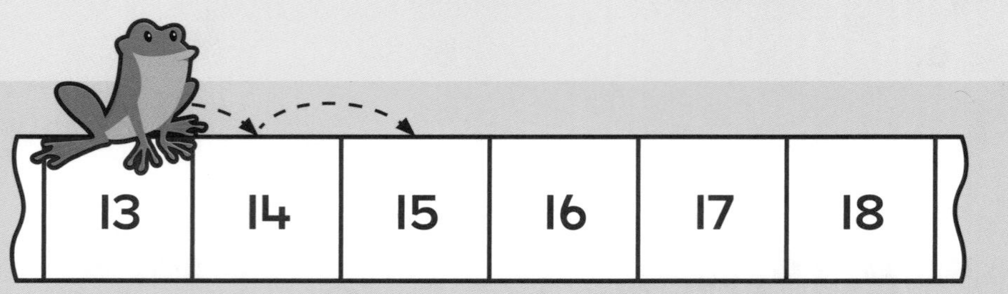

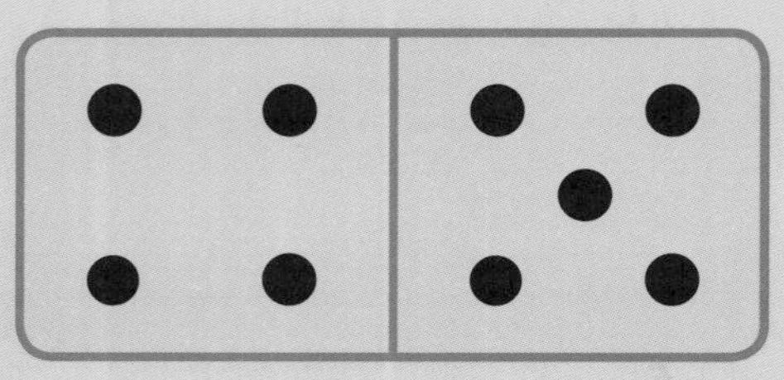

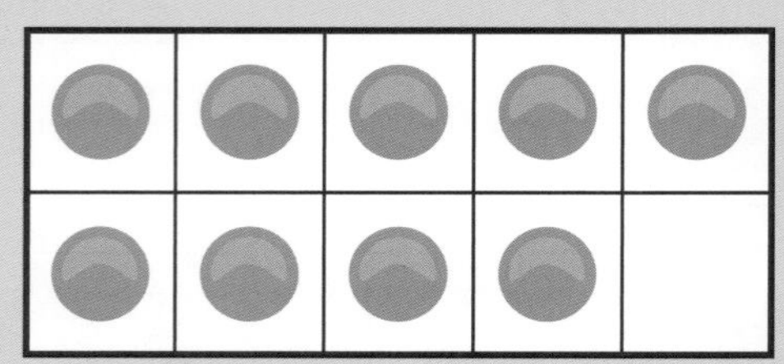

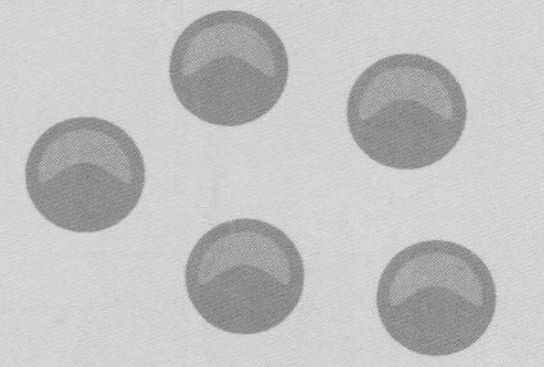

How could you figure out the total in each picture?

Which addition strategy would you use?

Which addition strategy would you use to solve each of these facts?

6 + 7 = ______ 2 + 9 = ______ 5 + 8 = ______

Step Up

1. Write the answer. Then color the circle green, blue, or orange to show the strategy you used to figure out the total.

Addition Strategy
- count-on
- doubles
- make-ten

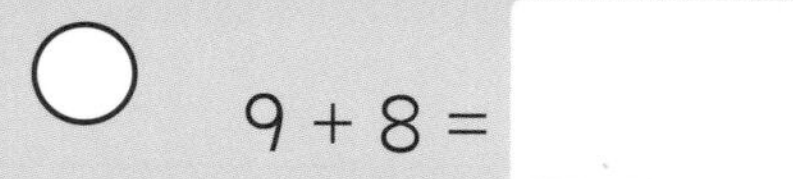

○ 13 + 1 = ______	○ 9 + 8 = ______	
○ 5 + 6 = ______	○ 3 + 9 = ______	○ 2 + 16 = ______
○ 8 + 8 = ______	○ 9 + 2 = ______	○ 7 + 9 = ______

2. Write the answer. Then draw a line to the strategy you used to figure it out.

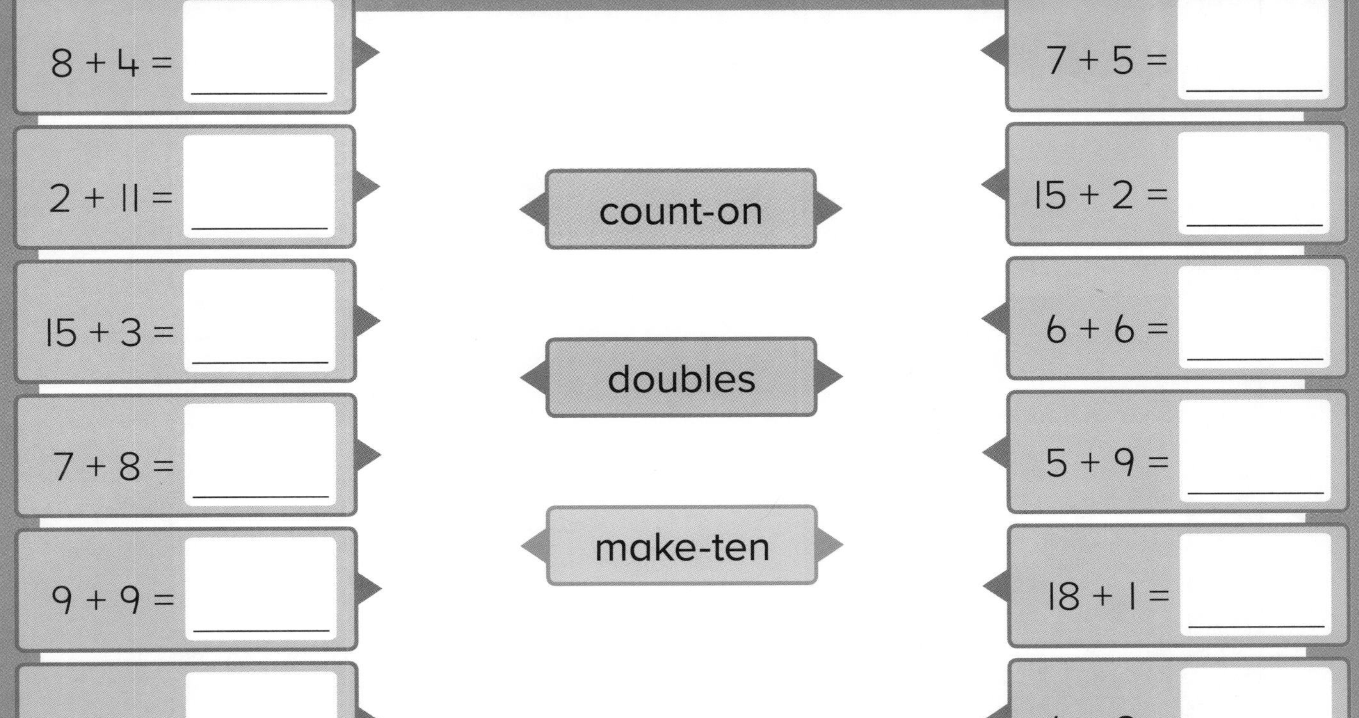

Step Ahead You can use more than one strategy to solve the same fact. Complete these to show the different ways these totals can be figured out.

a. Use the make-ten strategy

9 + 8 = ____

is the same as

10 + ____ = ____

Use the double-plus-1 strategy

9 + 8 = ____

is the same as

double ____ plus ____ = ____

b. Use the make-ten strategy

8 + 6 = ____

is the same as

____ + ____ = ____

Use the double-plus-2 strategy

8 + 6 = ____

is the same as

double 6 plus ____ = ____

7.7 Applying Addition Strategies

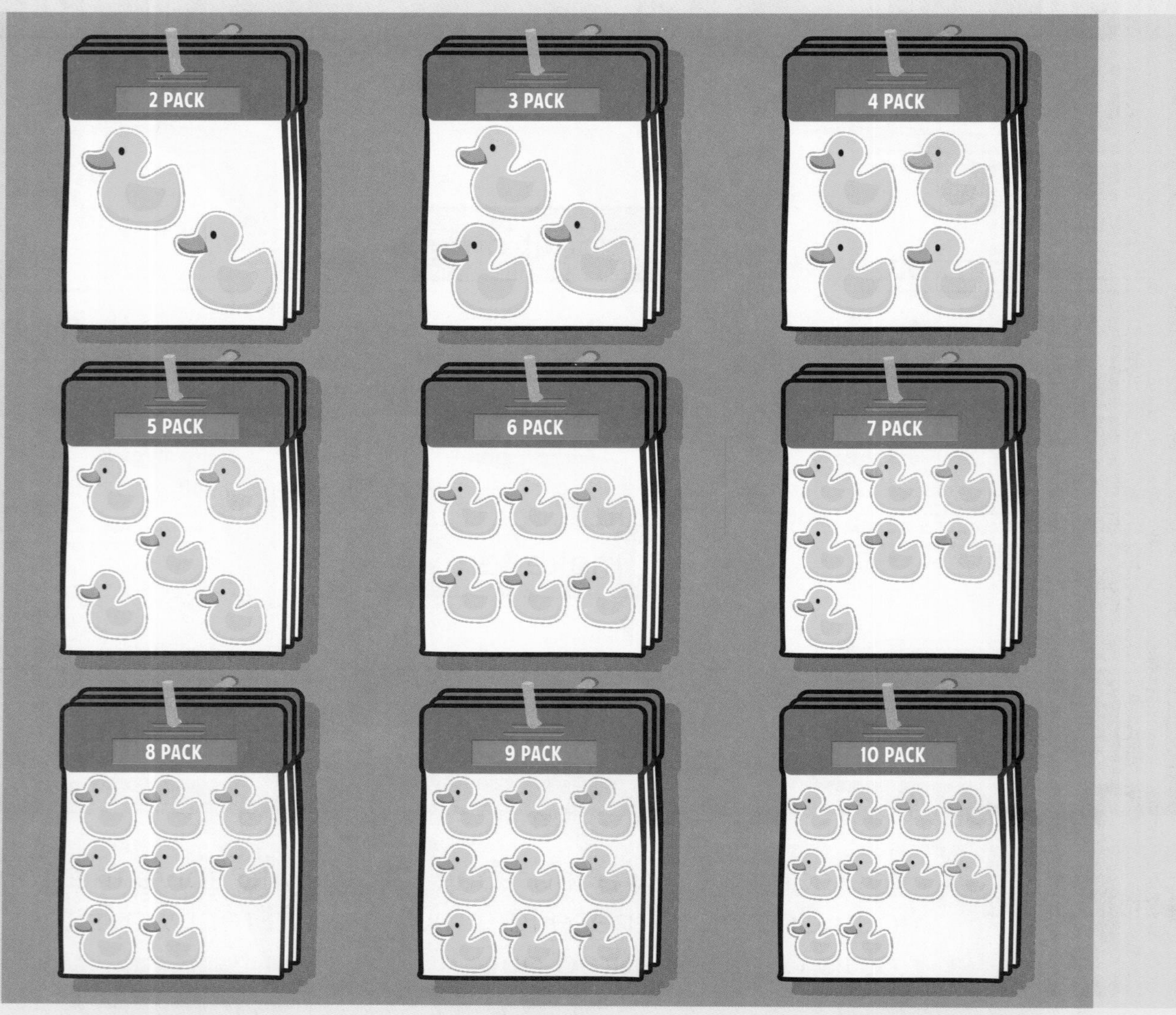

Choose two sheets of stickers with numbers that are easy to add.

How did you decide?

What is an addition story that matches the sheets you chose?

What addition sentence could you write to match?

What strategy did you use to figure out the total?

Choose one sheet of stickers from each row.
Use numbers that are easy to add.

How did you decide?

What is an addition story that matches the sheets you chose?

What addition sentence could you write to match?

What strategy did you use to figure out the total?

Step Up

a. Write an addition sentence to match the picture.
Then write a word story to match.

b. Write an addition sentence to figure out the total in these three jars.
Then write a word story to match.

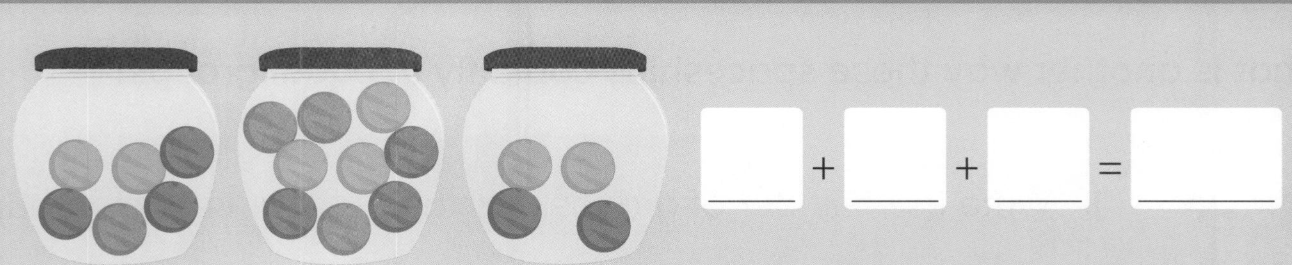

Step Ahead

Imagine you had one of each sheet of stickers shown on page 164. How many stickers would you have in total? Try to make tens first, then find the total.

7.8 Working with Equal Groups

Look at these groups of spaceships. What do you notice?

How many groups are there?

How many spaceships are in each group?

What is the total? How do you know?

What is another way these spaceships could fly in equal groups?

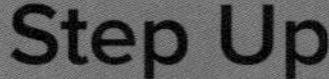

1. Write the number of groups and the number in each group.

a.

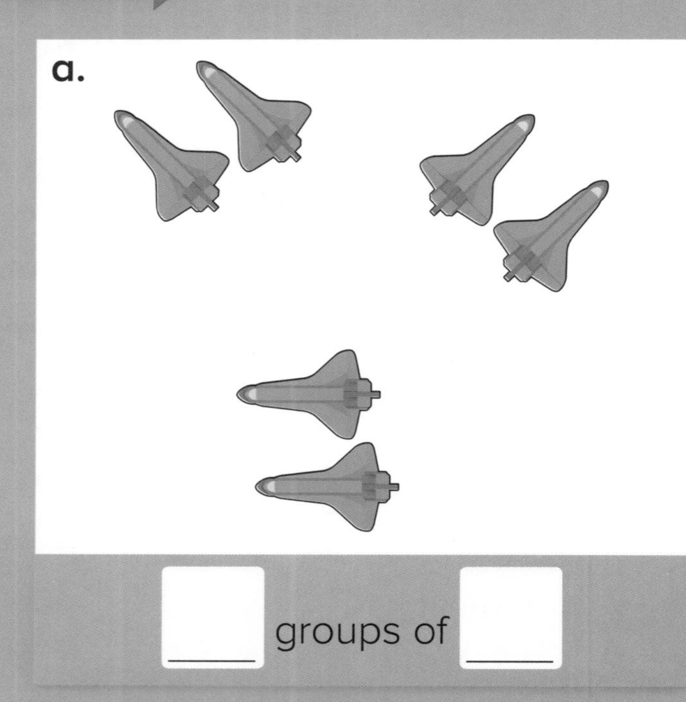

☐ groups of ☐

b.

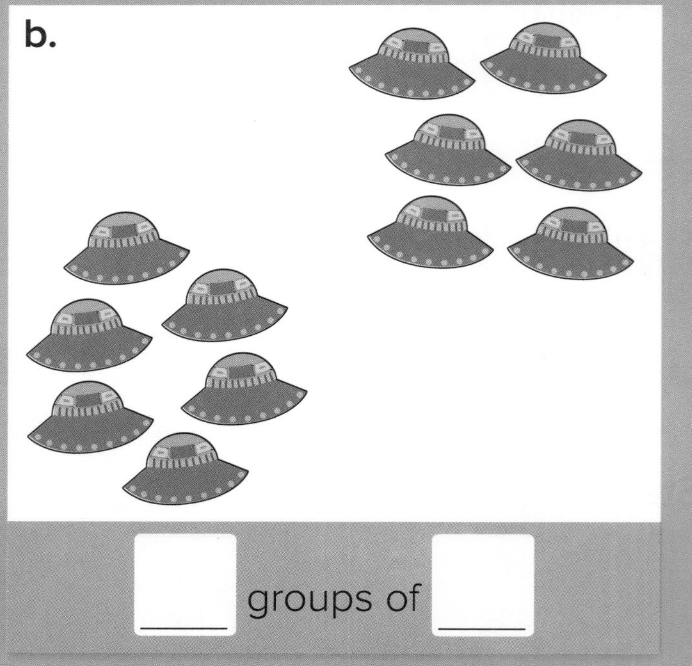

☐ groups of ☐

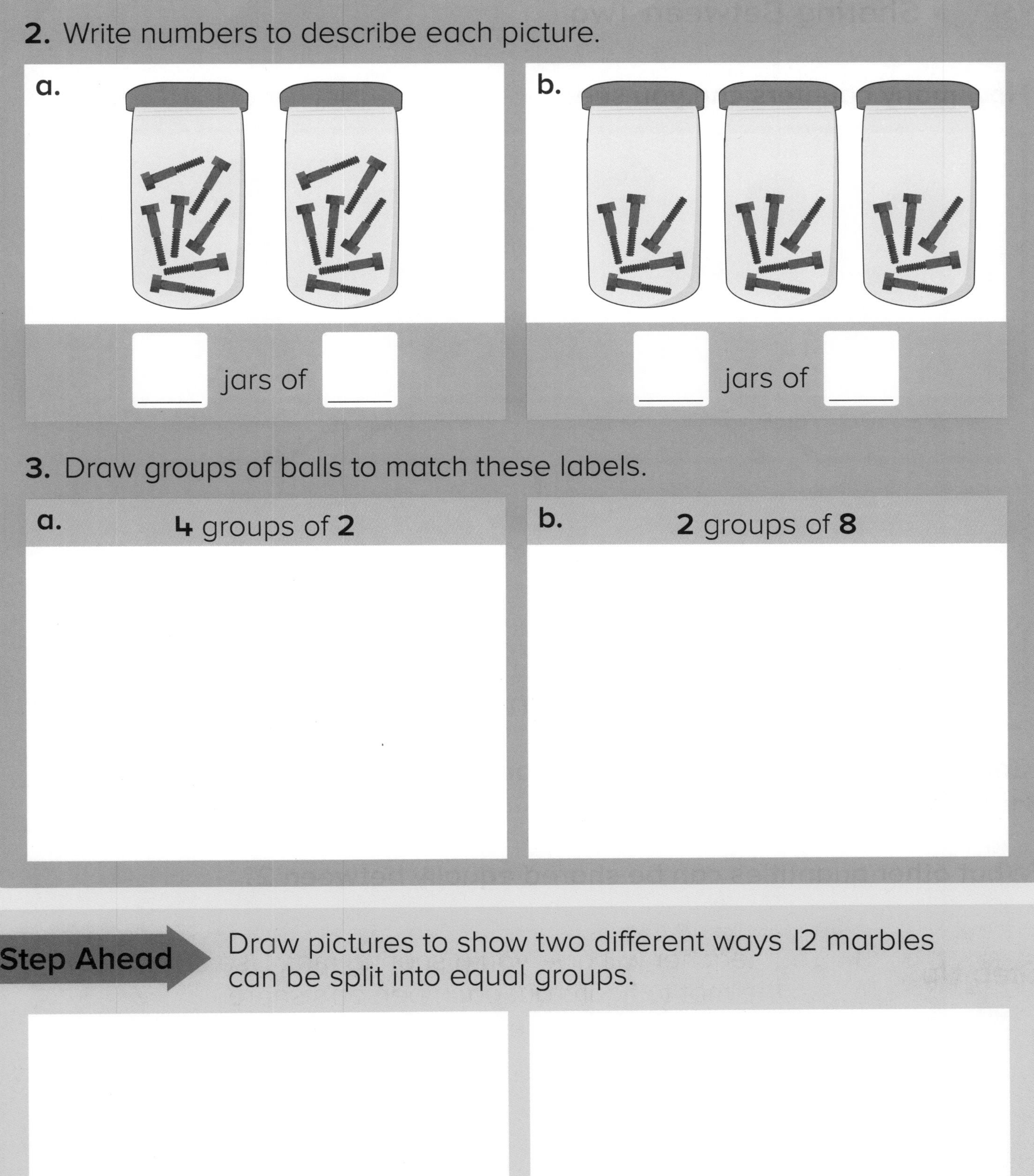

Step Ahead Draw pictures to show two different ways 12 marbles can be split into equal groups.

7.9 Sharing Between Two

How many counters can you see?

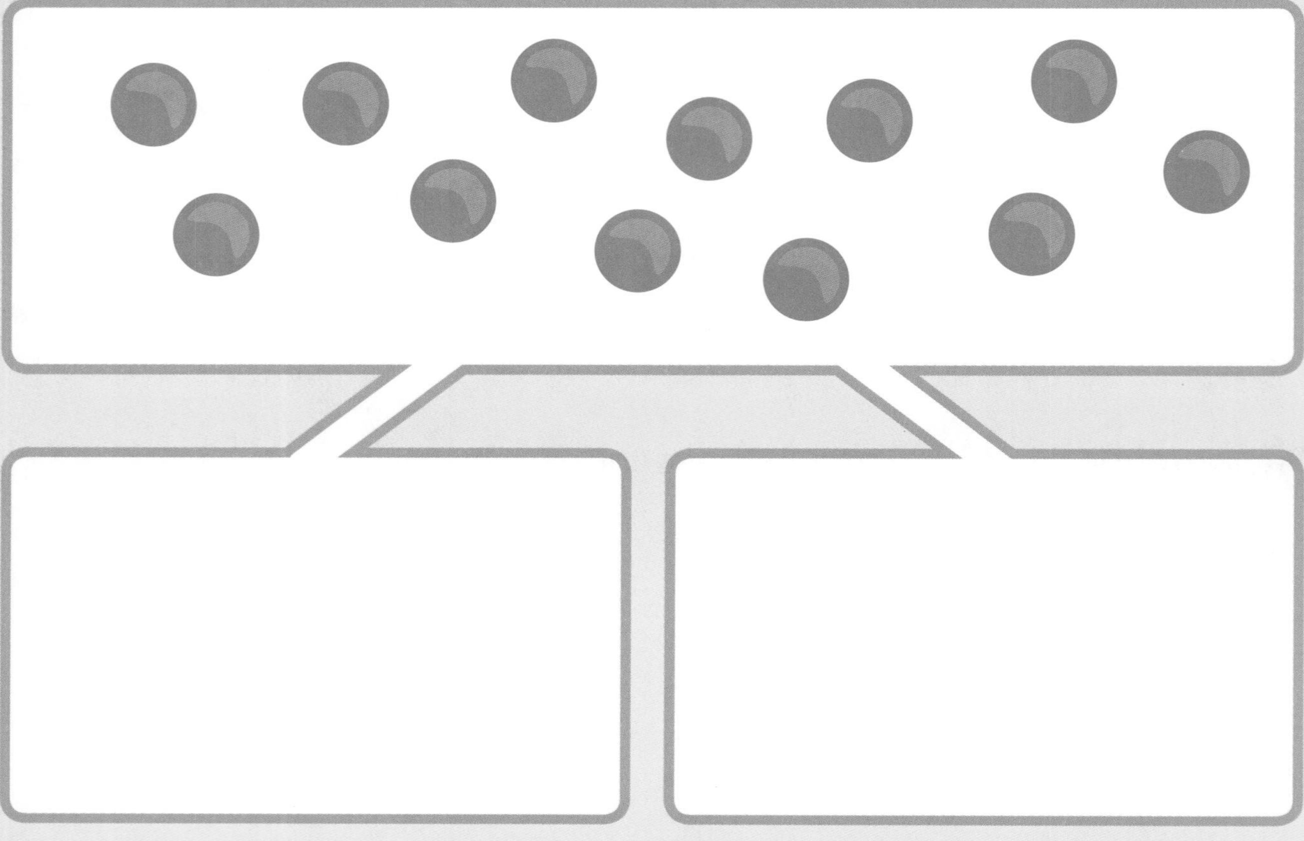

Can the counters be shared equally between two groups?
How do you know?

What other quantities can be shared equally between 2?

Step Up

1. Your teacher will give you a sharing mat. Use ones blocks on the mat to figure out each person's share.
Then complete each sentence.

a. 10 shared by 2 is ____ each.

b. 12 shared by 2 is ____ each.

c. 18 shared by 2 is ____ each.

d. 14 shared by 2 is ____ each.

e. 16 shared by 2 is ____ each.

f. 20 shared by 2 is ____ each.

2. a. Shade each number that can be shared equally between 2.

1	2	3	4	5	6	7	8	9	10
11	12	13	14	15	16	17	18	19	20
21	22	23	24	25	26	27	28	29	30
31	32	33	34	35	36	37	38	39	40

b. Describe the pattern you see.

____

____

c. Write some more numbers that can be shared equally between 2.

____

Step Ahead Write a story about sharing to match this picture.

____

____

____

____

7.10 Identifying One-Half of a Collection

Look at this sheet of paper.

How many parts can you see?

What do you notice about the parts?

What is another way you could fold the paper to show two parts the same size?

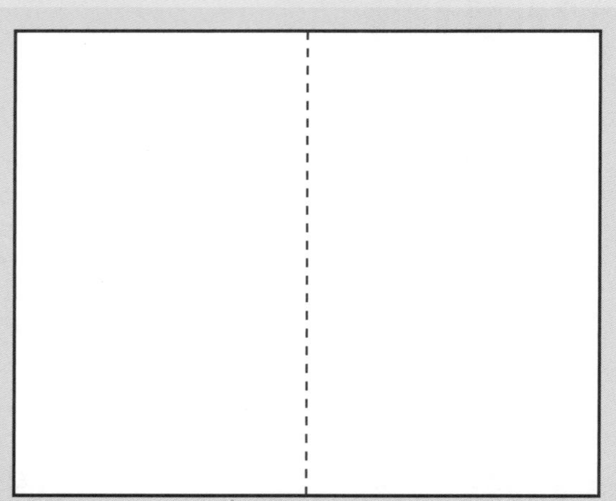

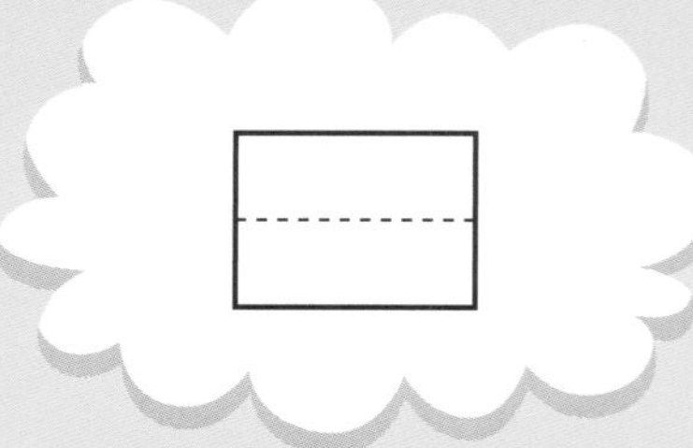

How many cubes can you see?

How many cubes are in each share?

How many cubes are in one-half?

Write numbers to complete this sentence.

One-half of ______ is ____.

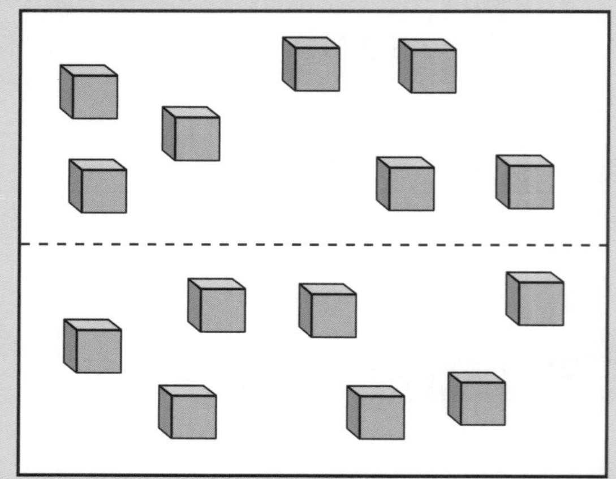

Step Up 1. Loop **one-half** of each group. Then complete each sentence.

a.

One-half of 6 is ____.

b.

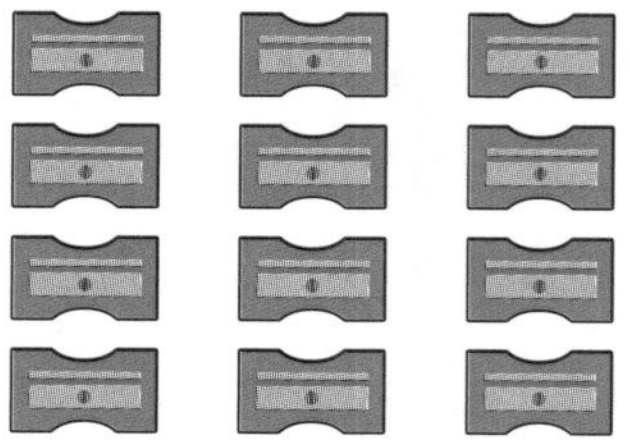

One-half of 12 is ____.

2. Loop **one-half**. Then write numbers to complete each sentence.

a.

One-half of ____ is ____.

b.

One-half of ____ is ____.

c.

One-half of ____ is ____.

d.

One-half of ____ is ____.

3. Complete the sentence. Draw dots to help.

a.

One-half is 7, so the **total** is ____.

b.

One-half is 10, so the **total** is ____.

Step Ahead Color parts of each picture to show **one-half** in two different ways.

7.11 Identifying One-Half of Amounts of Money

Look at these pennies.

What is the total value?

How can you figure out one-half of the total?

What are some other amounts you can halve?

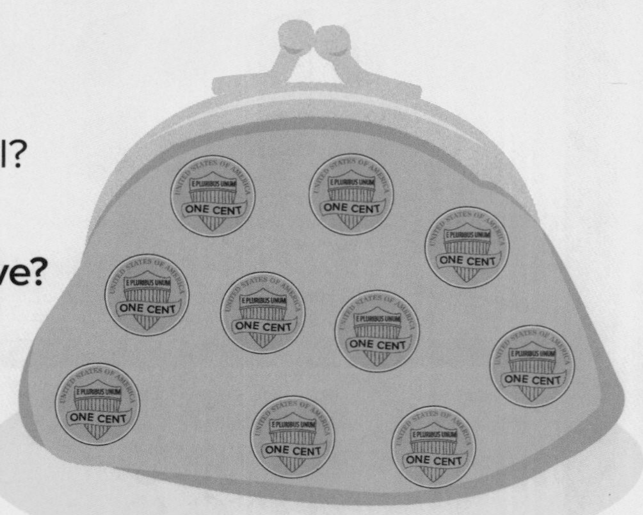

How do you know if an amount can be halved?

Step Up

1. Write the total value.
Then loop **one-half** and complete the sentence.

a. The total is ______ cents.

One-half is ____ cents.

b. The total is ______ cents.

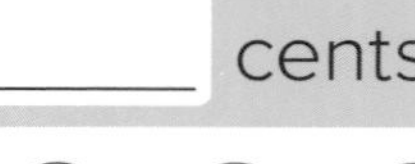

One-half is ____ cents.

c. The total is ______ cents.

One-half is ____ cents.

d. The total is ______ cents.

One-half is ____ cents.

2. Write the total value. Then loop **one-half** and complete the sentence.

a. The total is ______ cents.

One-half is ______ cents.

b. The total is ______ cents.

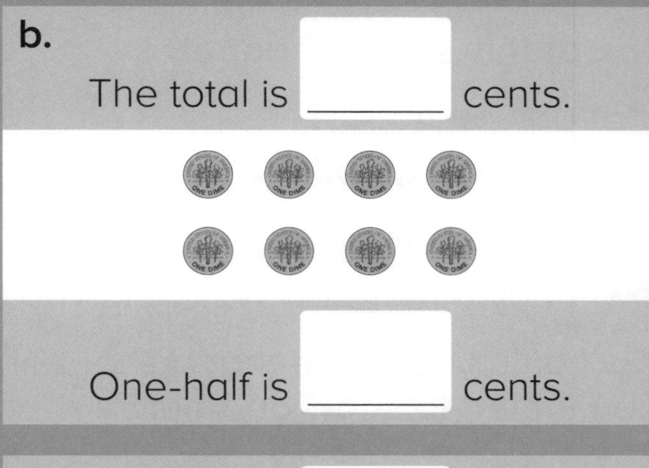

One-half is ______ cents.

c. The total is ______ cents.

One-half is ______ cents.

d. The total is ______ cents.

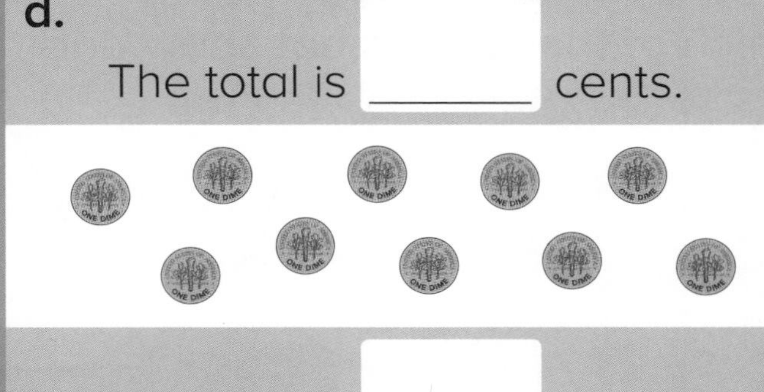

One-half is ______ cents.

Step Ahead Can these pennies be shared equally by 2?
Explain your thinking. You can draw a picture to help.

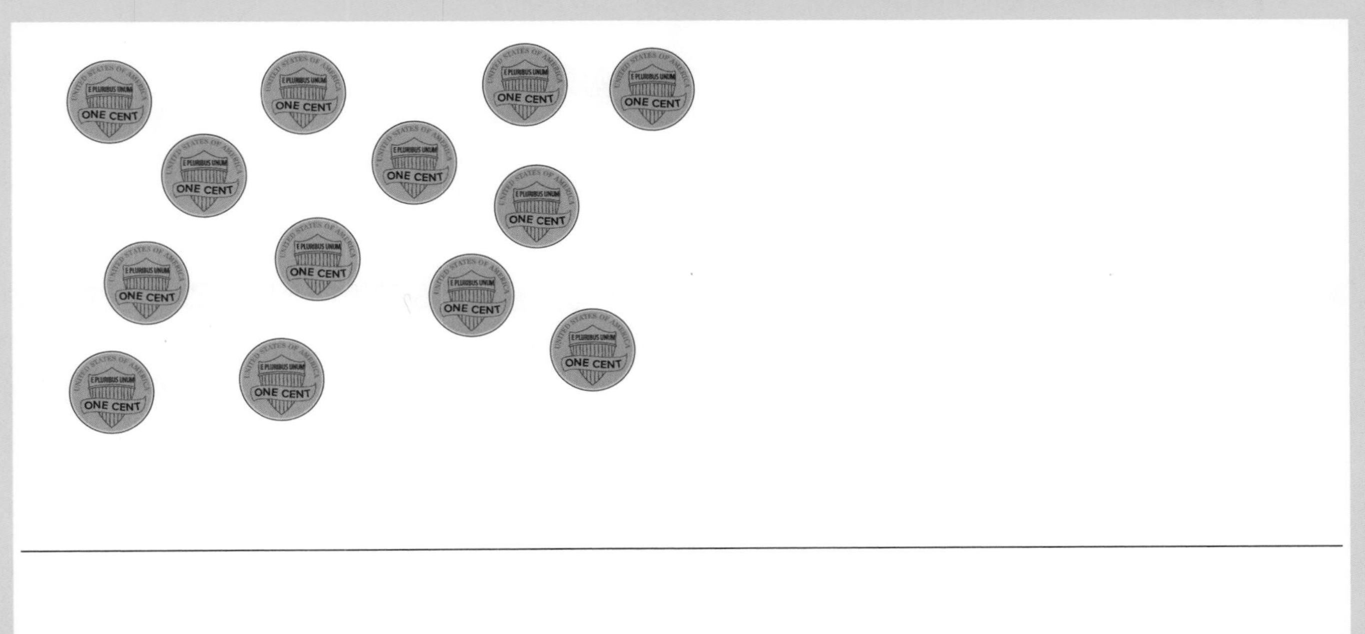

____

____

7.12 Identifying One-Half of a Region

Look at this sheet of paper.

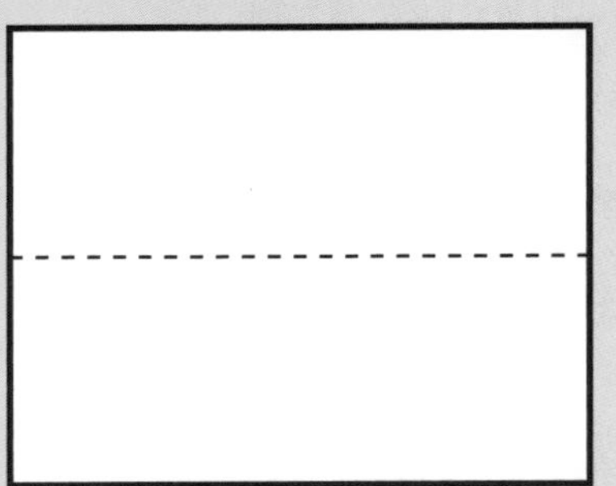

What do you notice?

What is another way you could fold the sheet to show one-half?

How many different ways could you show one-half?

How could you prove that a sheet of paper has been folded to show one-half?

Which of these does not show one-half? How do you know?

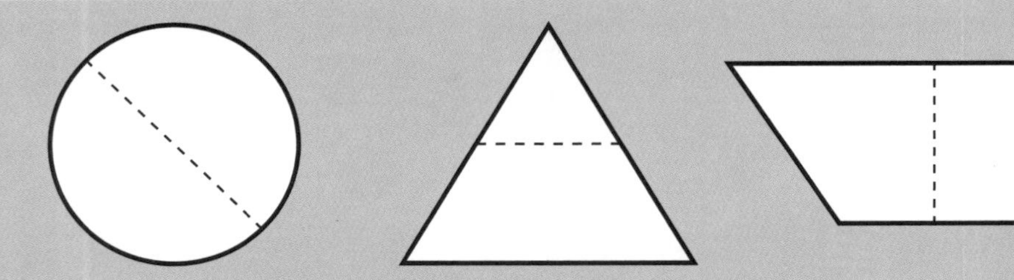

Step Up 1. Draw a line on each to show **one-half**.

a.

b.

c.

d.

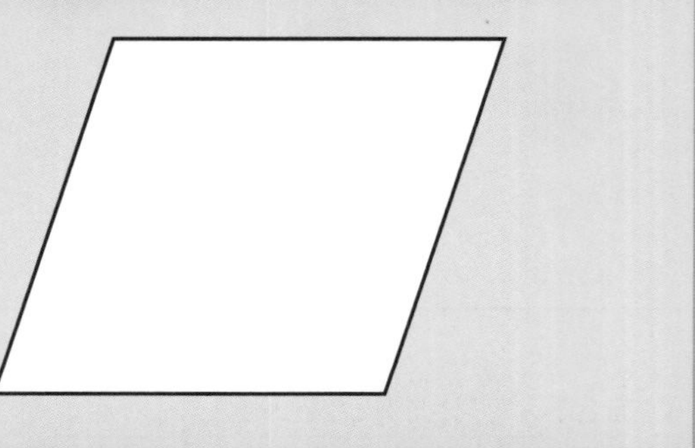

2. Color red one of the parts in each.
Then loop each picture that shows one-half in red.

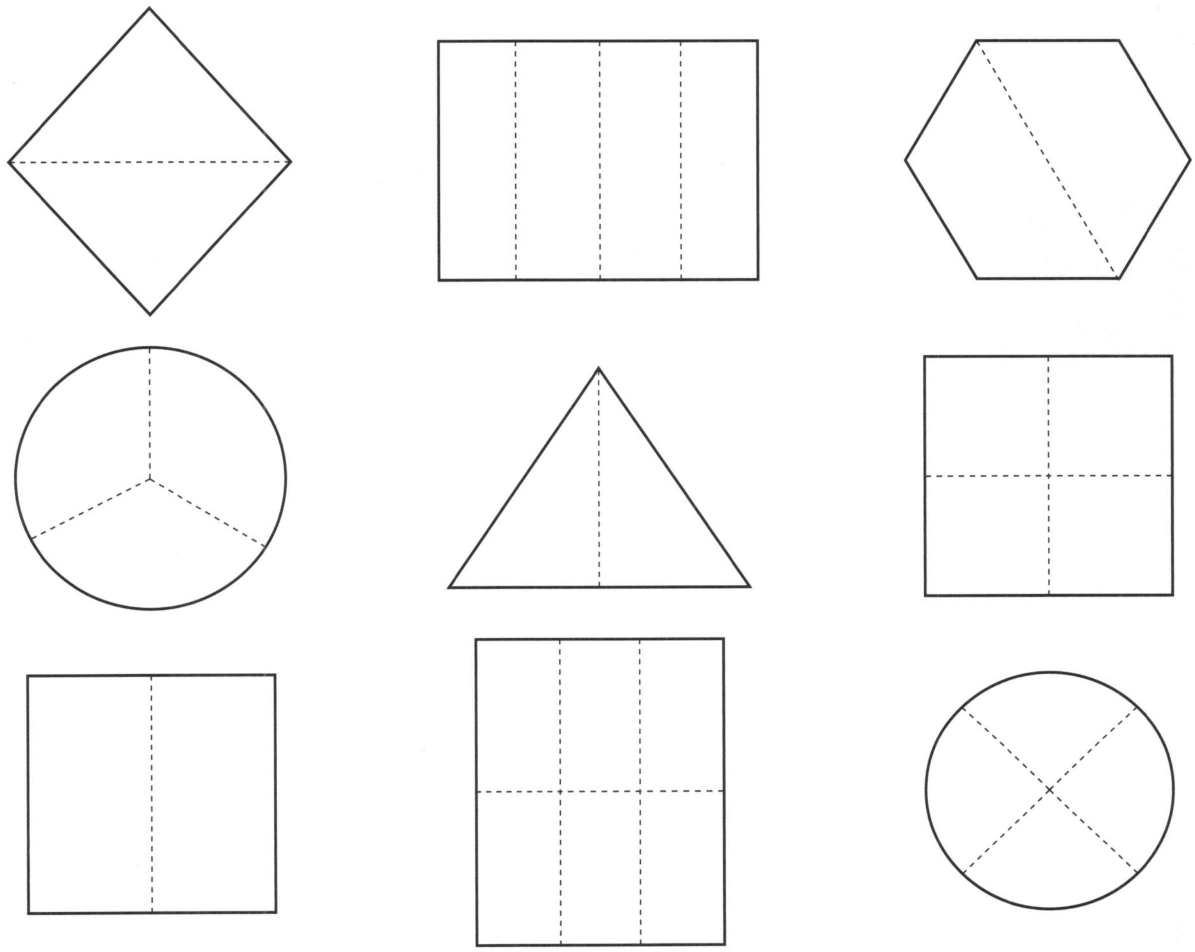

Step Ahead Color parts to match each label.

a.

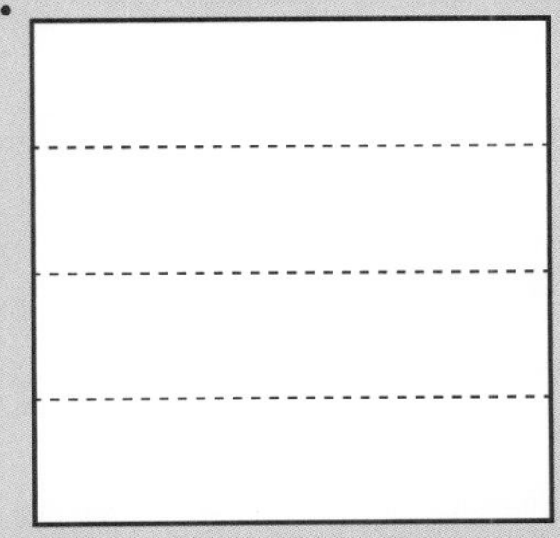

Less than one-half

b.

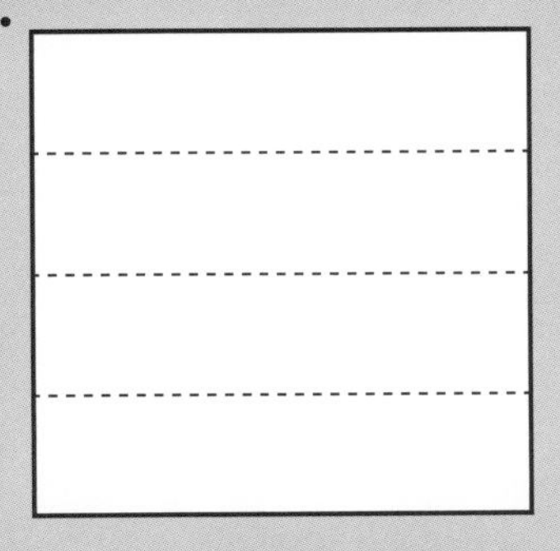

One-half

c.

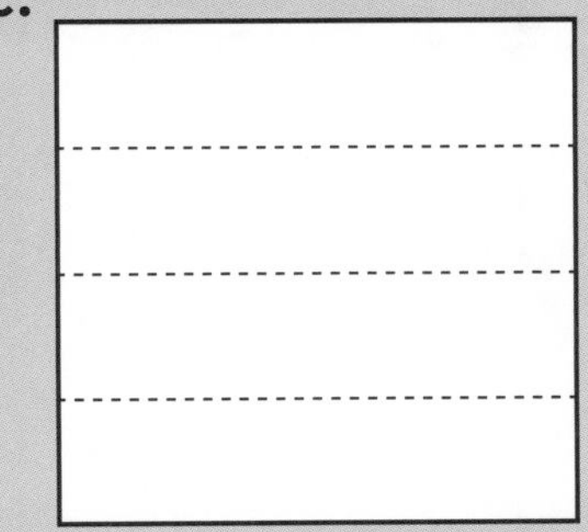

More than one-half

8.1 Identifying the Parts and Total

Look at this picture.

What addition story could you say about the picture?

Which number is the **total** in your story?

Which numbers are **parts** of the total?

What subtraction story could you say about the picture?

Which number is the **total** in your story?

Which numbers are **parts** of the total?

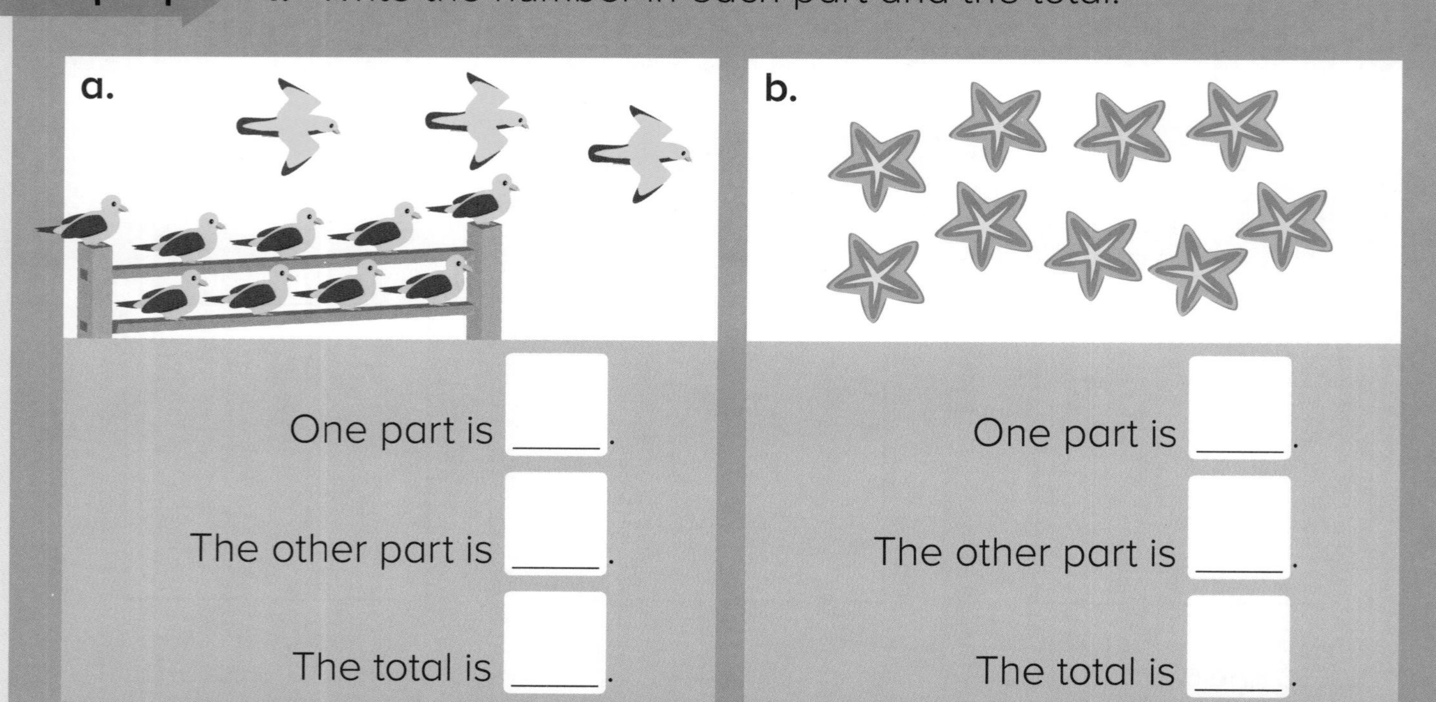

Step Up 1. Write the number in each part and the total.

a.

One part is _____.

The other part is _____.

The total is _____.

b.

One part is _____.

The other part is _____.

The total is _____.

2. Write an addition sentence to match each picture.
Then write a subtraction sentence to match each picture.

a.

4 + 6 = ____

____ − 4 = 6

b.

____ + ____ = ____

____ − ____ = ____

c.

____ + ____ = ____

____ − ____ = ____

d.

____ + ____ = ____

____ − ____ = ____

Step Ahead Draw a picture to match this addition sentence. **5 + 3 = 8**

8.2 Writing Related Addition and Subtraction Facts

Look at this picture.

What is an addition fact that matches the picture?

What is the **turnaround** fact?

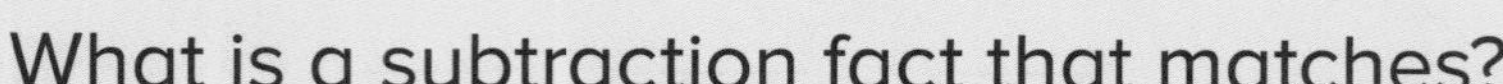

What is a subtraction fact that matches?

A subtraction fact does not have a turnaround fact.
It has a **related** fact.

What is the **related** subtraction fact?

8 − 3 = 5
is related to
8 − 5 = 3

Step Up I. Color the animals to show two groups. Then write an addition fact and subtraction fact to match each picture.

a.

___ + ___ = ___

___ − ___ = ___

b.

___ + ___ = ___

___ − ___ = ___

2. Color the animals to show two groups. Then write two addition facts and the two related subtraction facts to match each picture.

a.

___ − ___ = ___

___ − ___ = ___

b.

___ − ___ = ___

___ − ___ = ___

Step Ahead Draw a picture to match this addition sentence.

4 + 3 + 2 = 9

8.3 Writing Fact Families

Imagine this cube train is broken into two parts.

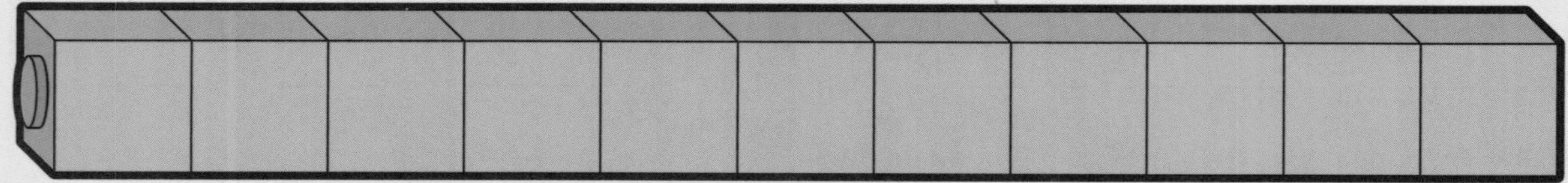

What two addition sentences could you write about the two parts?

What two subtraction sentences could you write to match?

The two addition facts and the two related subtraction facts make a **fact family.**

What is another fact family you know that goes with this cube train?

Step Up 1. Write the fact family to match each picture.

a.

____ + ____ = ____

____ + ____ = ____

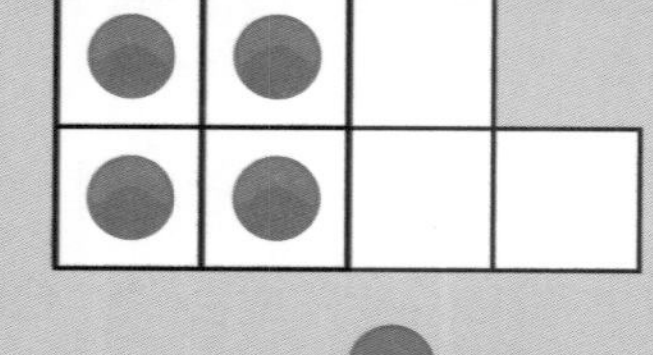

____ − ____ = ____

____ − ____ = ____

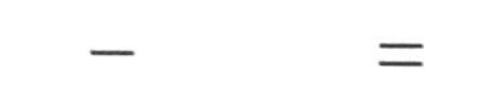

b.

____ + ____ = ____

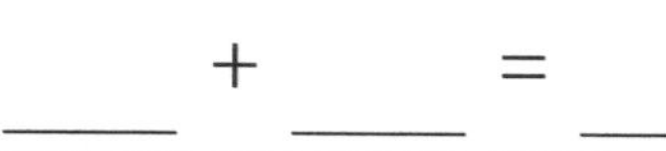

____ + ____ = ____

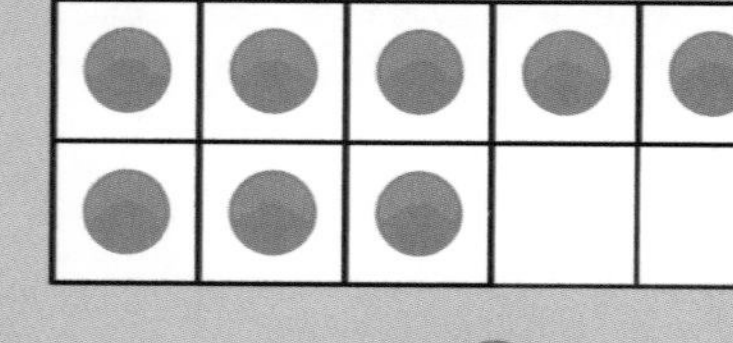

____ − ____ = ____

____ − ____ = ____

c.

____ + ____ = ____

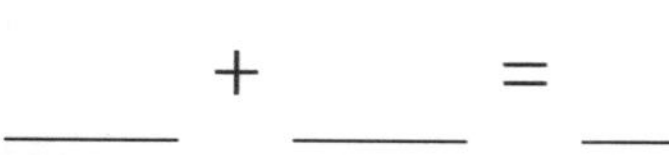

____ + ____ = ____

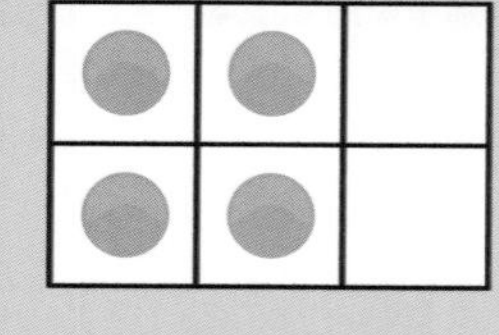

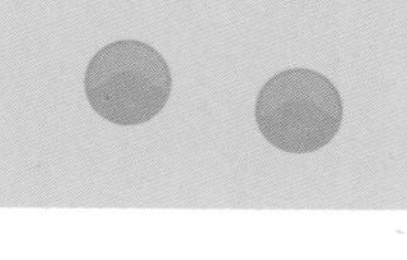

____ − ____ = ____

____ − ____ = ____

2. Draw lines to match facts to pictures.
Cross out the two facts that do not match a picture.

6 + 3 = 9		9 − 6 = 3
2 + 5 = 7	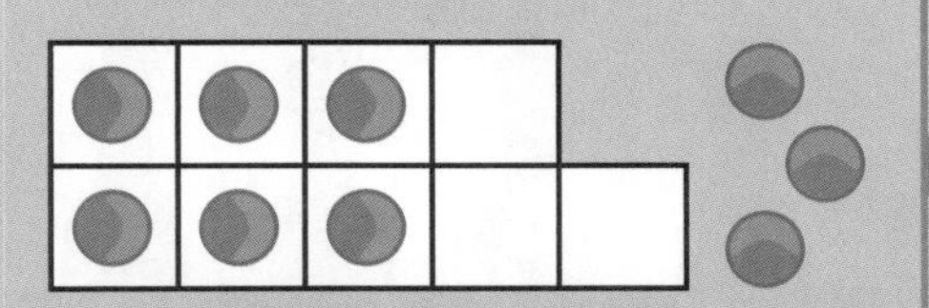	5 + 3 = 8
8 − 3 = 5		3 + 6 = 9
9 − 3 = 6		6 − 3 = 3
3 + 5 = 8		8 − 5 = 3

Step Ahead Write the missing facts to complete each fact family.

a.

___ + ___ = ___   ___ + ___ = ___

6 − 1 = 5   ___ − ___ = ___

b.

2 + 7 = 9   ___ + ___ = ___

___ − ___ = ___   ___ − ___ = ___

8.4 Introducing Unknown-Addend Subtraction

There were 12 carrots growing in the ground.
Some were taken during the night.

How many carrots were taken? How do you know?

What is the total? What are the parts?

Step Up 1. Draw more birds to match the total.
Then complete the addition sentence.

a.

1 + ___ = 5

b.

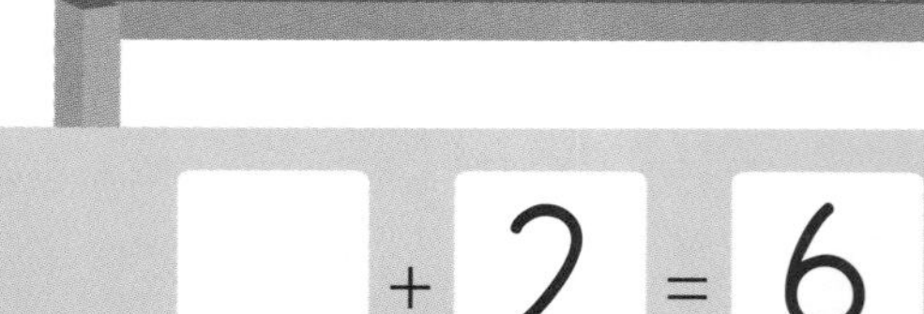

___ + 2 = 6

c.

___ + 6 = 8

d.

2 + ___ = 7

2. Write the fact family for each domino picture.

a. 7 dots in total

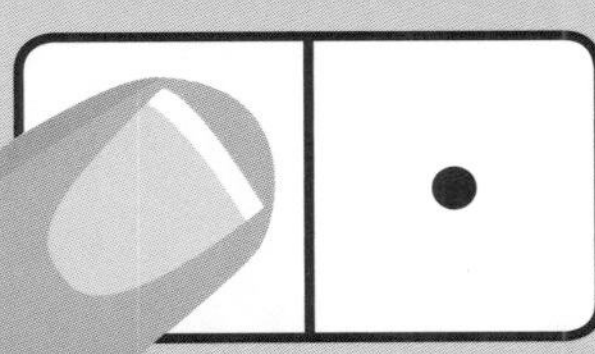

___ + ___ = ___   ___ − ___ = ___

___ + ___ = ___   ___ − ___ = ___

b. 6 dots in total

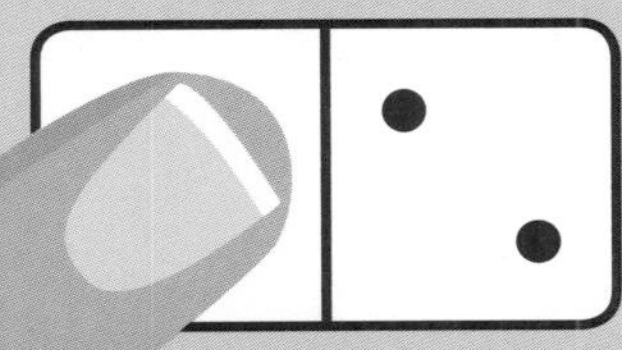

___ + ___ = ___   ___ − ___ = ___

___ + ___ = ___   ___ − ___ = ___

c. 8 dots in total

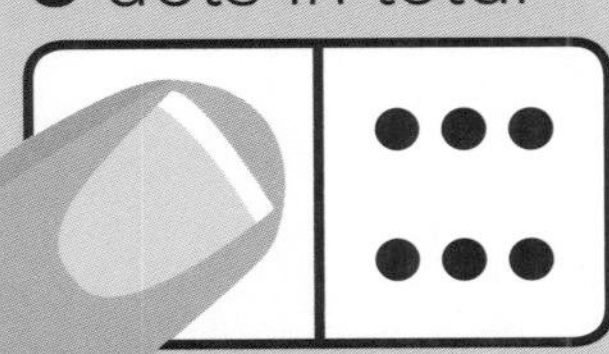

___ + ___ = ___   ___ − ___ = ___

___ + ___ = ___   ___ − ___ = ___

d. 11 dots in total

___ + ___ = ___   ___ − ___ = ___

___ + ___ = ___   ___ − ___ = ___

Step Ahead

Read the story. Write an addition fact that helps you figure out the answer. Then write the answer.

a. Jie had 7 toy cars. His brother gave him some more. Now Jie has 9 cars. How many more cars did his brother give him?

b. Ava caught 9 fish. Then she caught some more. Now Ava has 12 fish. How many more fish did she catch?

8.5 Using Addition to Solve Subtraction Problems

This card shows **two parts** and a **total**.

What do the numbers tell you?

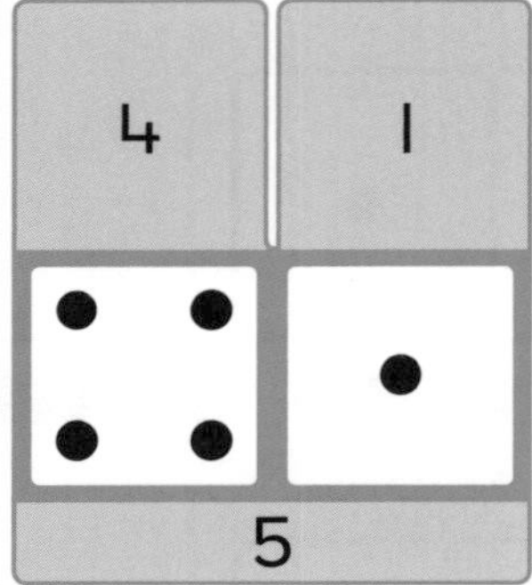

This card has one part hidden.

How can you use addition to help you figure out the part that is hidden?

3

5

I know the total is 5.
I know one of the parts is 3.
3 and 2 is 5 so the missing part must be 2.

Step Up

1. Write the missing numeral and draw the matching dots on each card. Then complete the addition facts.

a.

6 + ____ = 8

b.

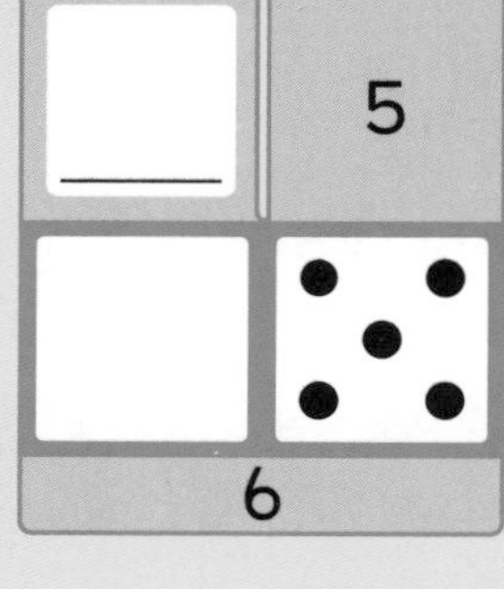

____ + 5 = 6

c.

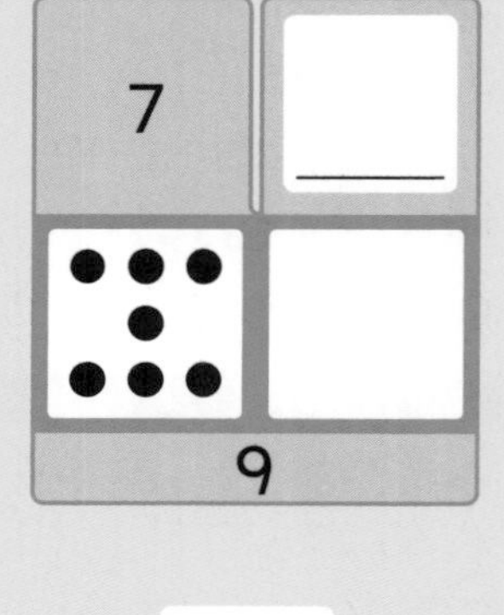

7 + ____ = 9

2. Complete the addition fact for each card.

a.

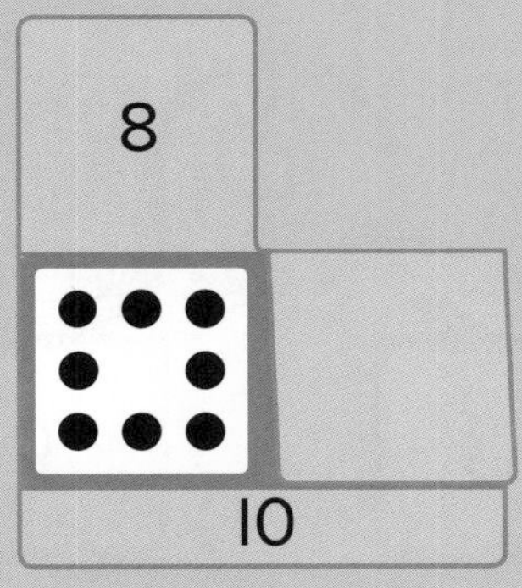

8 + ____ = 10

b.

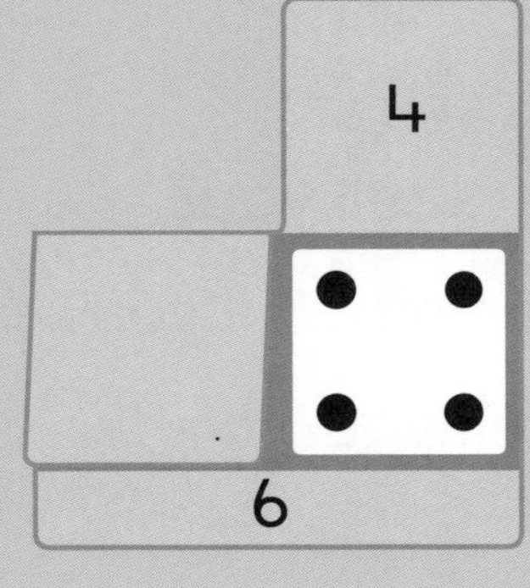

____ + 4 = 6

c.

____ + 7 = 8

3. Complete the addition fact. Then write a related subtraction fact.

a.

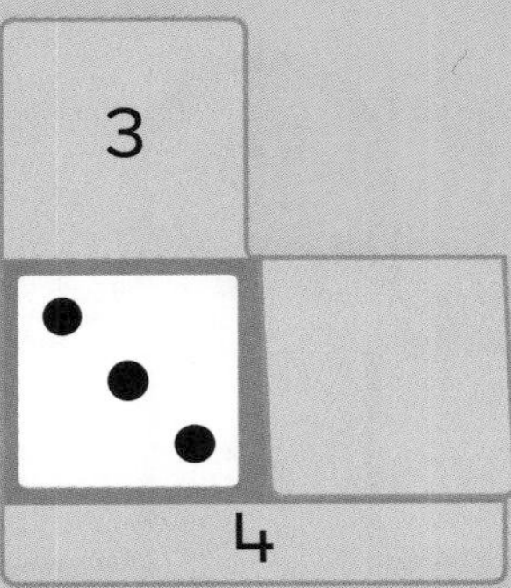

3 + ____ = 4

4 − ____ = ____

b.

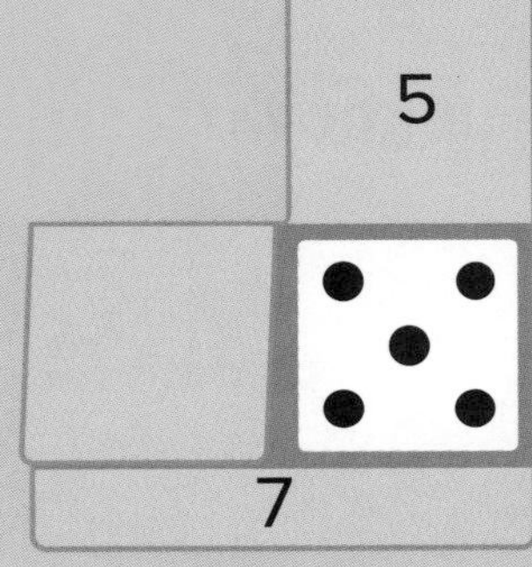

____ + 5 = 7

7 − ____ = ____

c.

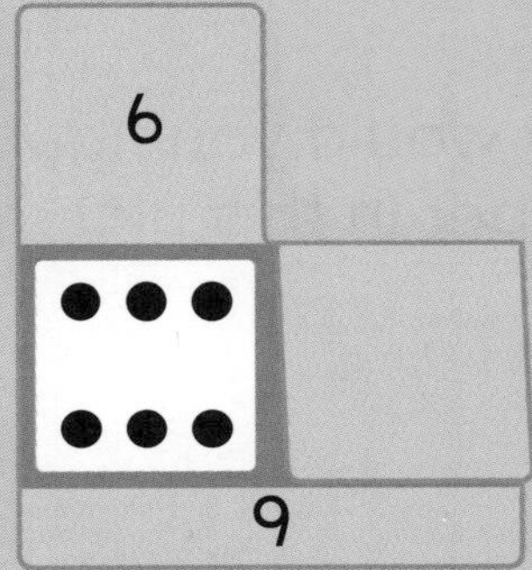

6 + ____ = 9

9 − ____ = ____

Step Ahead Write an addition fact that helps you figure out the answer. Then write the answer.

There were 9 birds on a fence. Some birds flew away. There are now 6 birds on the fence. How many birds flew away?

____ + ____ = ____ ____

8.6 Working with Addition and Subtraction

Look at this picture.

What do you think the numbers tell you?

What does the number in the circle tell you?

What do the other numbers tell you?

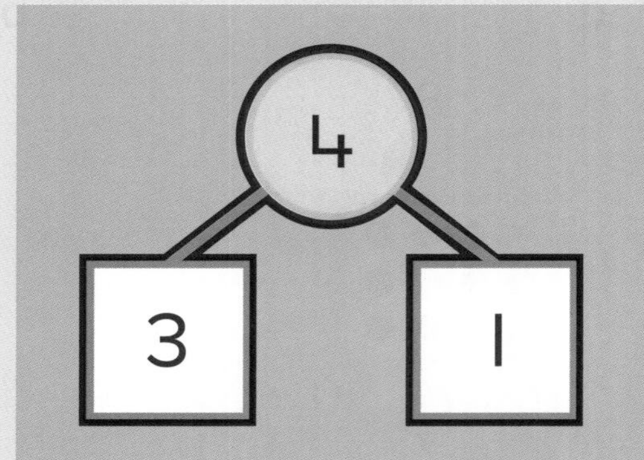

What two addition facts could you write to match the picture?

What two related subtraction facts could you write?

What do you call all these four facts together?

How would you figure out the unknown number in this picture?

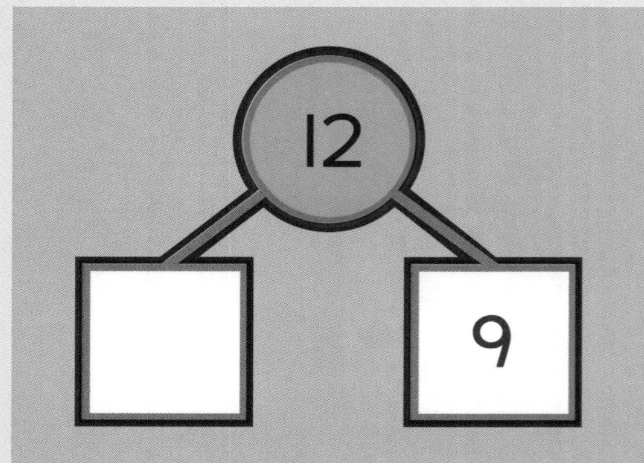

Step Up

1. Write the missing number in the picture. Then write one addition fact and one subtraction fact to match.

a.

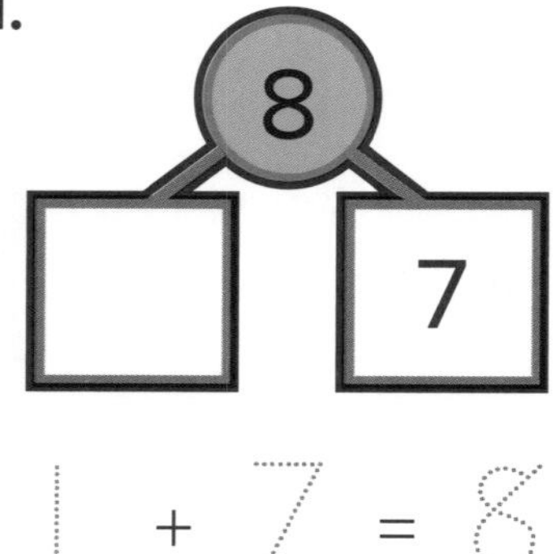

1 + 7 = 8

___ − ___ = ___

b.

___ + ___ = ___

___ − ___ = ___

c.

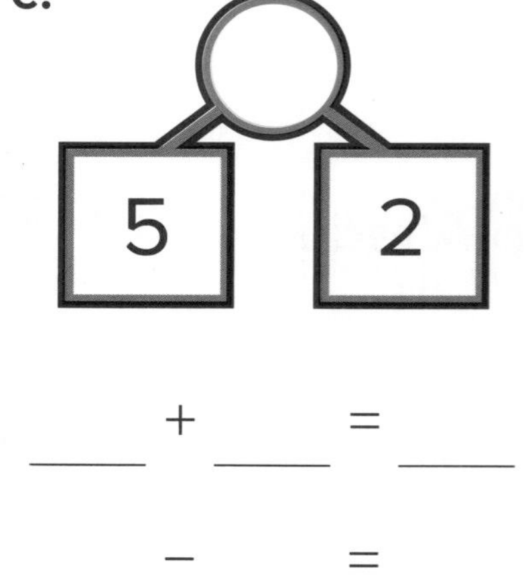

___ + ___ = ___

___ − ___ = ___

2. Complete each (number bond). Write the matching fact family.

a.

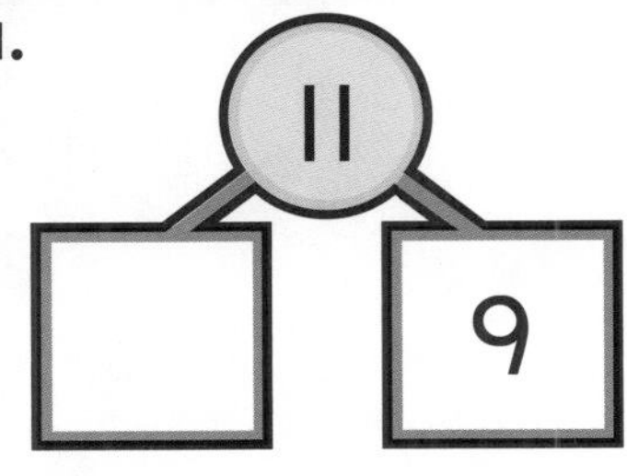

____ + ____ = ____

____ + ____ = ____

____ − ____ = ____

____ − ____ = ____

b.

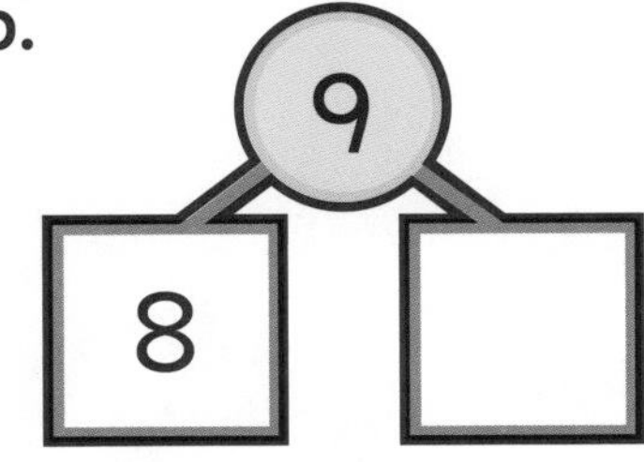

____ + ____ = ____

____ + ____ = ____

____ − ____ = ____

____ − ____ = ____

c.

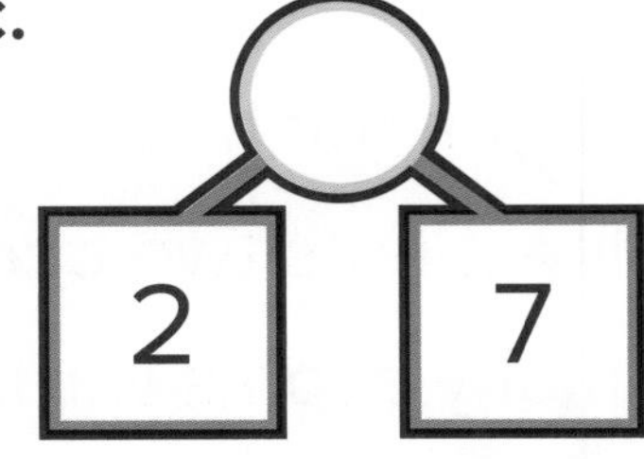

____ + ____ = ____

____ + ____ = ____

____ − ____ = ____

____ − ____ = ____

d.

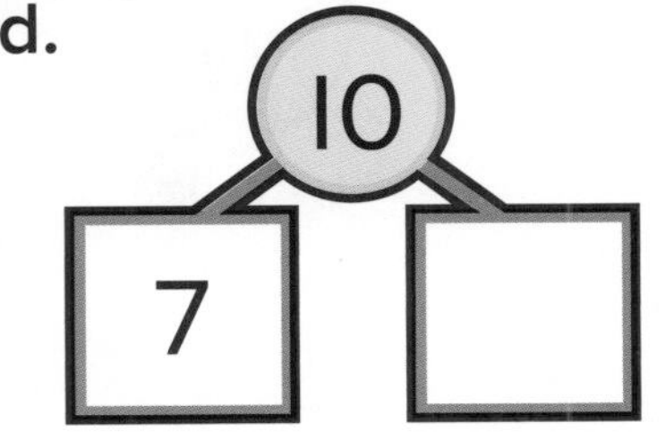

____ + ____ = ____

____ + ____ = ____

____ − ____ = ____

____ − ____ = ____

e.

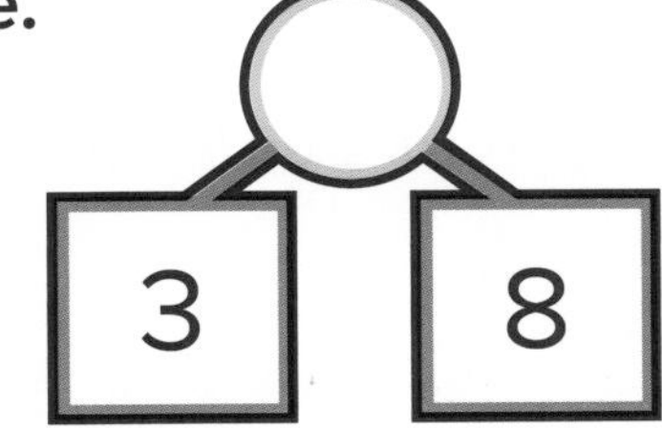

____ + ____ = ____

____ + ____ = ____

____ − ____ = ____

____ − ____ = ____

f.

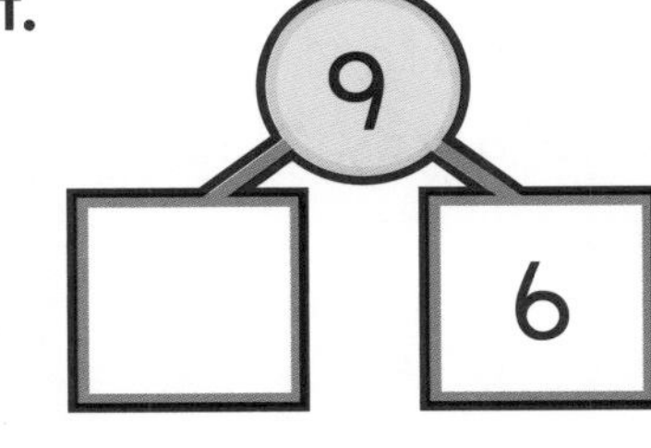

____ + ____ = ____

____ + ____ = ____

____ − ____ = ____

____ − ____ = ____

Step Ahead

The numbers in circles are totals.
The numbers in squares are parts.
Write the missing numbers.

8.7 Counting On and Back to Subtract

This chipmunk has 9 acorns.

Imagine it eats two acorns.

How many acorns will it have left?

How can you use this number track to figure out the answer?

1	2	3	4	5	6	7	8	9	10

I would start at 9 and jump **back** 2.
9 take away 2 is 7 so there would be 7 acorns left.

−2

1	2	3	4	5	6	7	8	9	10

Imagine the chipmunk had 9 acorns and ate 6 of them.

How could you use a number track to figure out the number of acorns it had left?

I would start at 6 and jump **on** to 9.
6 add 3 is 9 so there would be 3 acorns left.

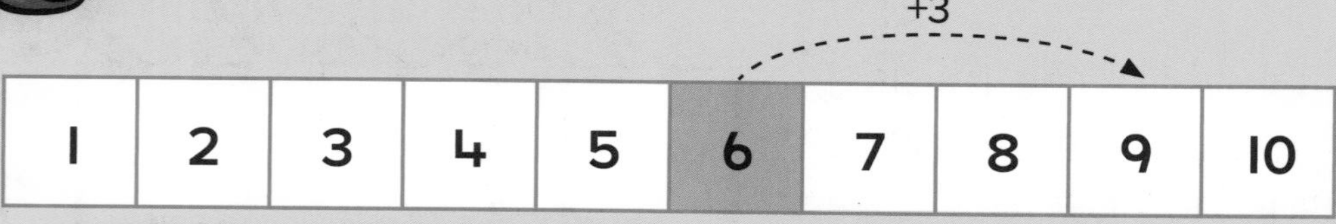

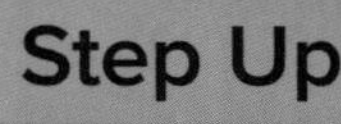

Step Up

Write a number sentence to show how many acorns will be left. You can use a number track on page 188 to help.

a. 8 acorns

I am going to eat 2 acorns.

________________ = ____

b. 6 acorns

I am going to eat 5 acorns.

________________ = ____

c. 8 acorns

I am going to eat 7 acorns.

________________ = ____

d. 9 acorns

I am going to eat 2 acorns.

________________ = ____

e. 7 acorns

I am going to eat 5 acorns.

________________ = ____

f. 10 acorns

I am going to eat 3 acorns.

________________ = ____

Step Ahead

Read the story. Then write the answer. You can draw a picture on a spare sheet of paper to help.

At the zoo, we bought 10 bags of animal food. In the morning, we fed 2 bags of food to the giraffes and 5 bags to the monkeys. How many bags did we have left?

____ bags

8.8 Decomposing a Number to Solve Subtraction Problems

Imagine you have 7 pennies.

How much more money do you need to buy this toy?

How could you use a number track to figure it out?

I would start at 7 and jump on to 10.
Then I would jump on from 10 to 12.
3 add 2 is 5 so I would need 5 cents.

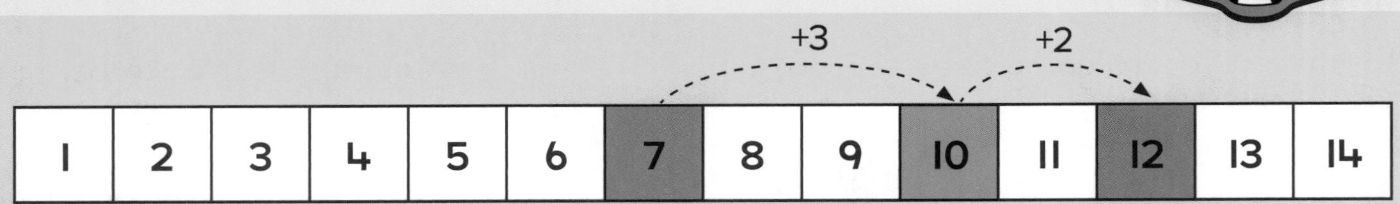

I would start at 12 and jump back to 10.
Then I would jump back from 10 to 7.
2 add 3 is 5 so I would need 5 cents.

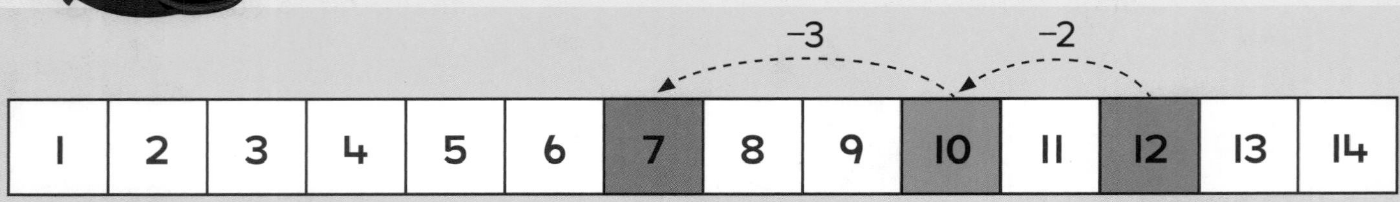

Step Up

1. Write how far each number is from 10.
You can use the number track to help you.

2. Figure out how much more money is needed to pay the price. Draw jumps on the number track to show your thinking.

a.

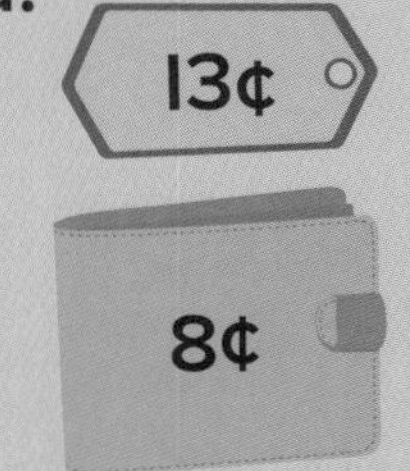

4	5	6	7	8	9	10	11	12	13	14

Amount needed is ____ ¢

b.

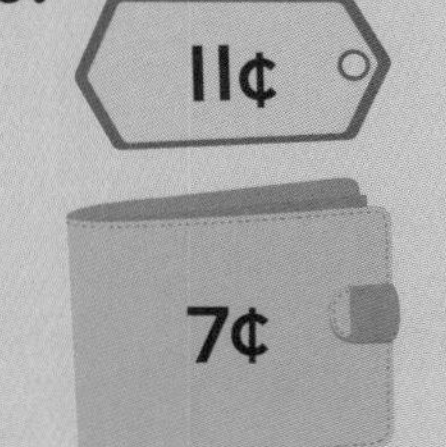

4	5	6	7	8	9	10	11	12	13	14

Amount needed is ____ ¢

c.

4	5	6	7	8	9	10	11	12	13	14

Amount needed is ____ ¢

d.

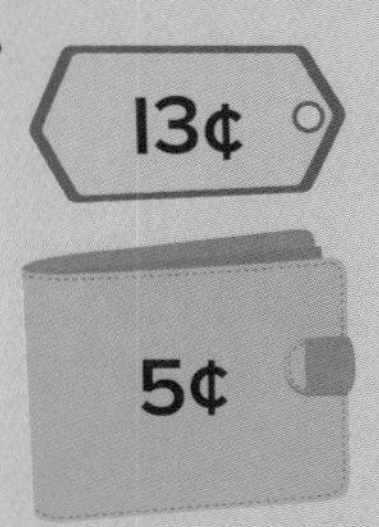

4	5	6	7	8	9	10	11	12	13	14

Amount needed is ____ ¢

Step Ahead Write an addition sentence or a subtraction sentence to match each question above.

a. ____________ = ____ ¢ b. ____________ = ____ ¢

c. ____________ = ____ ¢ d. ____________ = ____ ¢

8.9 Working with Cycles of Time

What do you know about the months of the year?

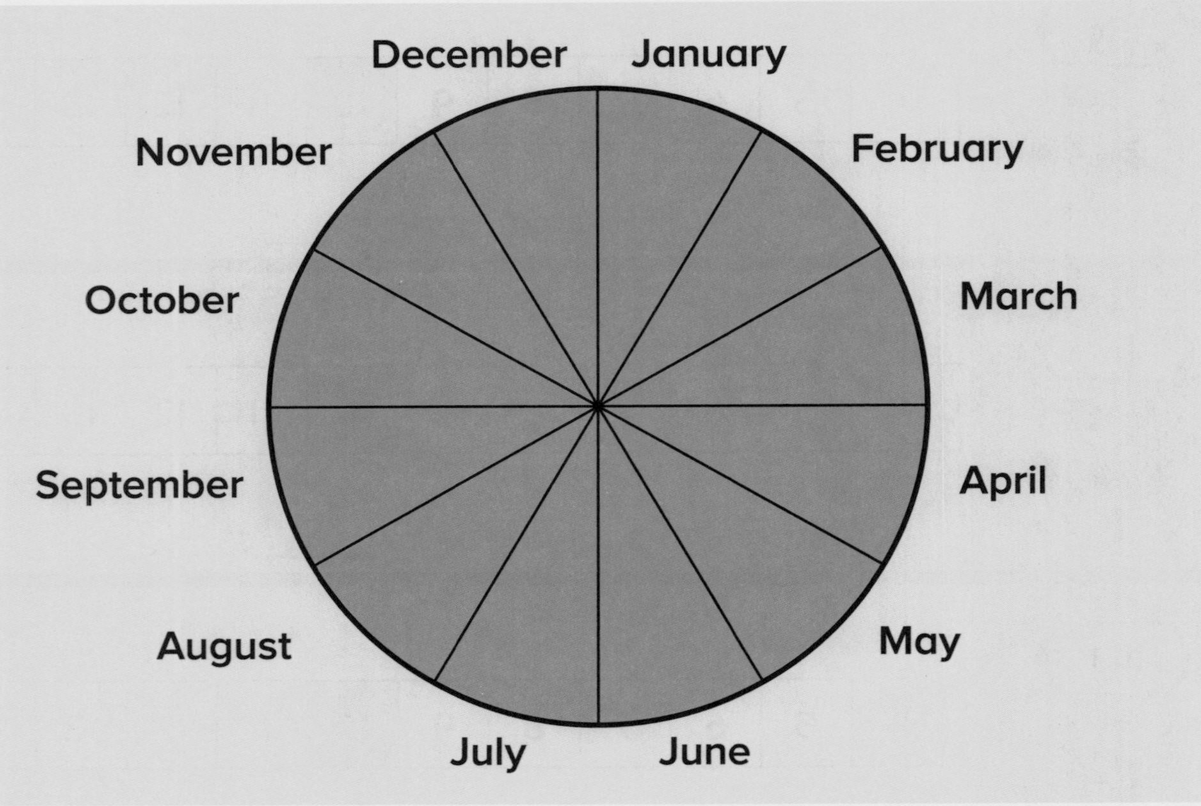

The months of the year make a **cycle.**

The cycle goes on and on without stopping, year after year.

What other cycles of time do you know?

Step Up

1. Write the month in which you were born.
Then write the month before and the month after.

Month just before	Month you were born	Month just after

2. **a.** How many months are in the first half of the year? ______ months

b. Which month starts the second half of the year? ____________

3. Look at this graph.

Birth Months of Grade 1 Students

Names of months

January	Sienna	Michael			
February	Kelly				
March	Noah	Amos	Aran		
April	Jack				
May	Carmen	Dakota	Cooper		
June	Julia				
July	Isabella	Jerome	Olivia		
August	Jessica				
September	Hernando	Riley	Ella	Thomas	Elena
October					
November	Gemma	Shauna	Sofia		
December	Jacinta	Joshua	Tien	Mia	

Number of students

a. How many students were born in these months?

March ____ April ____ May ____

b. In which month were 5 students born? ____________

c. In how many months were **exactly** 3 students born? ____

Step Ahead Write these months.

Natalie was born in October. Emma was born three months before Natalie.

She was born in ____________. Mika was born six months

after Natalie. He was born in ____________.

8.10 Introducing Time Half Past the Hour (Analog Clocks)

Look at this analog clock.

The short hand counts the hours and the long hand counts the minutes.

What time is this clock showing? How do you know?

How long does it take the minute hand to make one full turn around the clock?

Where would the minute hand point if it went halfway around?

When the minute hand is pointing at 6, it is **half past** an hour.

When the minute hand shows us a half-past time, what does the hour hand show us?

What time is this clock showing? How do you know?

Step Up 1. Write the time showing on each clock.

a.

Half past

2 o'clock

b.

Half past

4 o'clock

c.

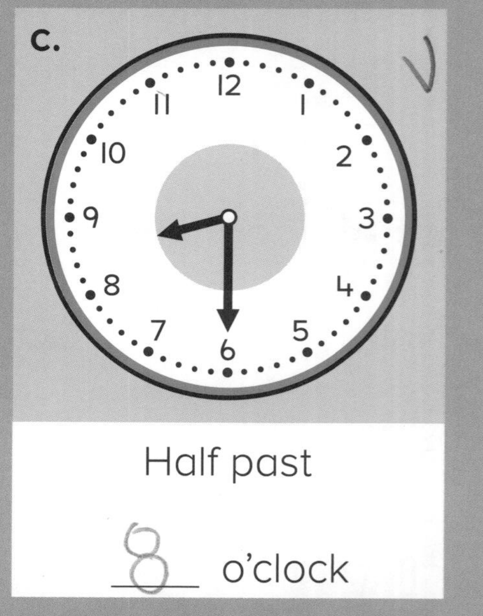

Half past

8 o'clock

2. Write each time.

a.

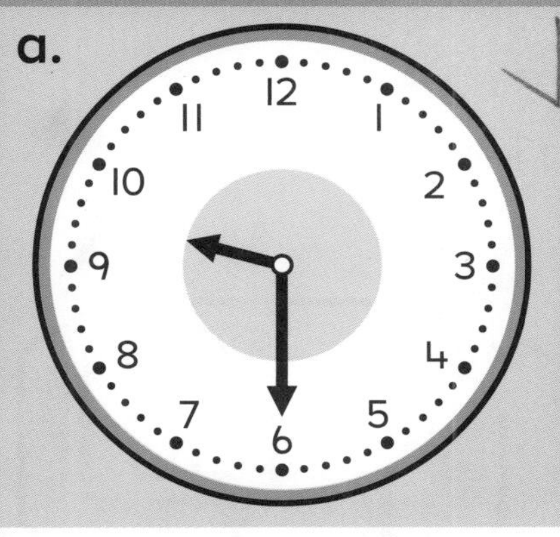

9:30

b.

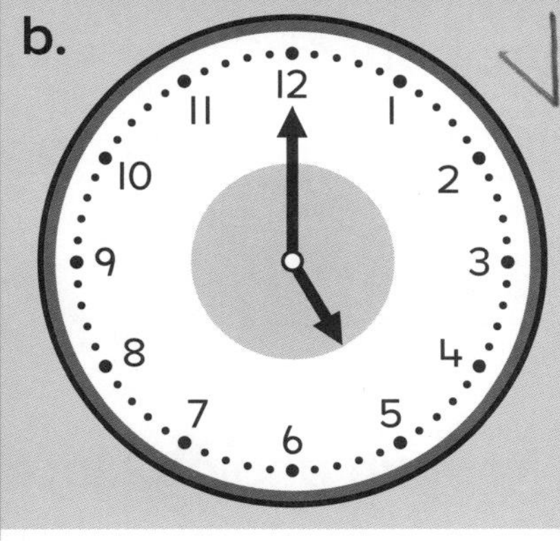

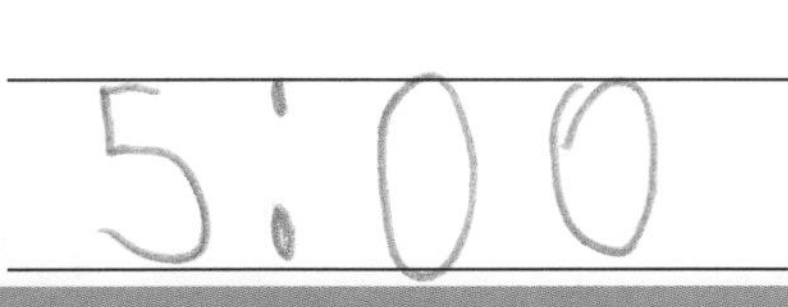

5:00

c.

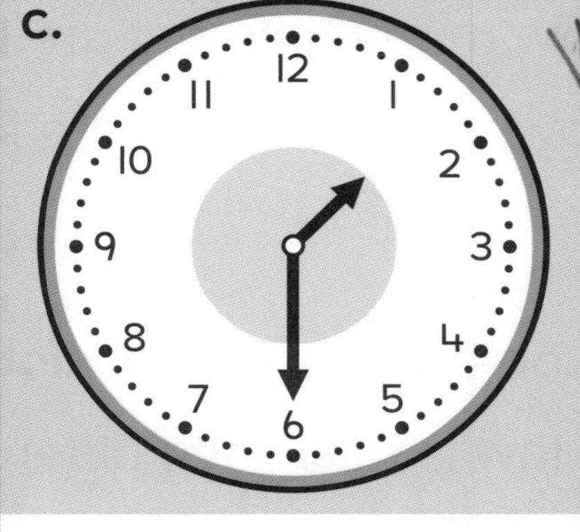

1:30

d.

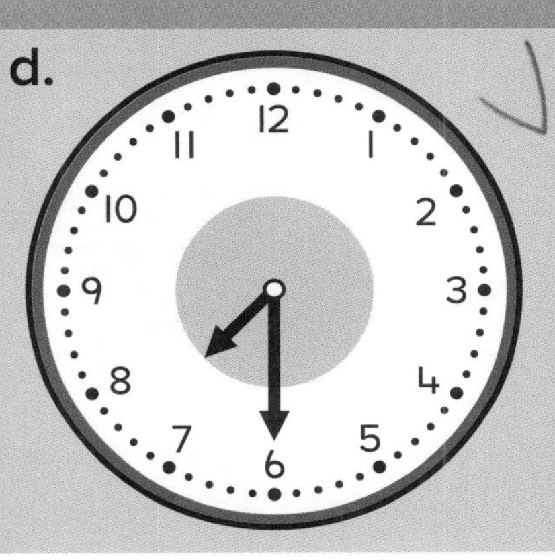

7:30

e.

2:00

f.

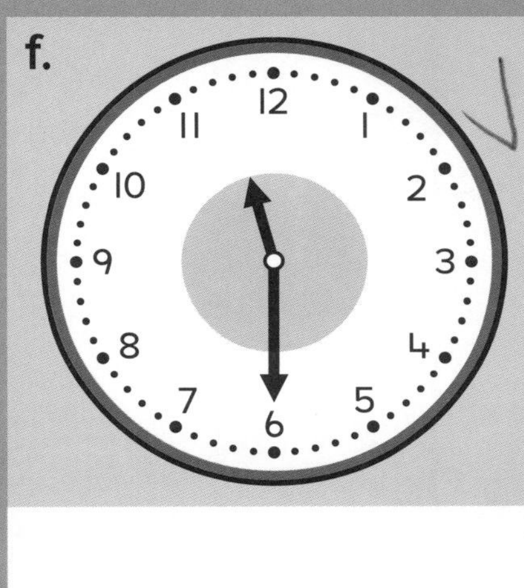

11:30

Step Ahead All these clocks show morning times. Loop the clocks that show times **between** half past 7 and 10 o'clock.

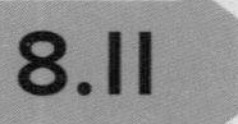

Reading and Writing Time Half Past the Hour (Digital Clocks)

How many minutes are in one hour?

How many minutes are in half an hour? How do you know?

Look at this digital clock.

How is this clock different from an analog clock?

What do you know about the time on this clock?

The 30 shows me the number of minutes. I know it is a half past time because 30 minutes is half of one hour.

What time is the clock showing?

Step Up

1. Draw a line from each label to a matching clock. Some clocks do not have a match.

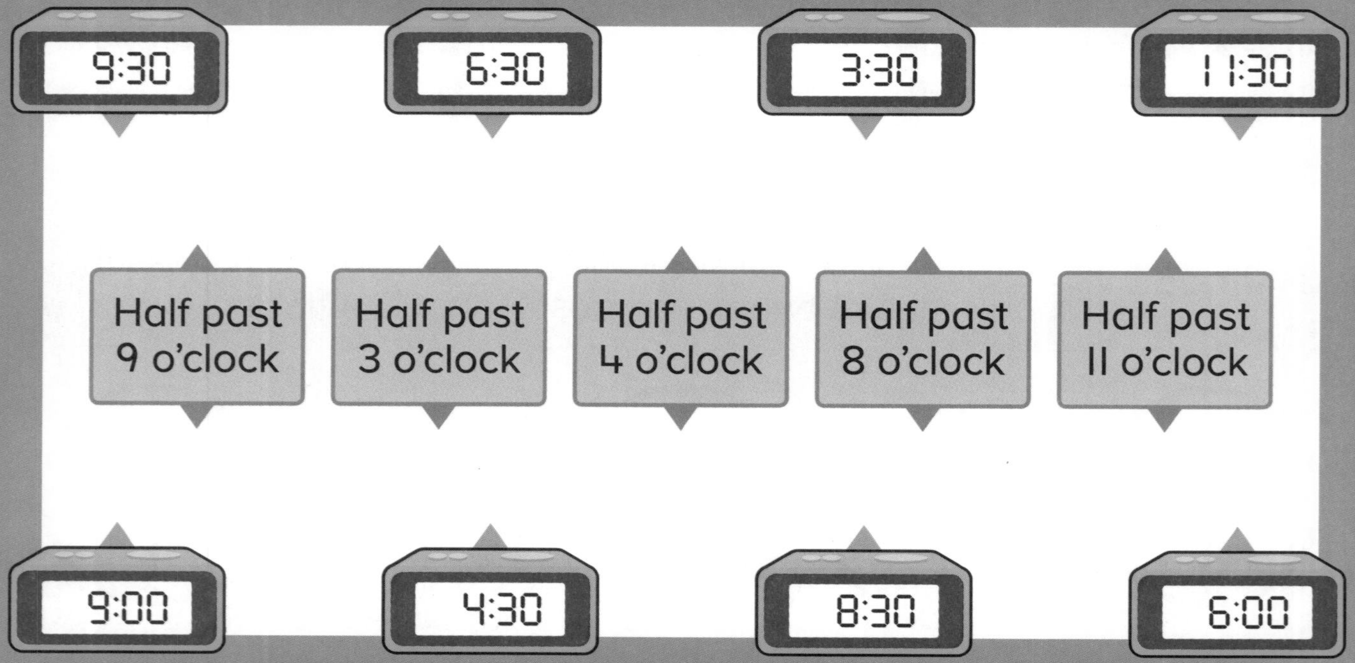

9:30 6:30 3:30 11:30

Half past 9 o'clock

Half past 3 o'clock

Half past 4 o'clock

Half past 8 o'clock

Half past 11 o'clock

9:00 4:30 8:30 6:00

2. Write each time in words.

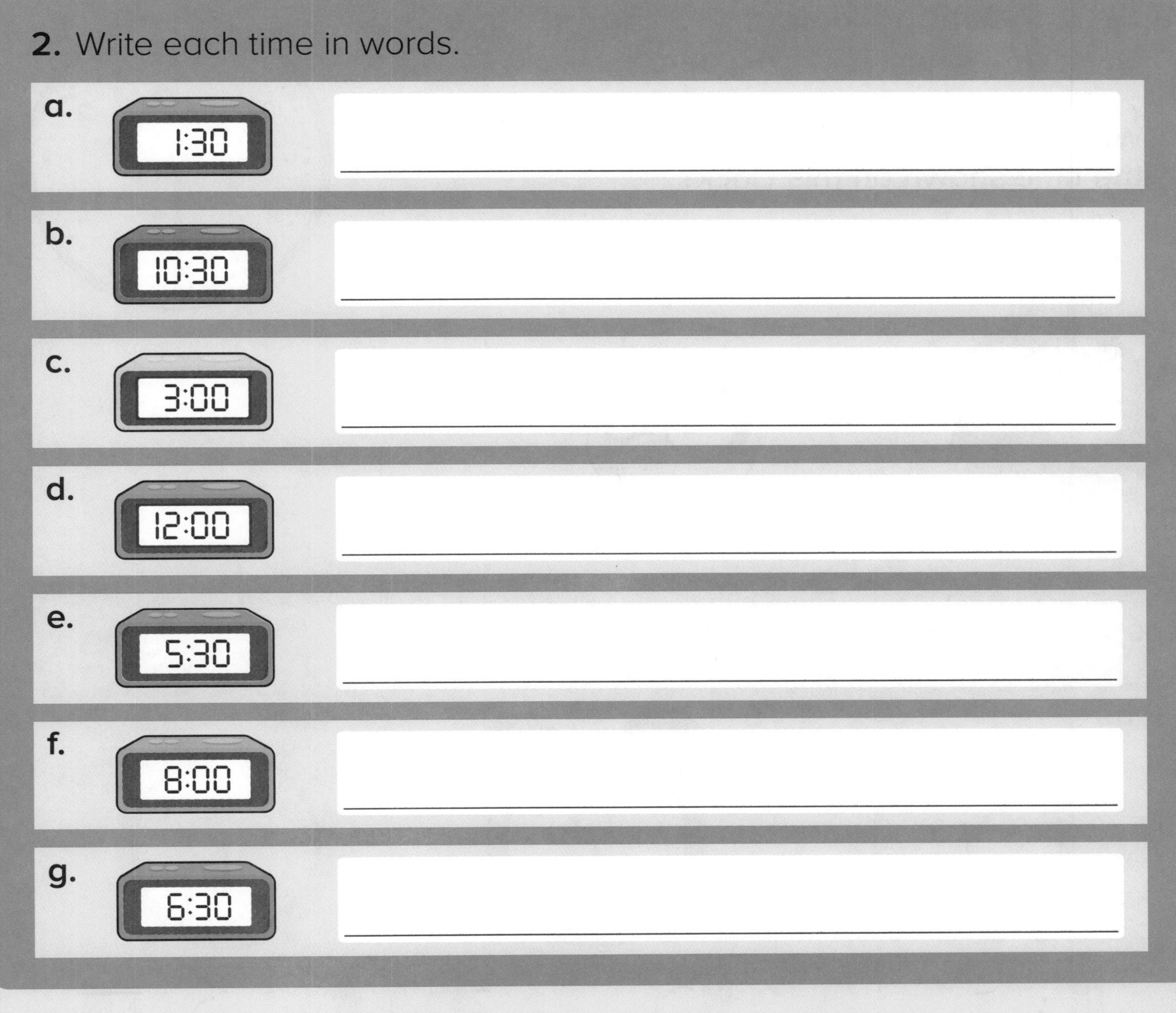

Step Ahead Complete the sentences.

a. 2:30

The time is half past ______.
One hour **later** will be half past ______.

b. 12:30

The time is half past ______.
One hour **later** will be half past ______.

8.12 Relating Analog and Digital Time

What different ways can you say the time shown on this clock?

Step Up

1. Write each time on the digital clock.

a.

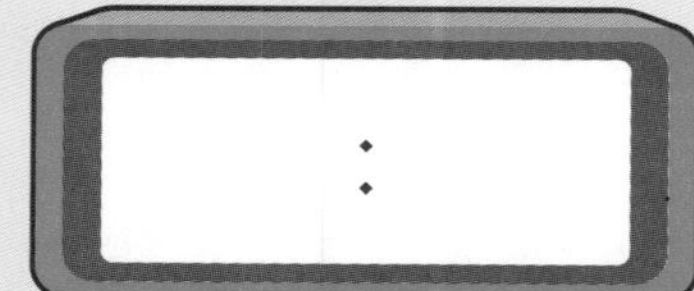

b.

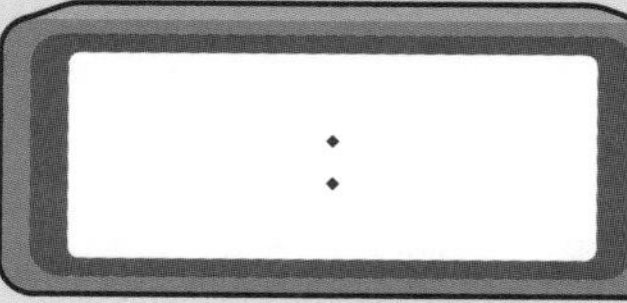

c.

d.

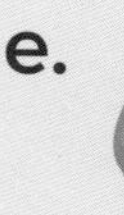

e.

f.

2. Draw lines to connect matching times.

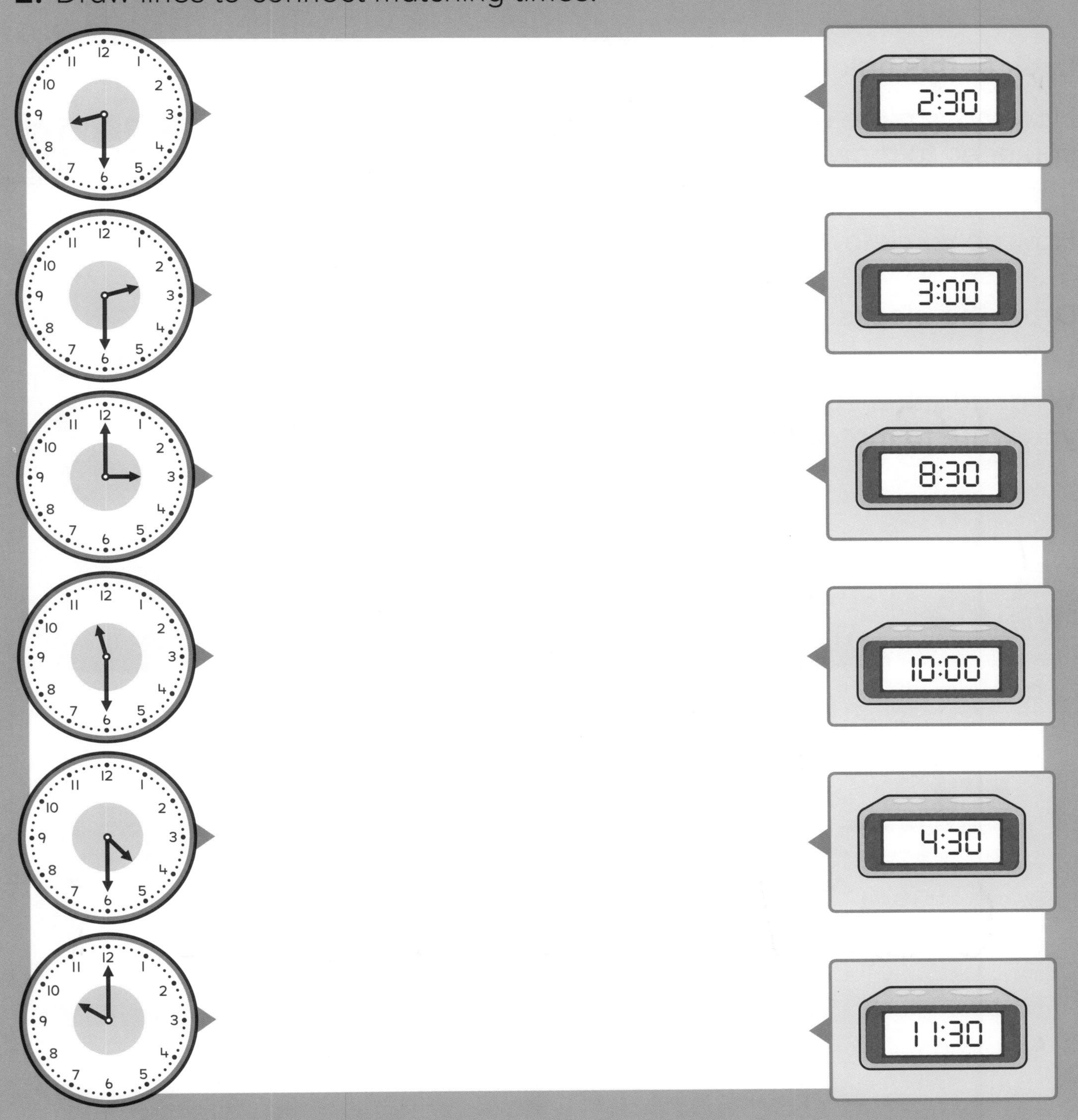

Step Ahead

James has breakfast at 7:00 on Monday morning.
He has baseball practice at 4:00 in the afternoon.

How many half past the hour times will there be on the clock between breakfast and the start of baseball training? ______

9.1 Balancing Equations (Two Addends)

Look at this balance picture.

How many more blocks do you need to draw to make the balance picture true?

How do you know?

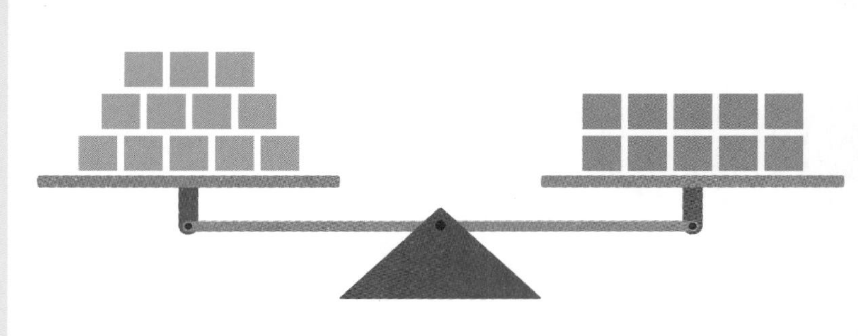

Draw the blocks.

What addition equation could you write to match the picture?

___ = ___ + ___

Step Up

1. Draw **more** blocks to make the balance picture true. Then write the matching equation.

a.

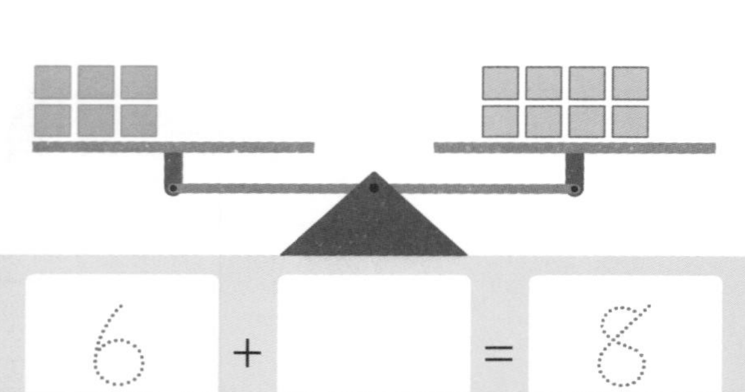

6 + ___ = 8

b.

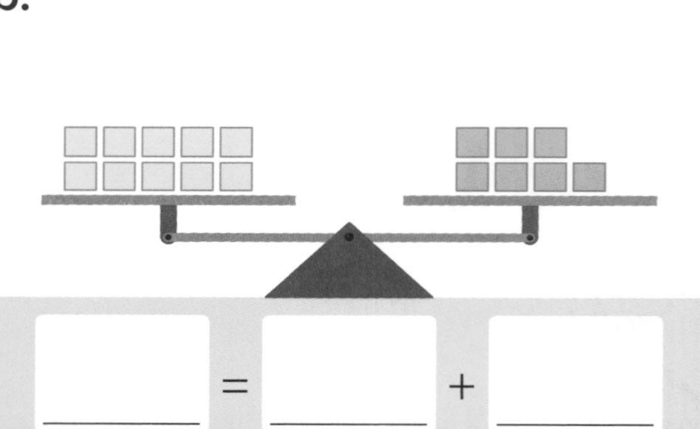

___ = ___ + ___

c.

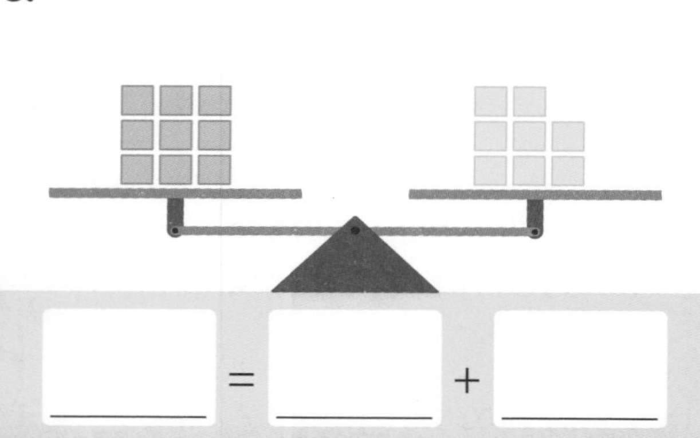

___ = ___ + ___

d.

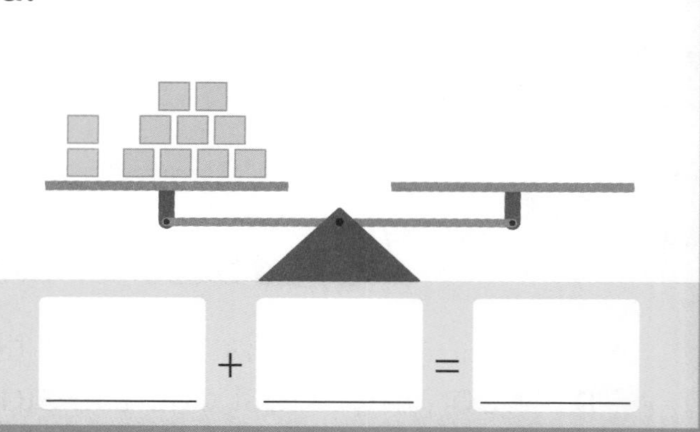

___ + ___ = ___

2. Write the missing numbers to make each balance picture true. Then write the matching equation.

a.

___ + ___ = ___

b.

___ = ___ + ___

c.

14 1

___ = ___ + ___

d.

___ + ___ = ___

e.

17 19

___ + ___ = ___

f.

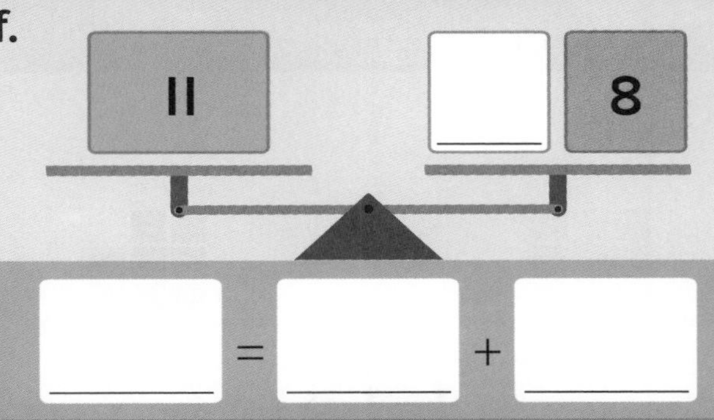

___ = ___ + ___

Step Ahead Write three different addition equations that would make this balance picture true.

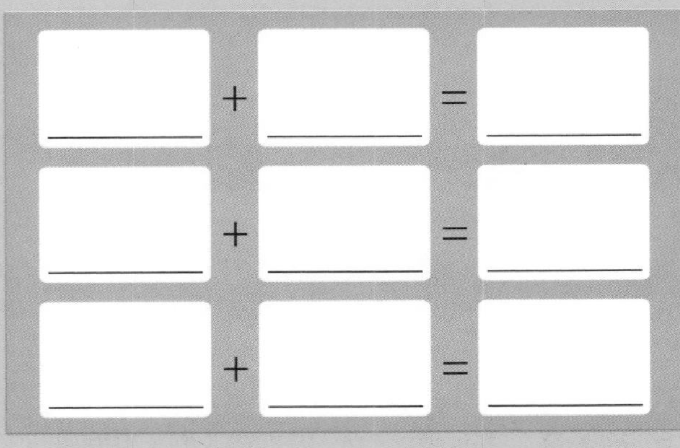

___ + ___ = ___

___ + ___ = ___

___ + ___ = ___

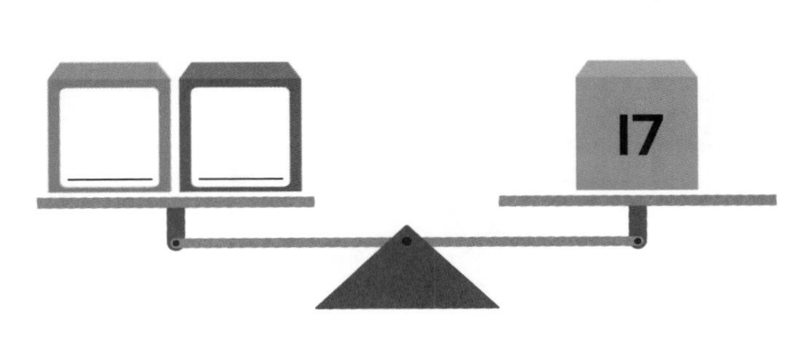

9.2 Balancing Equations (More Than Two Addends)

Look at this balance picture.

How many more blocks do you need to draw to make the balance picture true?

How do you know?

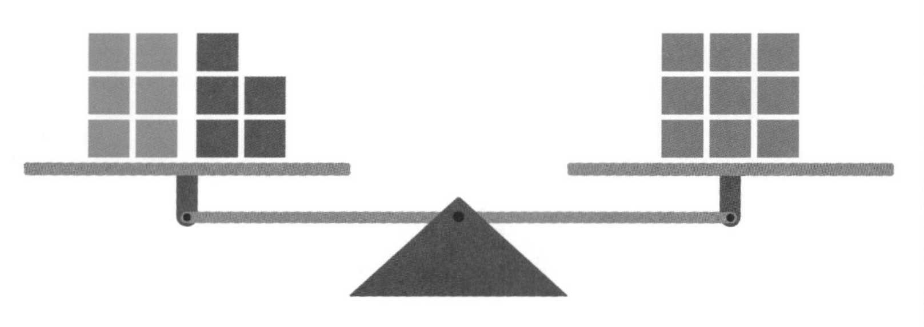

Draw the blocks.

What addition equation could you write to match the picture?

___ + ___ = ___ + ___

Step Up

I. Draw **more** blocks to make the balance picture true.
Then write the matching equation.

a.

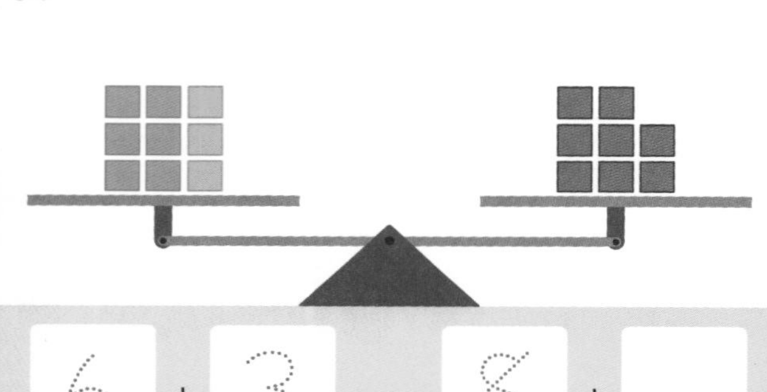

6 + 3 = 8 + ___

b.

___ + ___ = ___ + ___

c.

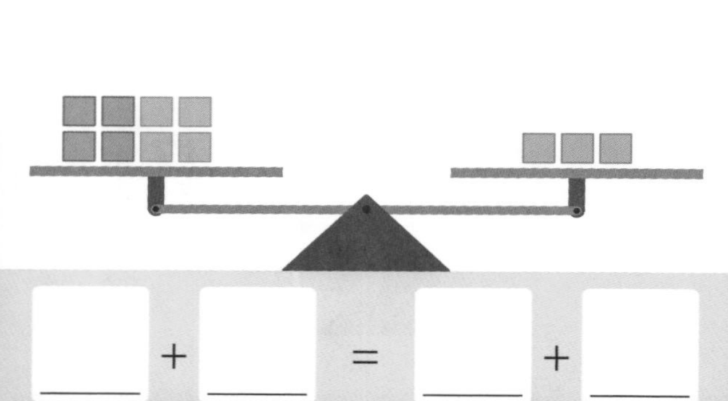

___ + ___ = ___ + ___

d.

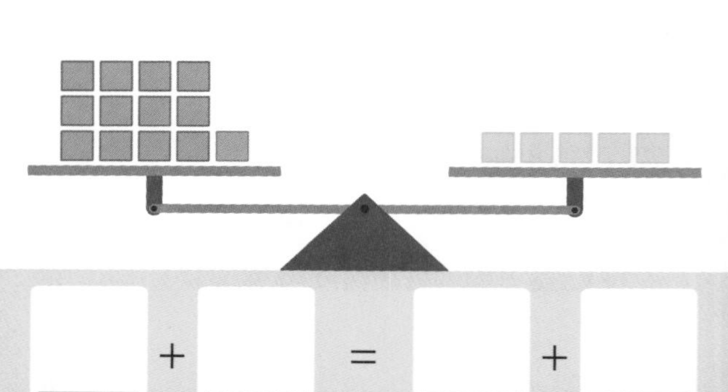

___ + ___ = ___ + ___

2. Write numbers to make each balance picture true.
Then write the matching equation.

a. 5 6 | 7 ___

5 + 6 = 7 + ___

b.

___ + ___ = ___ + ___

c. 6 ___ | 8 7

___ + ___ = ___ + ___

d.

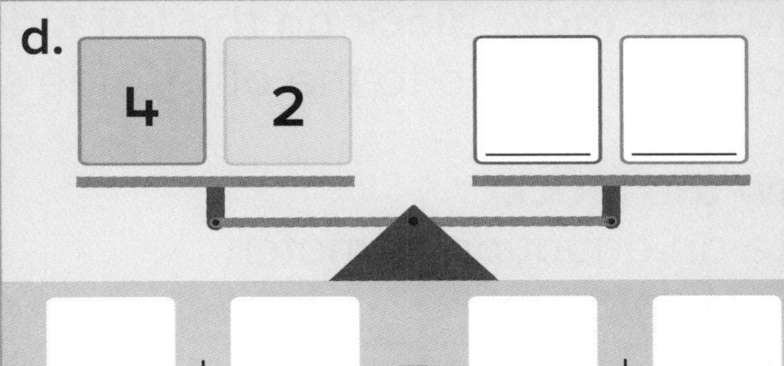

___ + ___ = ___ + ___

e.

___ + ___ = ___ + ___

f.

___ + ___ = ___ + ___

Step Ahead Write the missing numbers. Think carefully before you write.
Then write the matching equation.

a. 2 ___ | ___ 9

___ + ___ = ___ + ___

b.

___ + ___ = ___ + ___

9.3 Working with Equality

Look at this balance picture.

Write an addition equation to match.

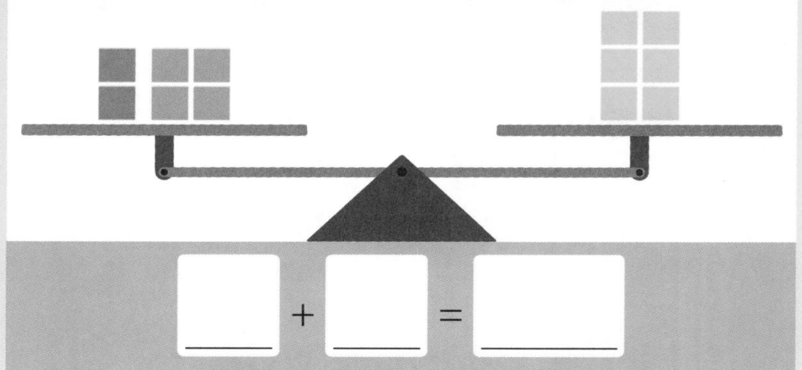

Draw one more block on the left side.
What must you do to the other side so that the quantities remain balanced?

Draw the block.
Write an equation to match the new picture.

___ + ___ = ___

Cross out three blocks on the right side.
What must you do to the other side so that the quantities remain balanced?

Cross out the blocks.
Write an equation to match the remaining blocks.

___ + ___ = ___

Step Up

1. Write an equation to match the balance picture.
Draw **more** blocks. Then write the new equation.

a.

___ + ___ = ___

Draw 2 more blocks on each side.

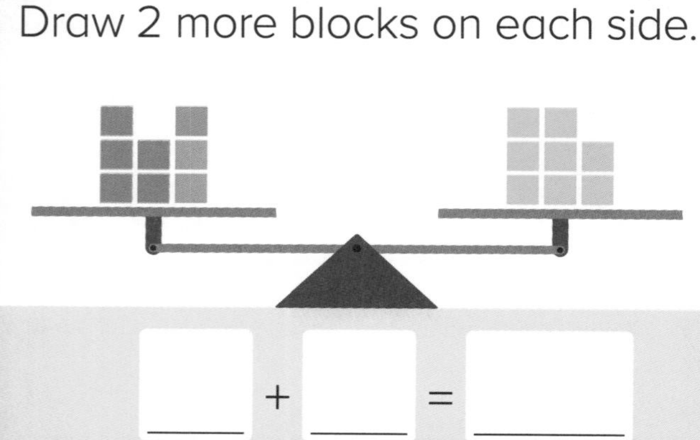

b.

___ + ___ = ___

Draw 3 more blocks on each side.

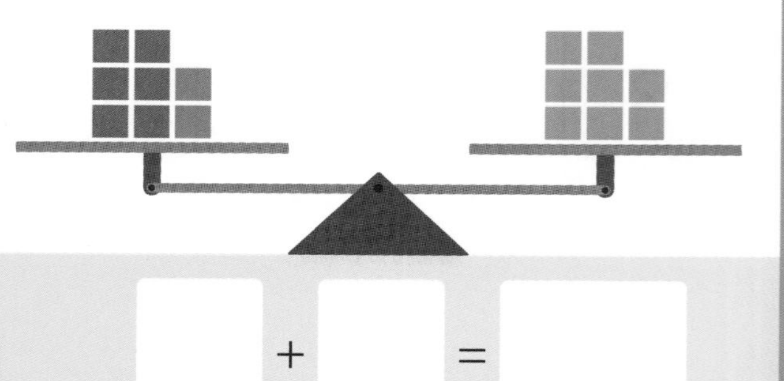

2. Write an equation to match the balance picture. **Cross out** blocks. Then write an equation to match the remaining blocks.

a. ____ + ____ = ____

Cross out 2 blocks on each side.

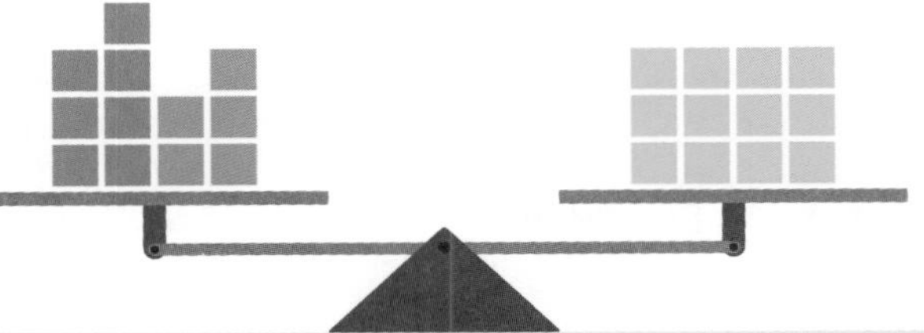

____ + ____ = ____

b. ____ + ____ = ____

Cross out 3 blocks on each side.

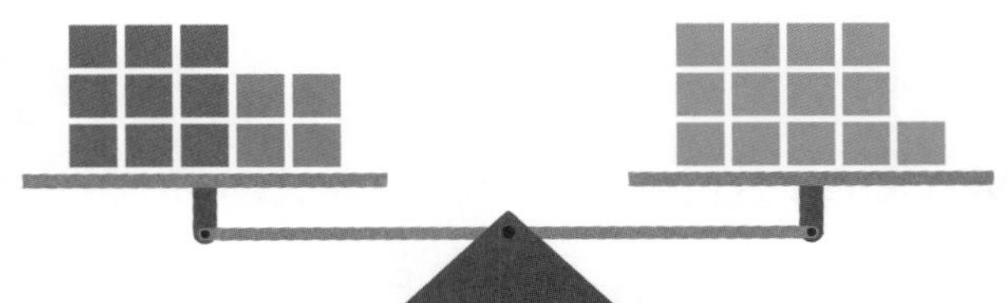

____ + ____ = ____

c. ____ + ____ = ____

Cross out 2 blocks on each side.

____ + ____ = ____

d. ____ + ____ = ____

Cross out 3 blocks on each side.

____ + ____ = ____

Step Ahead

There are 16 marbles in total. Alisa has 2 more marbles than Juan. How many marbles does each person have?

Alisa has ____ marbles.

Juan has ____ marbles.

9.4 Representing Word Problems

Mano has 7 cards.

Lela has 6 cards.

How many cards do they have in total?

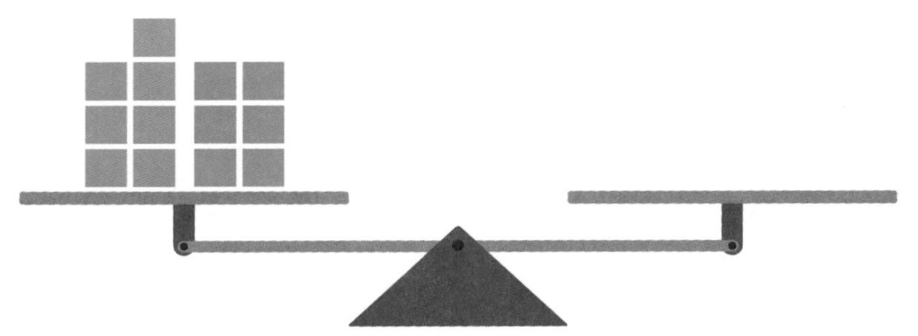

How does the balance picture match the word problem?

What do the pink and blue blocks show?

Draw more blocks to show the total.

Write an equation to match the picture. ____________________

Step Up

1. Read the story. Draw more blocks in the balance picture to match. Then write an equation to show your thinking.

a. There are 8 girls and 3 boys.

How many children in all?

____

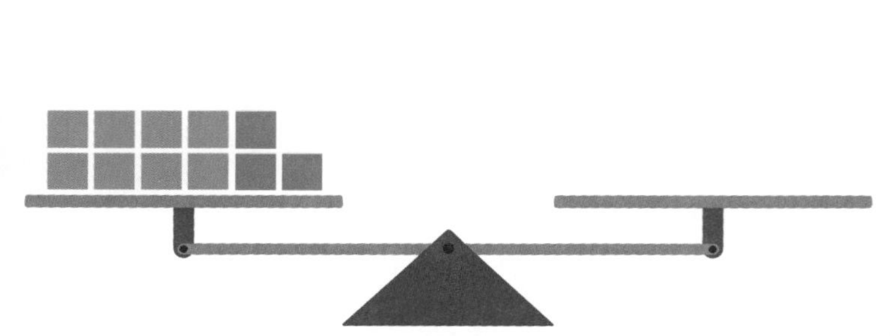

b. There are 12 dogs in the pet store. 6 have short hair. The others have long hair.

How many dogs have long hair?

____

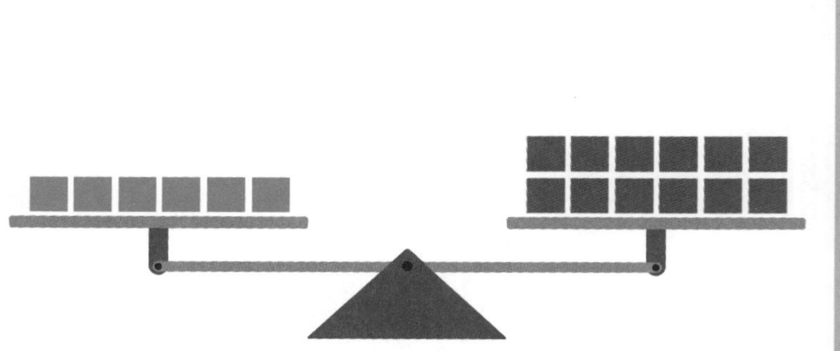

2. Read the story. Write numbers in the balance picture to match. Then write an equation to show your thinking.

a. There are 15 students in a class. There are 8 boys.

How many girls are there?

b. There were 12 chocolates in a box. Now there are 9 left.

How many were eaten?

c. There are 8 fish you can see. There are 9 fish hiding.

How many fish are in the tank?

Step Ahead Read the story. Then write an equation to match.

a. 12 eggs were used for breakfast on the weekend. More eggs were used on Saturday than on Sunday. How many eggs could have been used each day?

b. 18 students went on a school trip. There were fewer boys than girls. What numbers of boys and girls could there have been?

9.5 Working with Inequality

Look at this balance picture.
What do you notice?

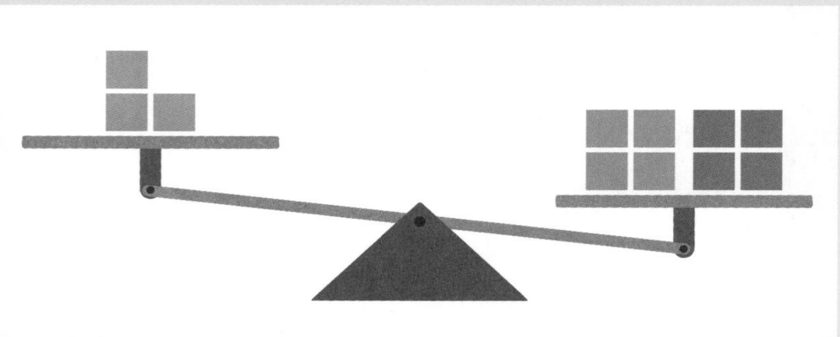

What numbers of blocks could you draw on the left side so that the balance is still not equal? How do you know?

If you drew 7 more blocks on the left side, what would happen? How do you know?

Step Up

1. Draw **more** blocks on each pan balance. Make sure each balance picture is true.

a.

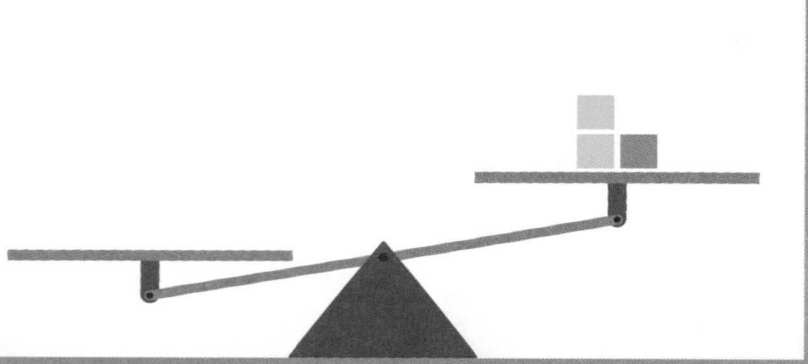

b.

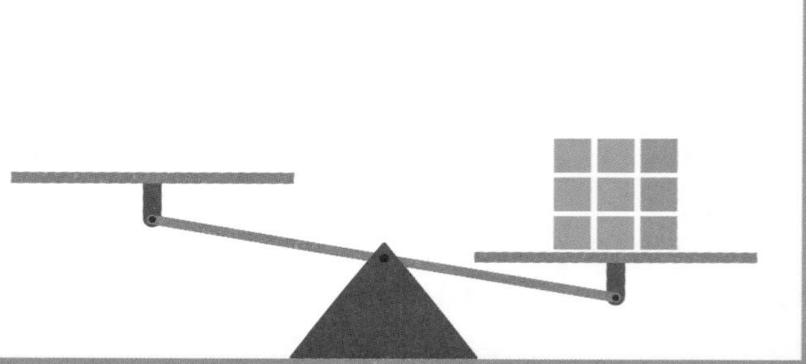

c.

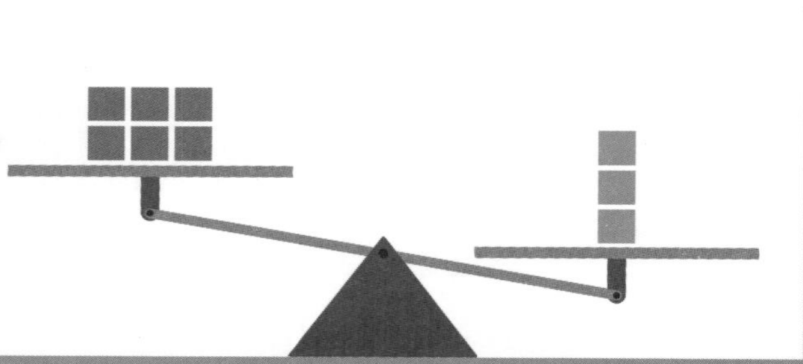

d.

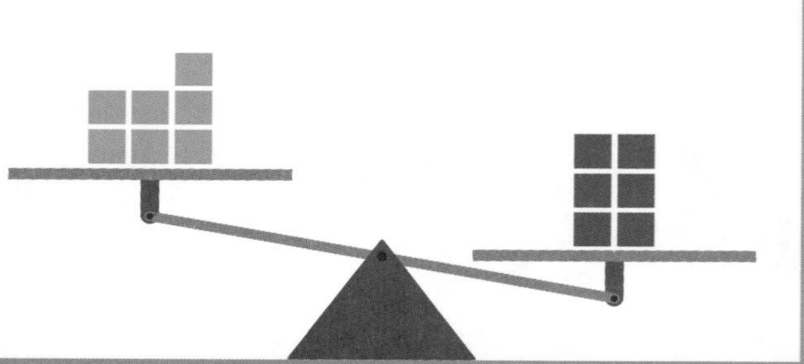

e.

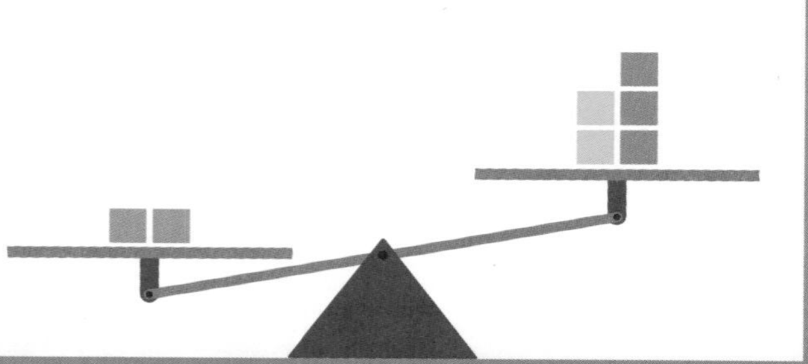

f.

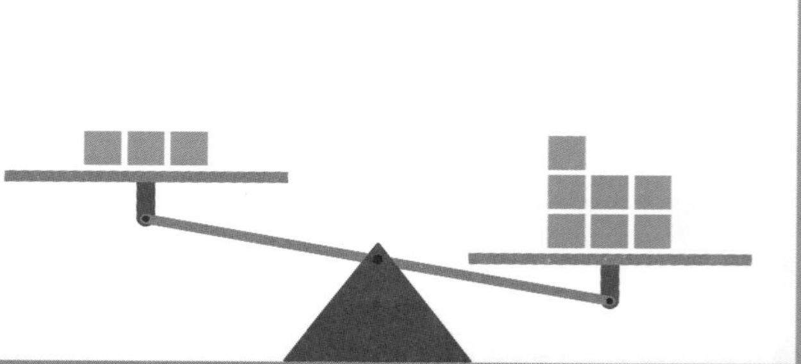

2. Write numbers in the boxes to make each balance picture true. Then complete the sentence.

a.

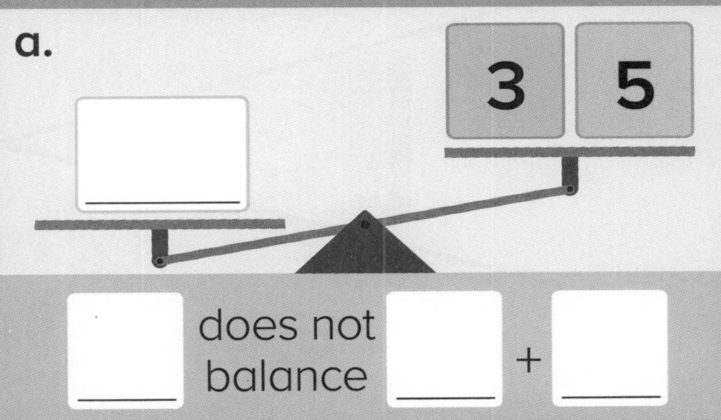

___ does not balance ___ + ___

b.

___ does not balance ___ + ___

c.

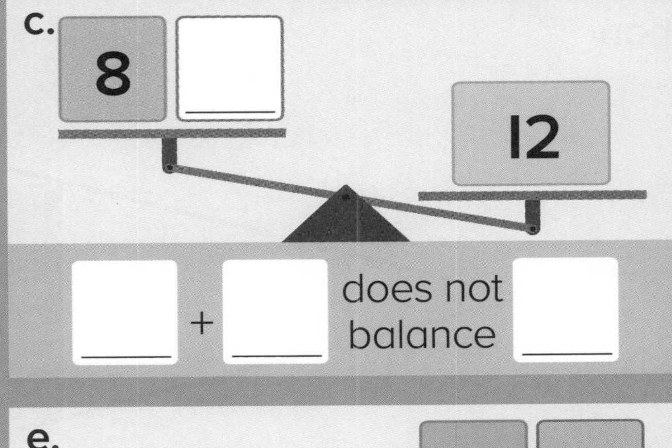

___ + ___ does not balance ___

d.

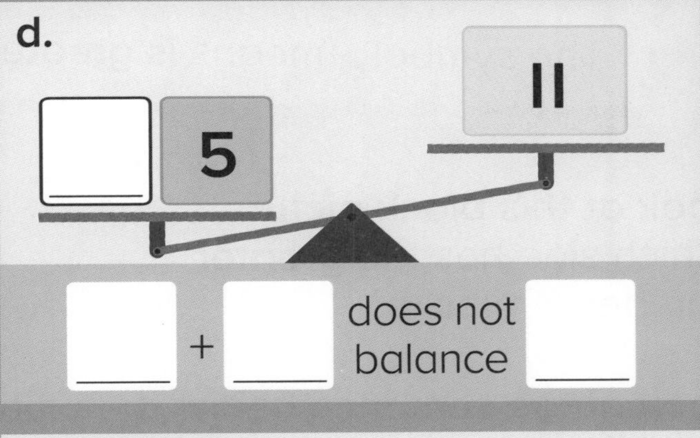

___ + ___ does not balance ___

e.

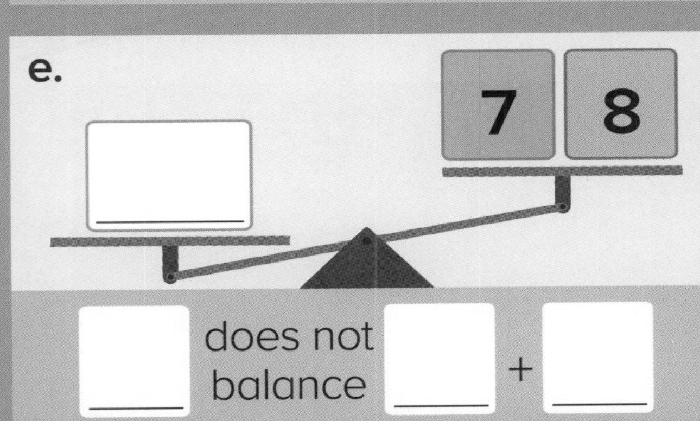

___ does not balance ___ + ___

f.

___ does not balance ___ + ___

Step Ahead Write numbers to make these balance pictures true. Think carefully before you write.

a.

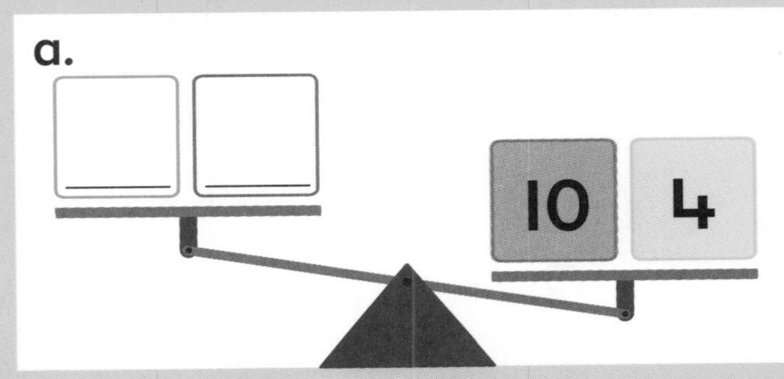

b.

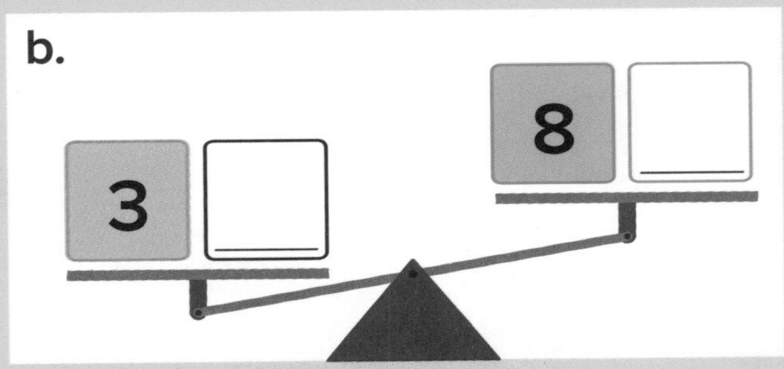

9.6 Introducing Comparison Symbols

Look at this block picture.
Which side has the greater number of blocks?

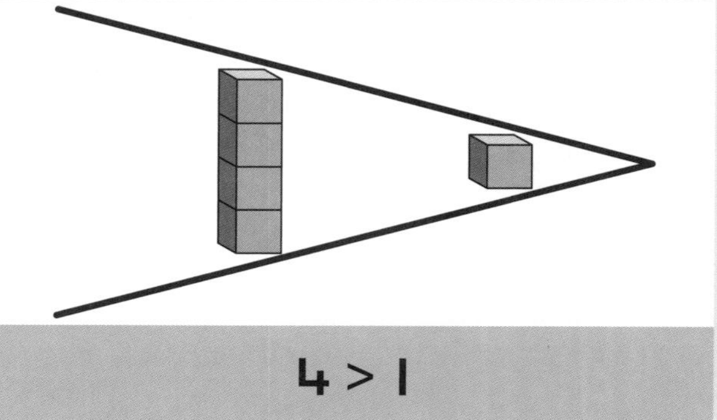

Look at the sentence below the picture.
How does it match the picture?

What does **>** mean? How do you know?

The symbol > means **is greater than.**

Look at this block picture.
Which side has the **greater** number of blocks?

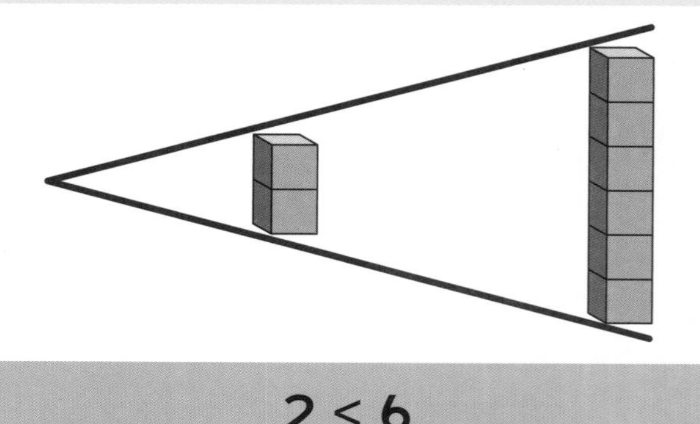

Look at the sentence below the picture.
How does it match the picture?

What does **<** mean? How do you know?

The symbol < means **is less than.**

Step Up 1. Compare each stack.
Then write **<** or **>** to complete each sentence.

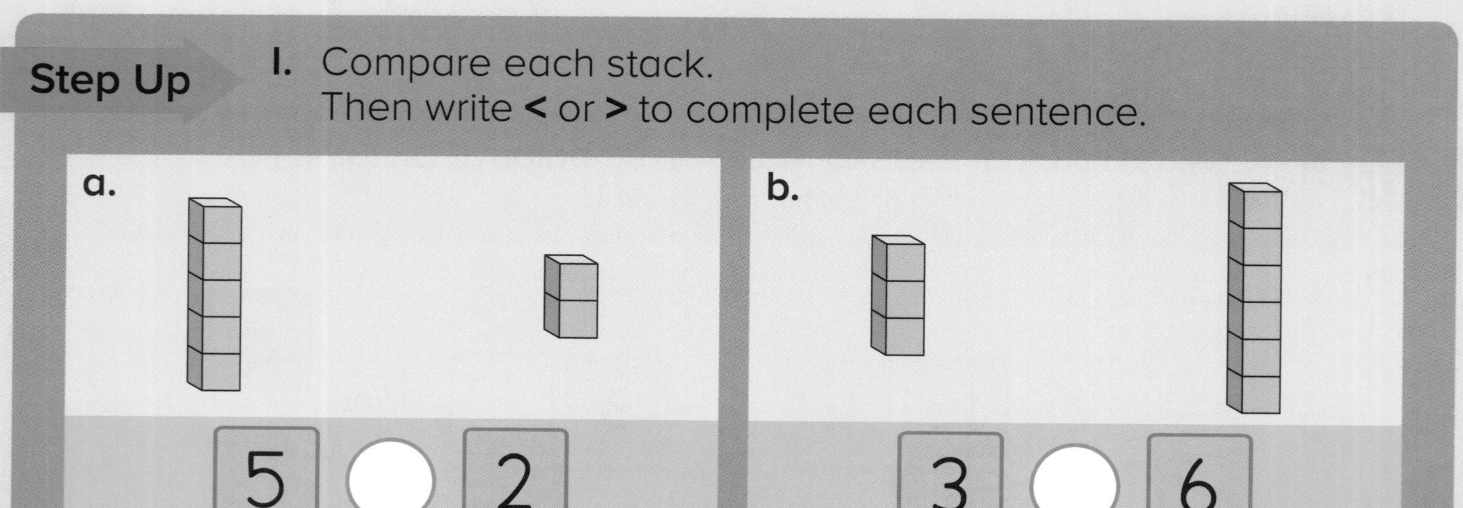

2. Write the numbers and **>** or **<** to complete each sentence.

a.

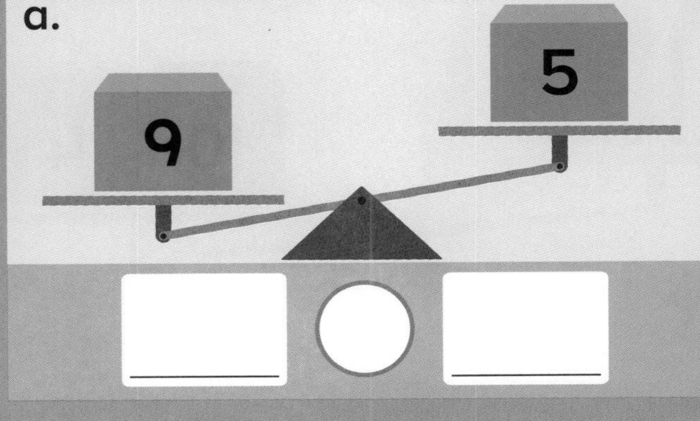

b.

c.

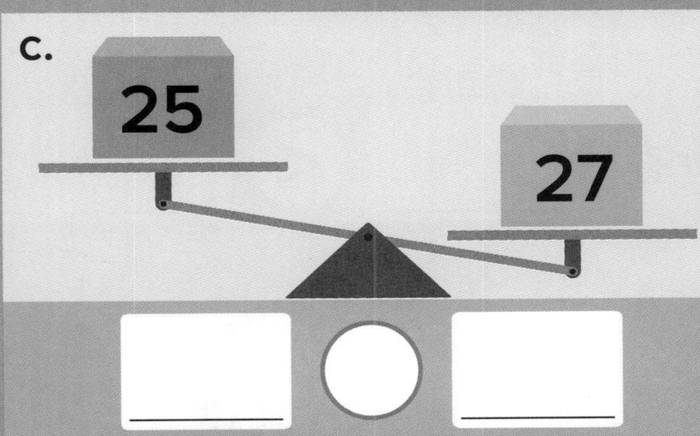

d.

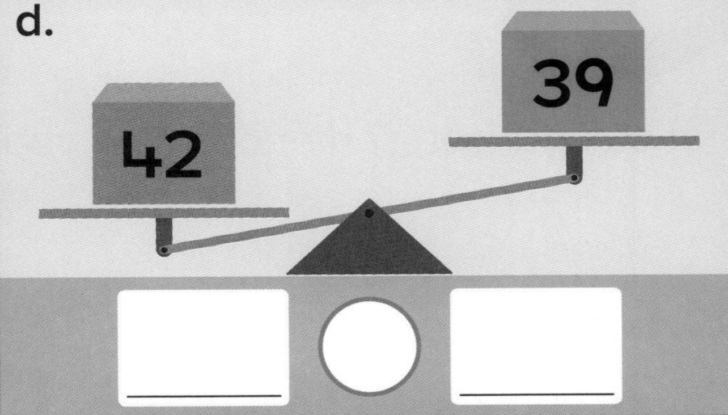

3. Loop the sentences that are true.

a. 19 **>** 16 **b.** 34 **<** 29 **c.** 8 **<** 10 **d.** 17 **>** 71

Step Ahead Use these numbers to make two true balance pictures. Then write comparison sentences to match.

13 

15 12

a.

b.

Recording Results of Comparisons with Symbols

Look at this balance picture.

What number could you write in the empty box on the left side? How do you know?

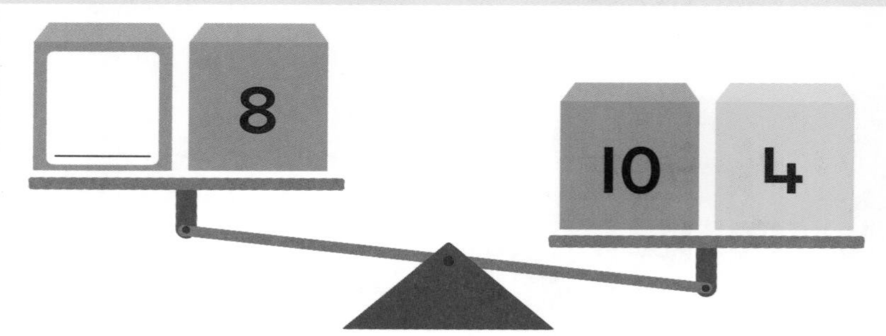

You could write any number less than 6 in the empty box.

What comparison sentence could you write? ______ < ______

Look at this balance picture.

What do you know about the numbers on the left side?

What numbers could you write?

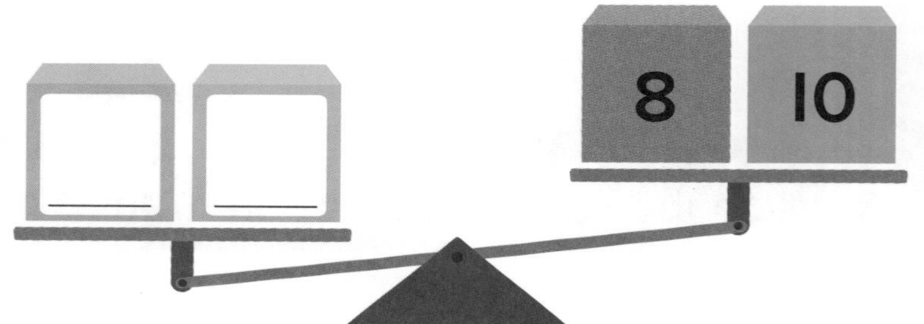

What comparison sentence could you write? ______

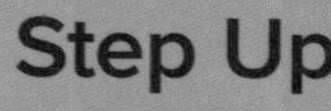

Step Up

1. Write a number to make the balance picture true.
Then write a comparison sentence using **<** or **>** to match.

a.

______

b.

______

2. Write numbers to make the balance picture true.
Then write the comparison sentence to match.

a. 13 5

____

b.

____

c. 14 6

____

d.

____

3. Write **<**, **>**, or **=** to make true comparison sentences.

a. 14 + 3 ◯ 16 + 2	**b.** 6 + 9 ◯ 4 + 15	**c.** 5 + 7 ◯ 1 + 11
d. 12 + 4 ◯ 7 + 8	**e.** 19 + 1 ◯ 3 + 17	**f.** 6 + 13 ◯ 8 + 9

Step Ahead Write **<**, **>**, or **=** to make true comparison sentences.

a. 9 + 6 + 2 ◯ 2 + 7 + 4	**b.** 7 + 2 + 8 ◯ 3 + 5 + 9
c. 1 + 2 + 9 ◯ 5 + 4 + 5	**d.** 7 + 5 + 3 ◯ 2 + 6 + 8
e. 19 − 8 ◯ 13 + 6	**f.** 17 − 2 ◯ 6 + 9

9.8 Sharing Among Four

How many counters can you see?

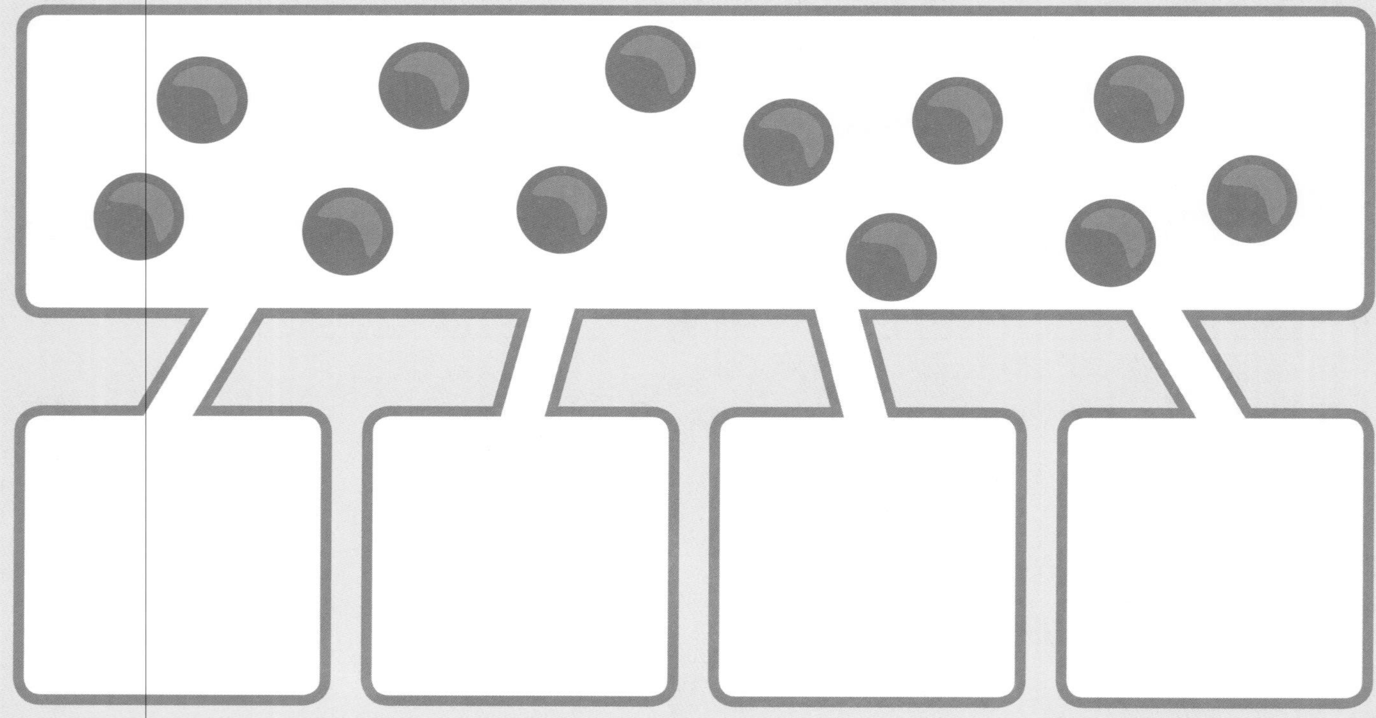

Can the counters be shared equally among 4 groups? How do you know?

How many counters will be in each group?

What other quantities can be shared equally among 4 groups?

Step Up

1. Your teacher will give you a sharing mat. Use ones blocks on the mat to figure out each person's share. Then complete each sentence.

a. 20 shared by 4 is ____ each.

b. 16 shared by 4 is ____ each.

c. 36 shared by 4 is ____ each.

d. 28 shared by 4 is ____ each.

e. 32 shared by 4 is ____ each.

f. 24 shared by 4 is ____ each.

2. a. Shade each number that can be shared equally among 4.

1	2	3	4	5	6	7	8	9	10
11	12	13	14	15	16	17	18	19	20
21	22	23	24	25	26	27	28	29	30
31	32	33	34	35	36	37	38	39	40
41	42	43	44	45	46	47	48	49	50

b. Describe the pattern that you see.

c. Imagine the number board above went to 60.
Write some **extra** numbers that can be equally shared among 4.

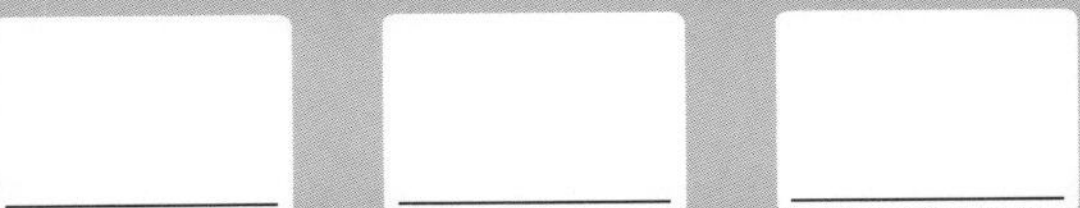

Step Ahead

a. Write some numbers that can be shared equally by 2 **and** by 4.

b. Write some numbers that can be shared by 2 but **not** by 4.

9.9 Identifying One-Fourth of a Collection

Look at this sheet of paper.

How has it been folded?

How many parts can you see?
What do you notice about the parts?

What name is used to describe one of the four parts?

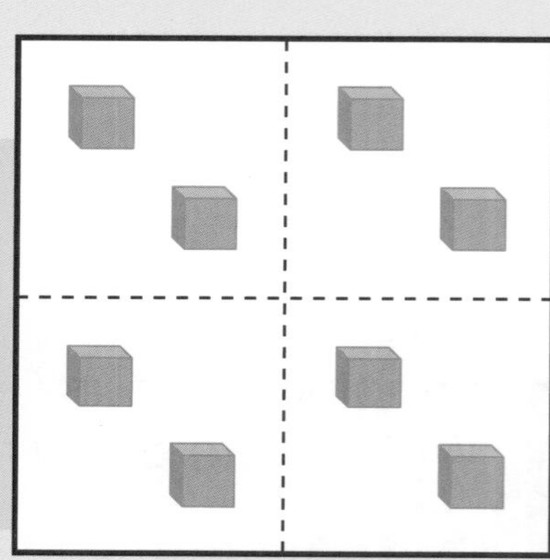

What do you notice about the cubes that have been placed on the folded sheet of paper?

How many cubes are in each equal share?

How many cubes are in one-fourth of 8?

Step Up I. Complete each sentence.

a.

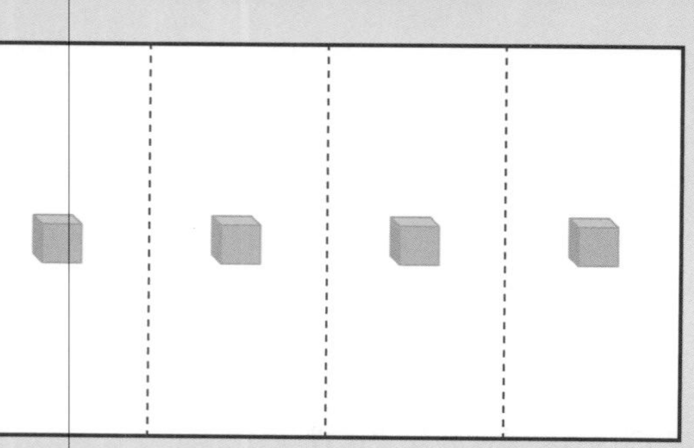

One-fourth of 4 is ____.

b.

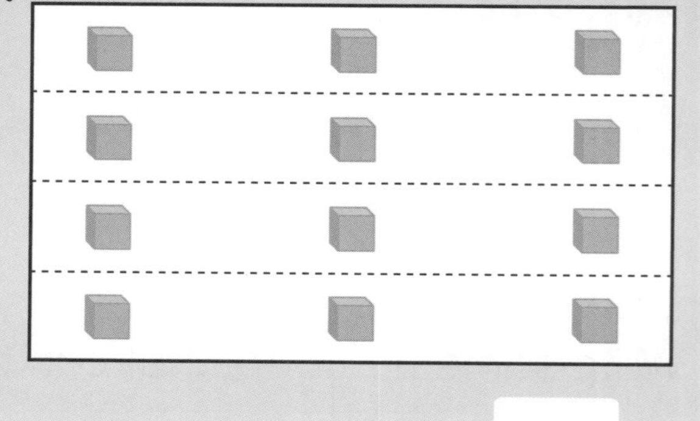

One-fourth of 12 is ____.

2. Loop **one-fourth** of each group. Then complete the sentence.

a.

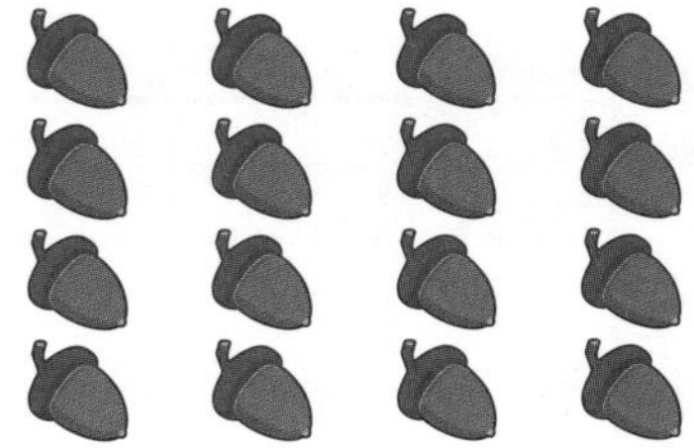

One-fourth of 16 is ____.

b.

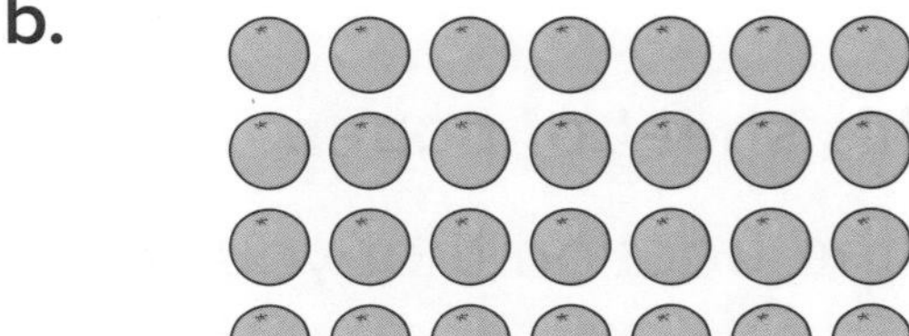

One-fourth of 28 is ____.

c.

One-fourth of 32 is ____.

d.

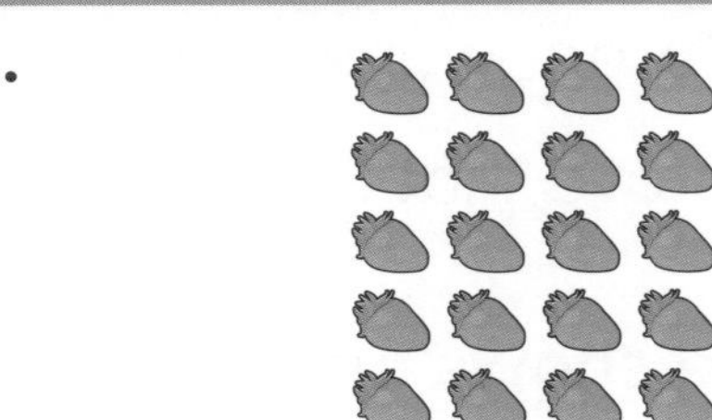

One-fourth of 20 is ____.

e.

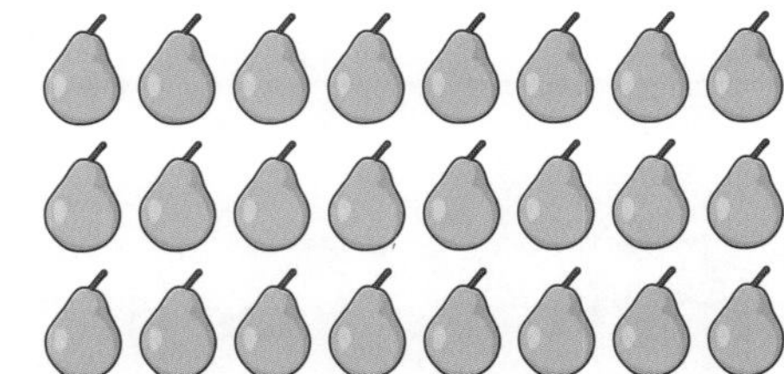

One-fourth of 24 is ____.

f.

One-fourth of 36 is ____.

Step Ahead

Twelve students voted on their favorite yogurt flavor. One-half liked blueberry. One-fourth liked strawberry. The others liked vanilla. Color these faces to show how many students voted for each flavor.

Color

- Blueberry – blue
- Strawberry – red
- Vanilla – yellow

9.10 Identifying One-Fourth of a Region

Look at this sheet of paper.

Describe the fraction that you see.

What is another name for one-fourth?

What other ways could you fold the paper to show one-fourth?

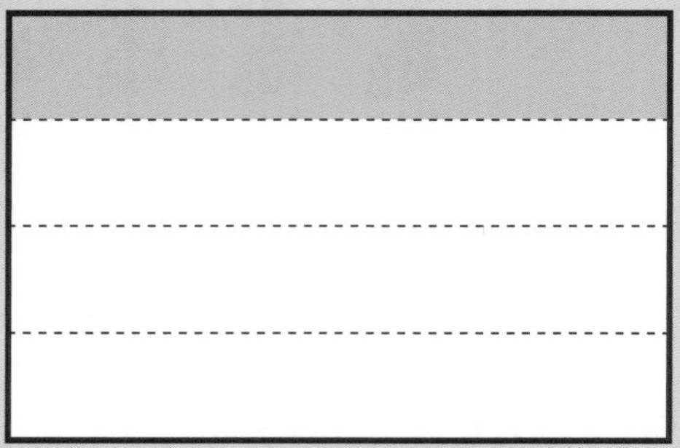

How many different ways can you show one-fourth?

How can you prove that a sheet of paper has been folded to show one-fourth?

Which of these shows one-fourth? How do you know?

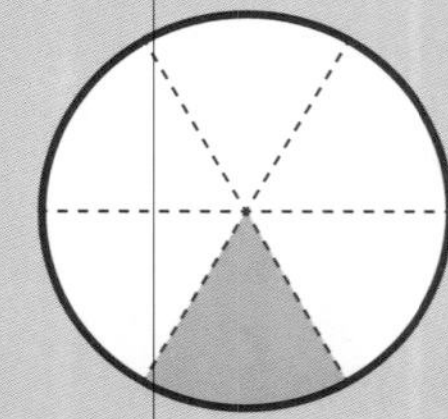

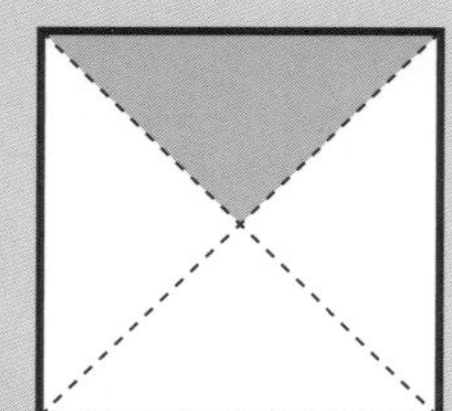

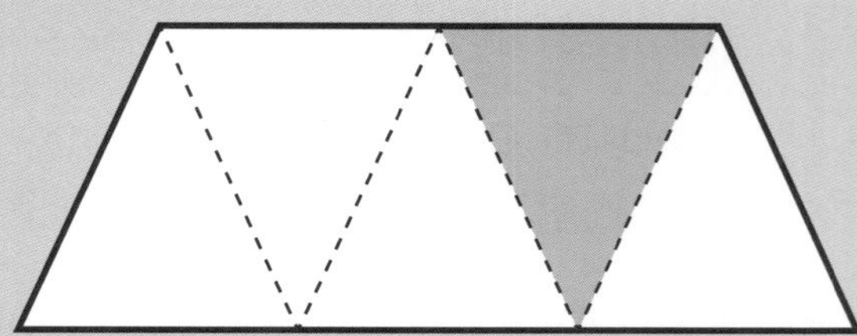

Step Up

1. Draw one more line to show four parts the same size. Then color **one-fourth**.

a.

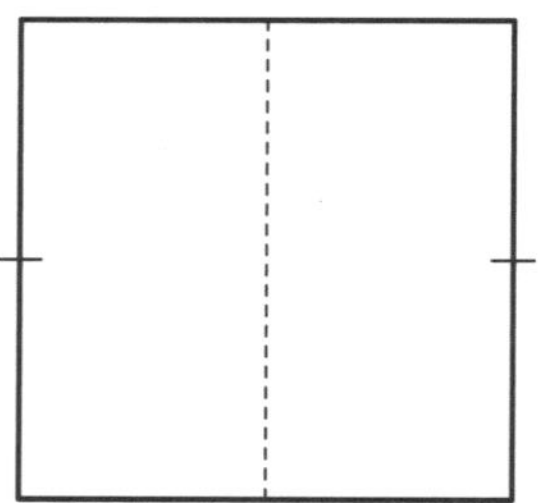

b.

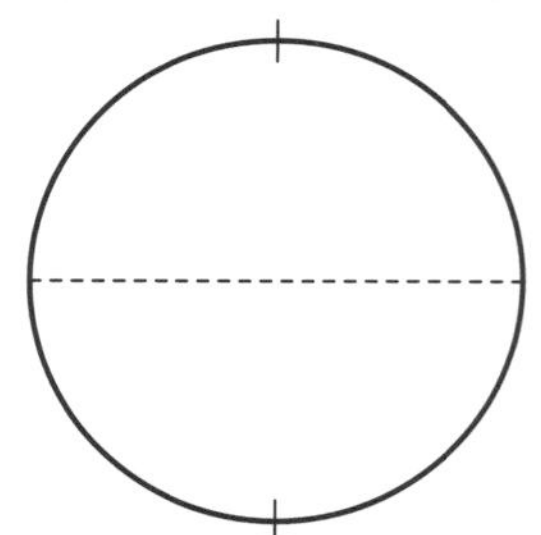

c.

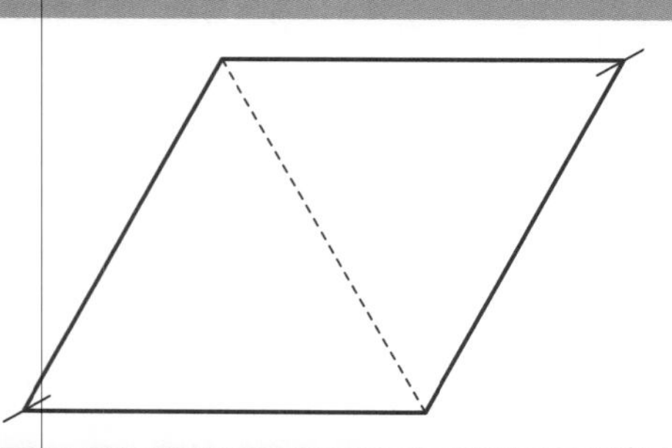

d.

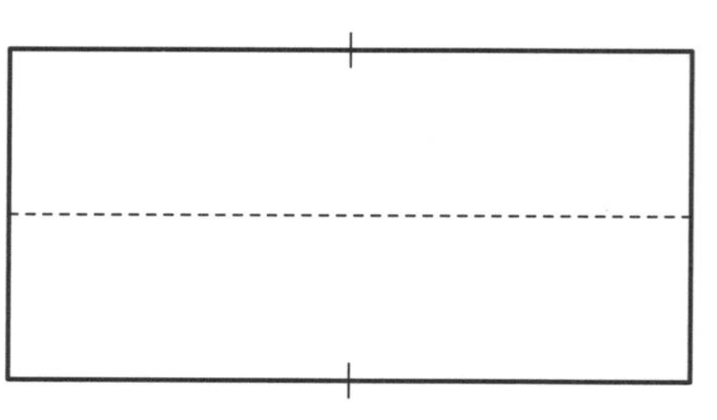

2. Color blue **one** of the parts in each.
Then loop each picture that shows one-fourth in blue.

a.

b.
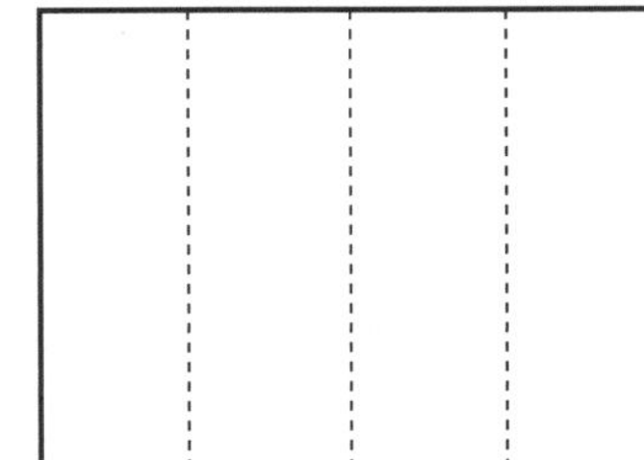

c.
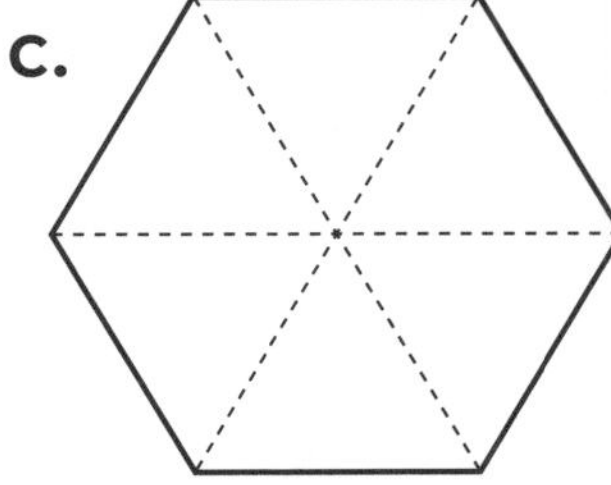

d.
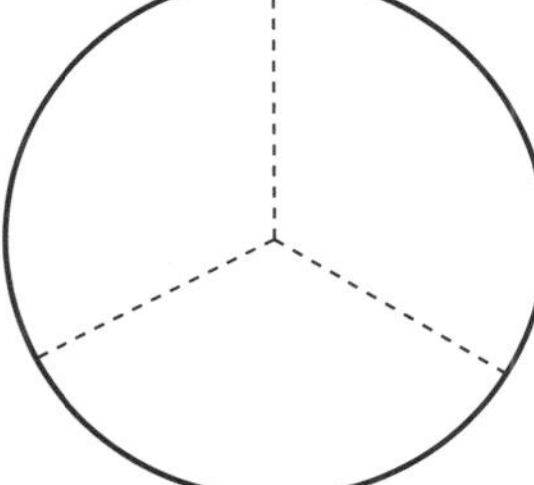

e.
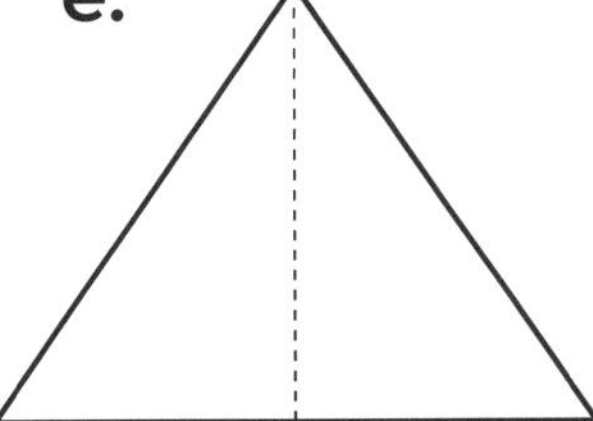

f.
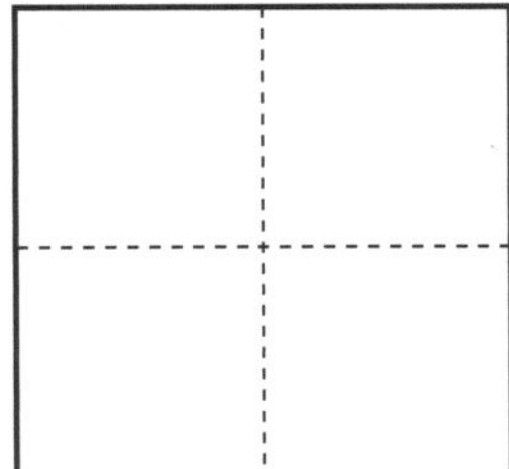

g.
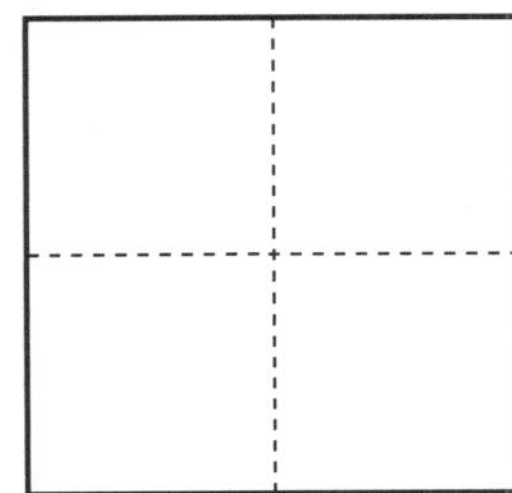

h.
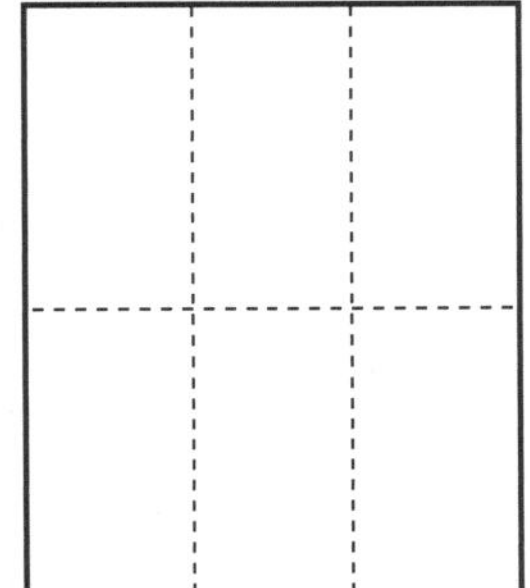

i.
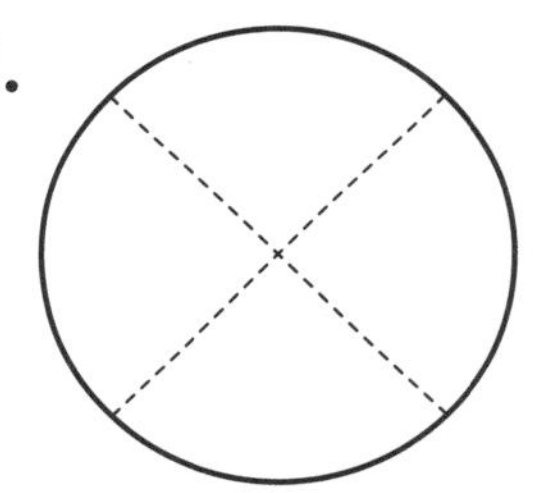

Step Ahead Write **two** different ways to sort these.

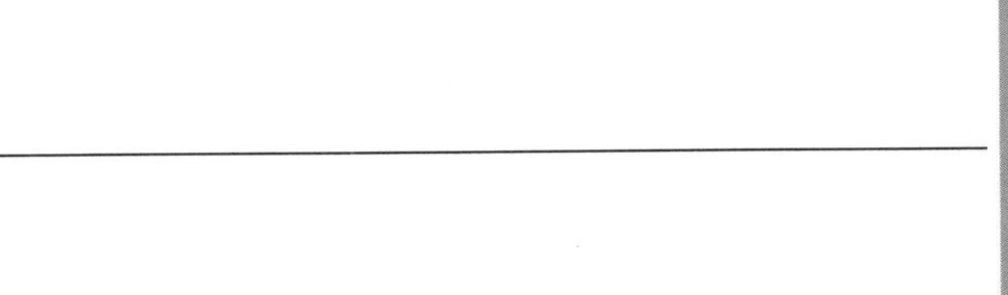

1.

2.

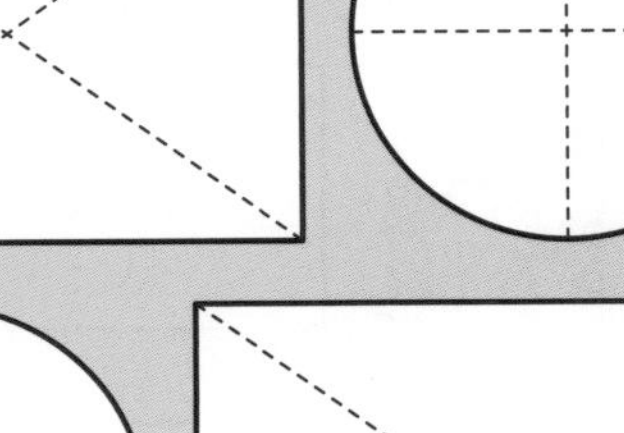

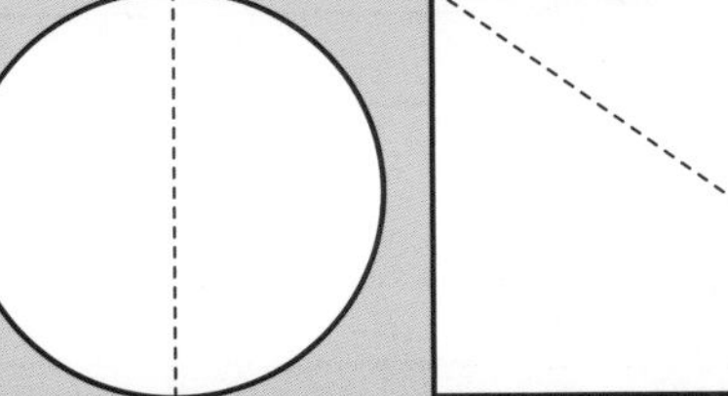

9.11 Identifying One-Half and One-Fourth of a Region

What do you notice about each of these pictures?

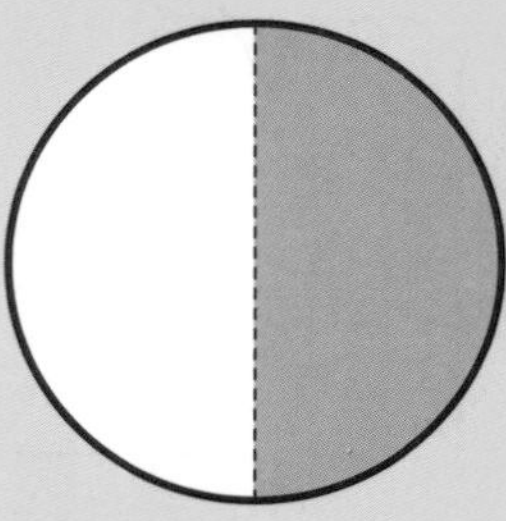
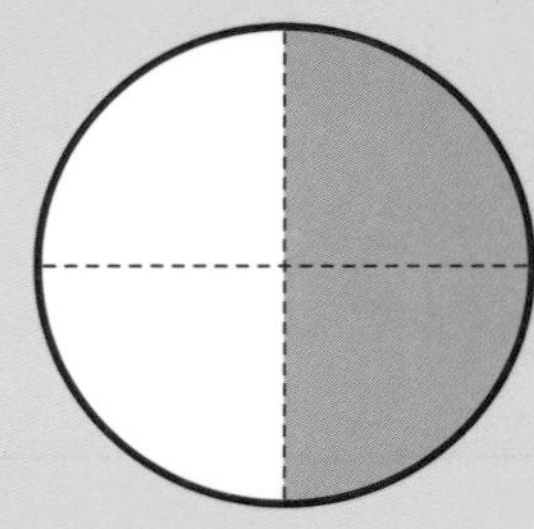
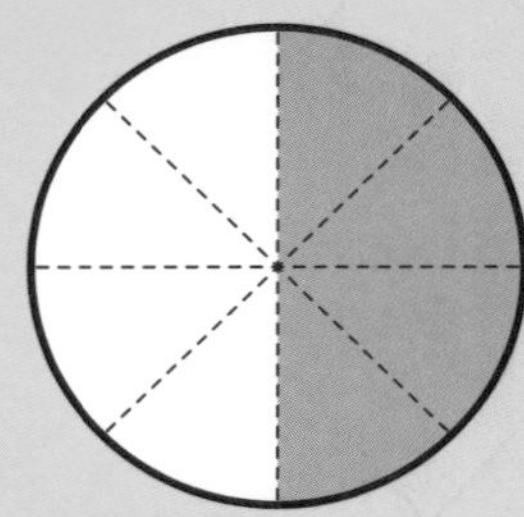

How many parts of each have been shaded?

Does each picture show the same amount shaded? How do you know?

Color one-half of each of these.

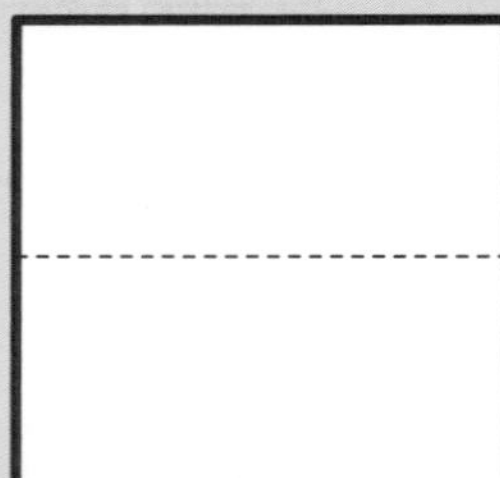
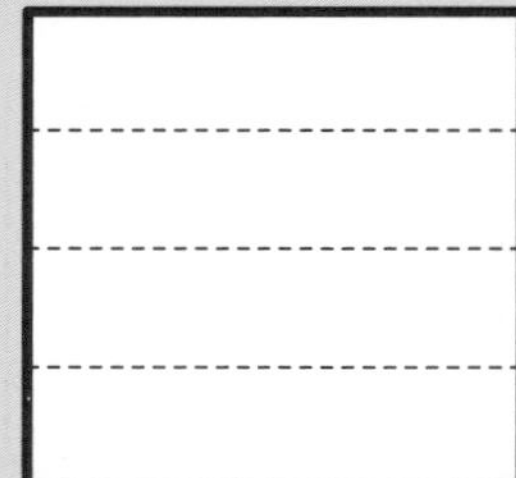
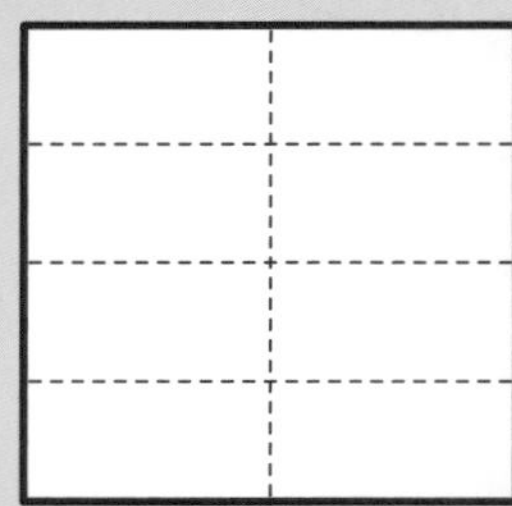

Can a different number of parts show the same amount? How?

Step Up

1. Color **one-half** of each picture.

2. Color **one-fourth** of each picture.

3. Color **one-half** of each.

a.

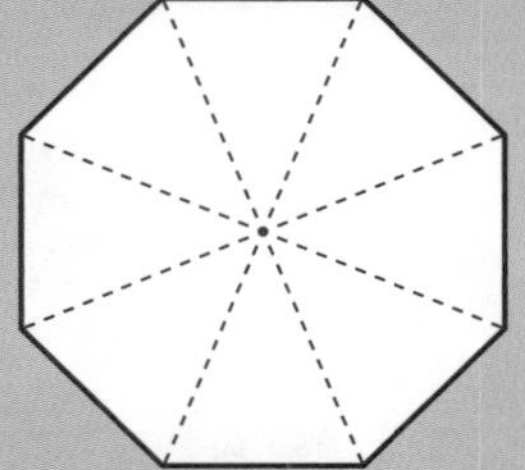

b.

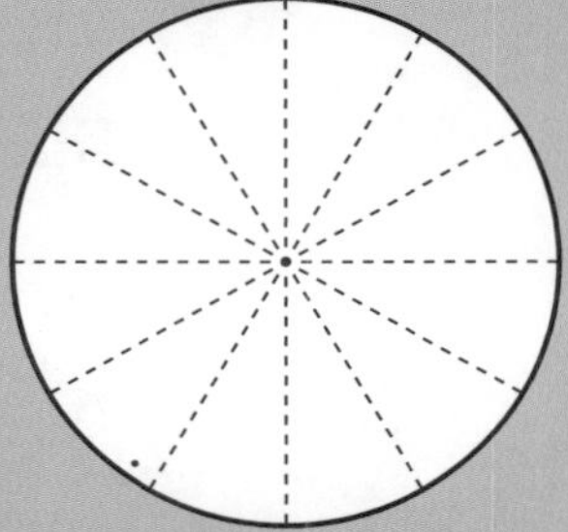

c.

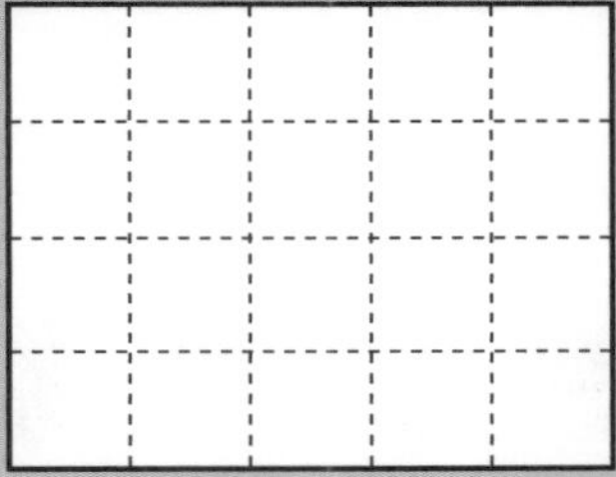

d.

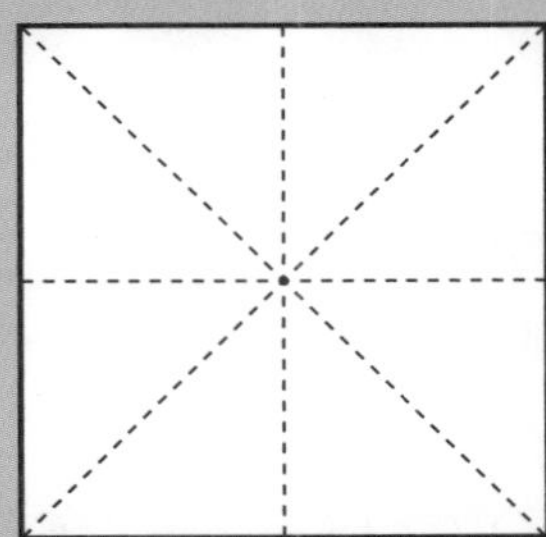

4. Color **one-fourth** of each.

a.

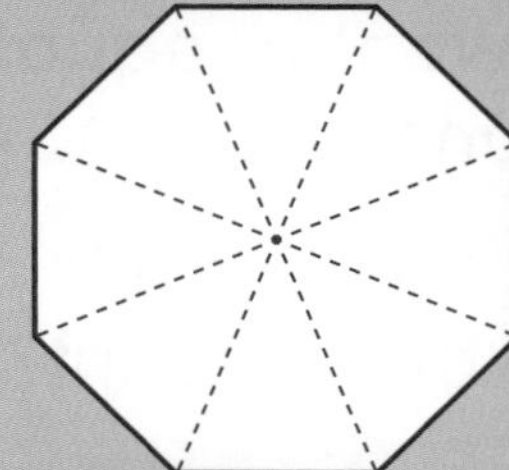

b.

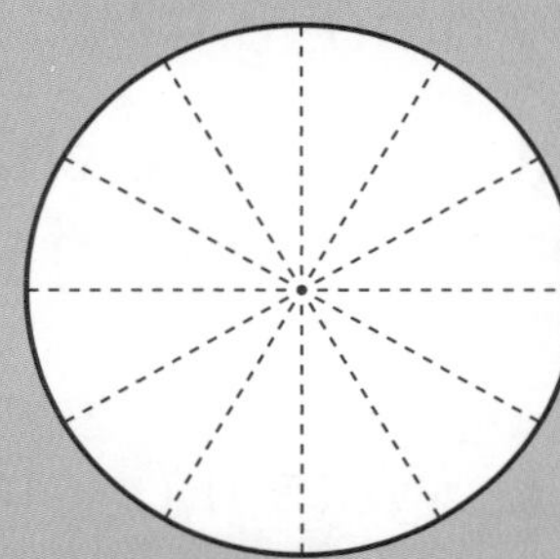

c.

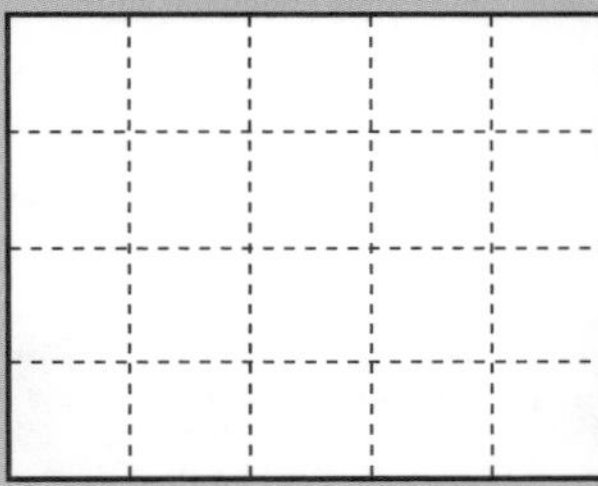

d.

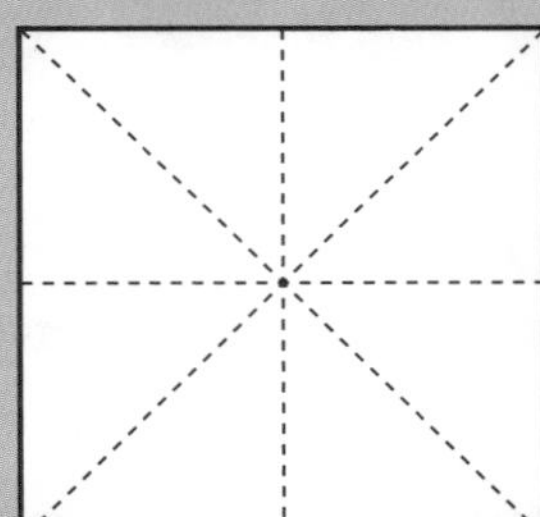

Step Ahead Color these to show one-fourth in **four** different ways.

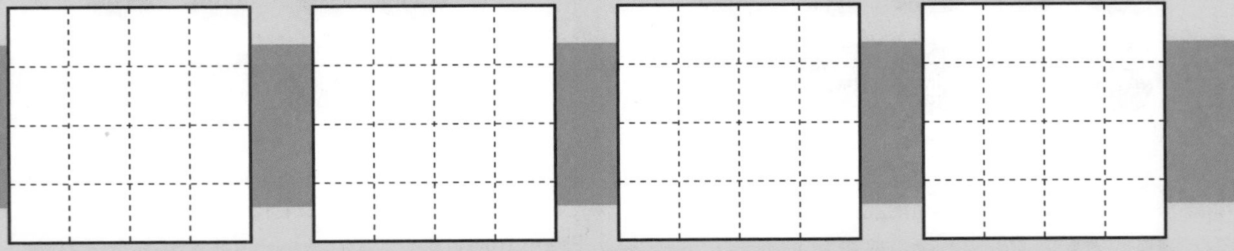

9.12 Identifying One-Fourth of Amounts of Money

Four friends want to equally share this money.

How can you figure out one-fourth of this amount?

What other amounts can you share equally among 4?

What amount cannot be shared equally among 4? How do you know?

Step Up

I. Write the total value.
Then loop **one-fourth** and complete the sentence.

a.

The total is ____ cents.

One-fourth is ____ cents.

b.

The total is ____ cents.

One-fourth is ____ cents.

c.

The total is ____ cents.

One-fourth is ____ cents.

d.

The total is ____ cents.

One-fourth is ____ cents.

2. Write the total value. Then loop **one-fourth** and complete the sentence.

a.

The total is _______ cents.

One-fourth is _______ cents.

b.

The total is _______ cents.

One-fourth is _______ cents.

c.

The total is _______ cents.

One-fourth is _______ cents.

d.

The total is _______ cents.

One-fourth is _______ cents.

Step Ahead

Four friends share the cost of this toy. How much will each person pay? Draw coins to show your thinking.

10¢

1¢

$1

Each person will pay _______ ¢.

10.1 Extending the Count-On Strategy Beyond the Facts

Look at this piece of a number track.

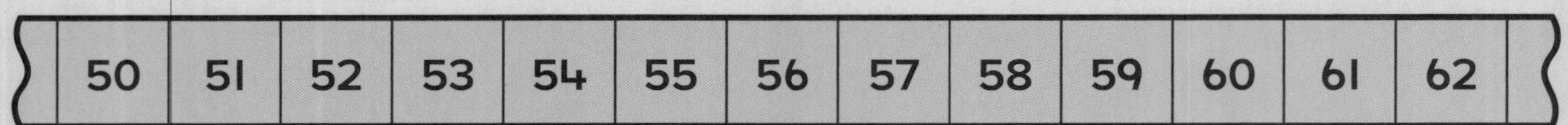

Imagine you were standing on 53 and made one jump to 55.
How can you show your jump on the number track?

You could draw an arrow like this.

50	51	52	53	54	55	56	57	58	59	60	61	62

What number sentence could you write to show what you did?

____ + ____ = ____

What other jumps could you make on this piece of number track?
What number sentences could you write to show what you did?

Step Up 1. Write the totals.

a. 24 + 1 = ____ b. 27 + 1 = ____ c. 31 + 1 = ____

2. Write the totals. Draw jumps on the number track to help you.

47	48	49	50	51	52	53	54	55	56	57

a. 49 + 1 = ____ **b.** 51 + 2 = ____ **c.** 54 + 3 = ____

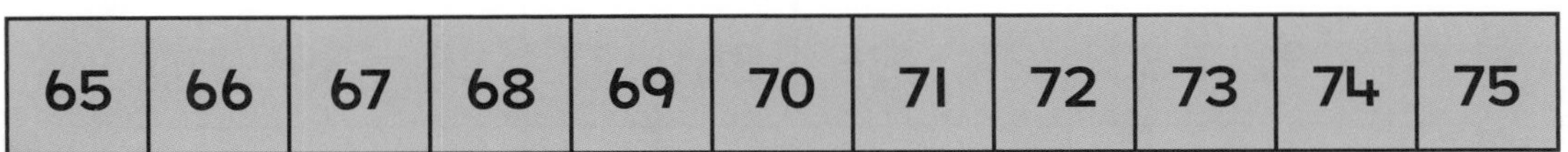

65	66	67	68	69	70	71	72	73	74	75

d. 66 + 1 = ____ **e.** 69 + 2 = ____ **f.** 72 + 3 = ____

3. Use this number track to complete different addition sentences.

84	85	86	87	88	89	90	91	92	93	94

a. ____ + 2 = ____ **b.** ____ + 1 = ____

c. ____ + 3 = ____ **d.** ____ + 2 = ____

e. ____ + 1 = ____ **f.** ____ + 3 = ____

Step Ahead Use the number track in Question 3 to help you figure out the answer.

Chloe has 87 cents.
Ramon has 2 cents more than Chloe.
Keisha has 3 cents more than Ramon.
Will has 2 cents more than Keisha.

How much money does Will have? ____ ¢

10.2 Exploring Addition Patterns

Look at these numbers.

1	2	3	4	5	6	7	8	9	10
11	12	13	14	15	16	17	18	19	20
21	22	23	24	25	26	27	28	29	30
31	32	33	34	35	36	37	38	39	40
41	42	43	44	45	46	47	48	49	50

What number is 1 more than 37? How do you know?

What number is 2 more than 25? How do you know?

What do you know about all the numbers that have 9 in the ones place?

Step Up 1. Write the totals.

a.	b.	c.
2 + 1 = ____	14 + 2 = ____	5 + 3 = ____
12 + 1 = ____	24 + 2 = ____	15 + 3 = ____
22 + 1 = ____	34 + 2 = ____	25 + 3 = ____
32 + 1 = ____	44 + 2 = ____	35 + 3 = ____
52 + 1 = ____	64 + 2 = ____	75 + 3 = ____
72 + 1 = ____	84 + 2 = ____	95 + 3 = ____

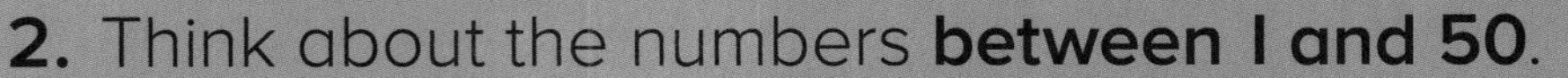

2. Think about the numbers **between 1 and 50**.

   a. Write all the numbers that have 3 in the ones place.

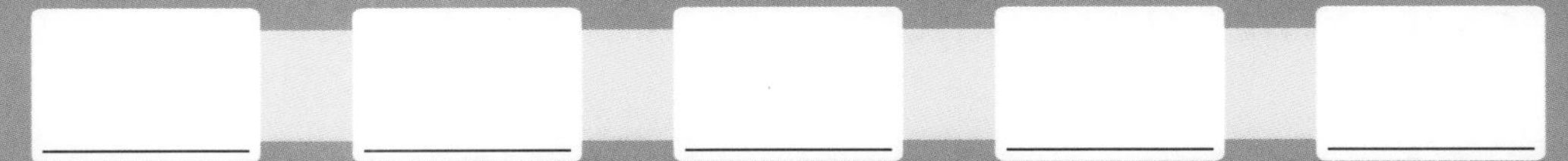

   b. Write the numbers that are **2 more** than each number you wrote.

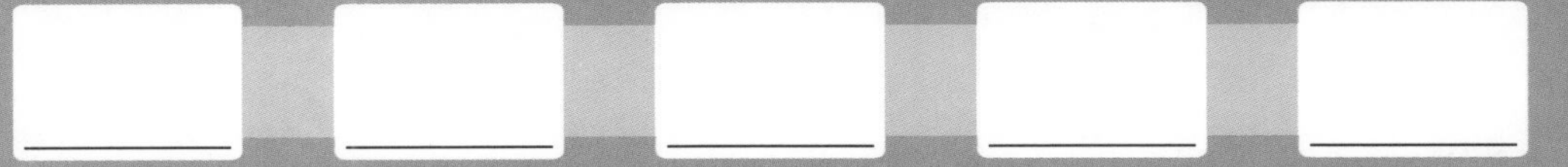

3. Think about the numbers **between 50 and 100**.

   a. Write all the numbers that have 6 in the ones place.

   b. Write the numbers that are **2 more** than each number you wrote.

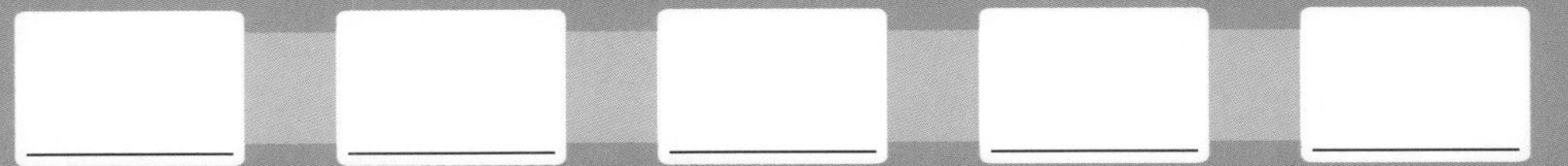

4. Write numbers **between 11 and 50** to complete these to show different addition sentences.

a. ____ + 3 = ____	b. ____ + 2 = ____	c. ____ + 3 = ____
d. ____ + 2 = ____	e. ____ + 1 = ____	f. ____ + 2 = ____

Step Ahead

Deven had 55 cents. He found 4 cents more in his school bag. Kristina had 56 cents. Her mother gave her 2 cents more. Jerome had 58 cents.

a. Who had the most money in total? ____________

b. Write the addition sentences you used to help you.

____

____

10.3 Counting Multiples of 10 (Off the Decade)

Look at this pattern. What do you notice?

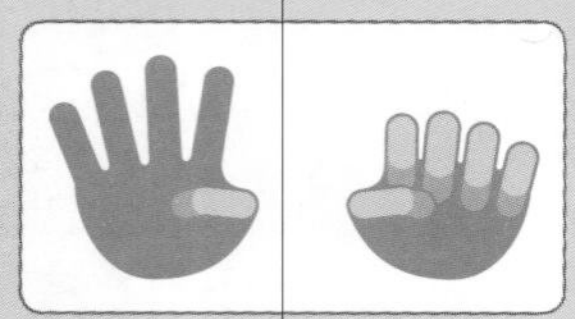

Picture 1

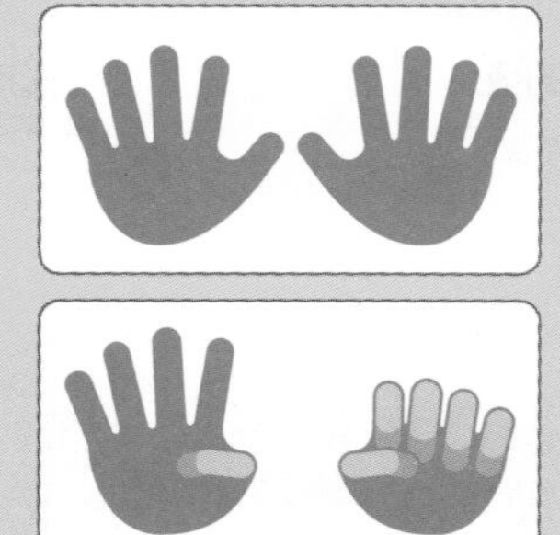

Picture 2

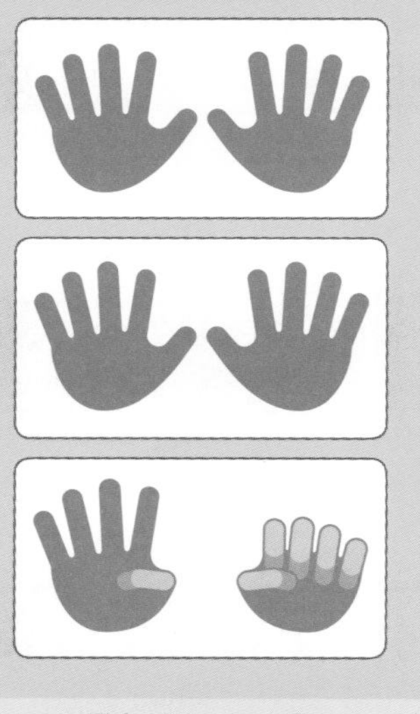

Picture 3

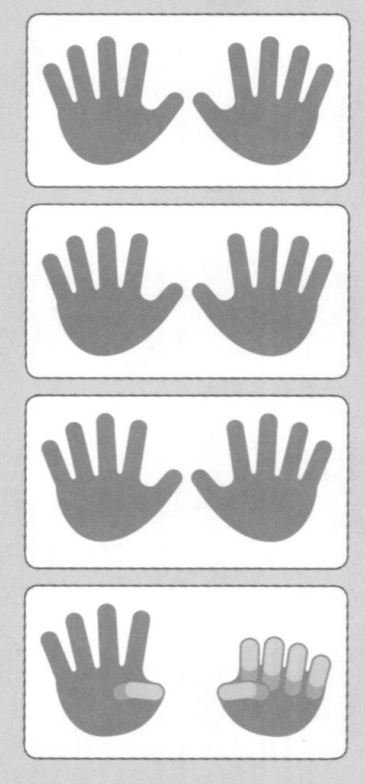

Picture 4

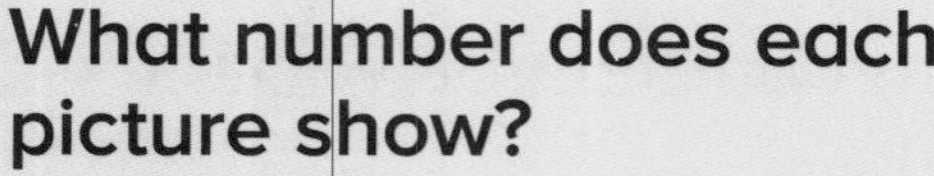

What number does each picture show?

What is the next number in the pattern? How do you know?

How many students will be needed to show the next number in the pattern?

How do you know?

Step Up

1. How many students will be needed to show these numbers with their fingers?

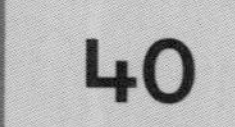

a.	40	____	b.	20	____
c.	80	____	d.	50	____
e.	60	____	f.	70	____
g.	90	____	h.	30	____

2. Find these numbers on the hundred chart.
Count in steps of 10 to the matching shape. Write the numeral.

a. 12 ______

b. 33 ______

c. 5 ______

d. 54 ______

e. 46 ______

f. 68 ______

g. 27 ______

h. 19 ______

i. 71 ______

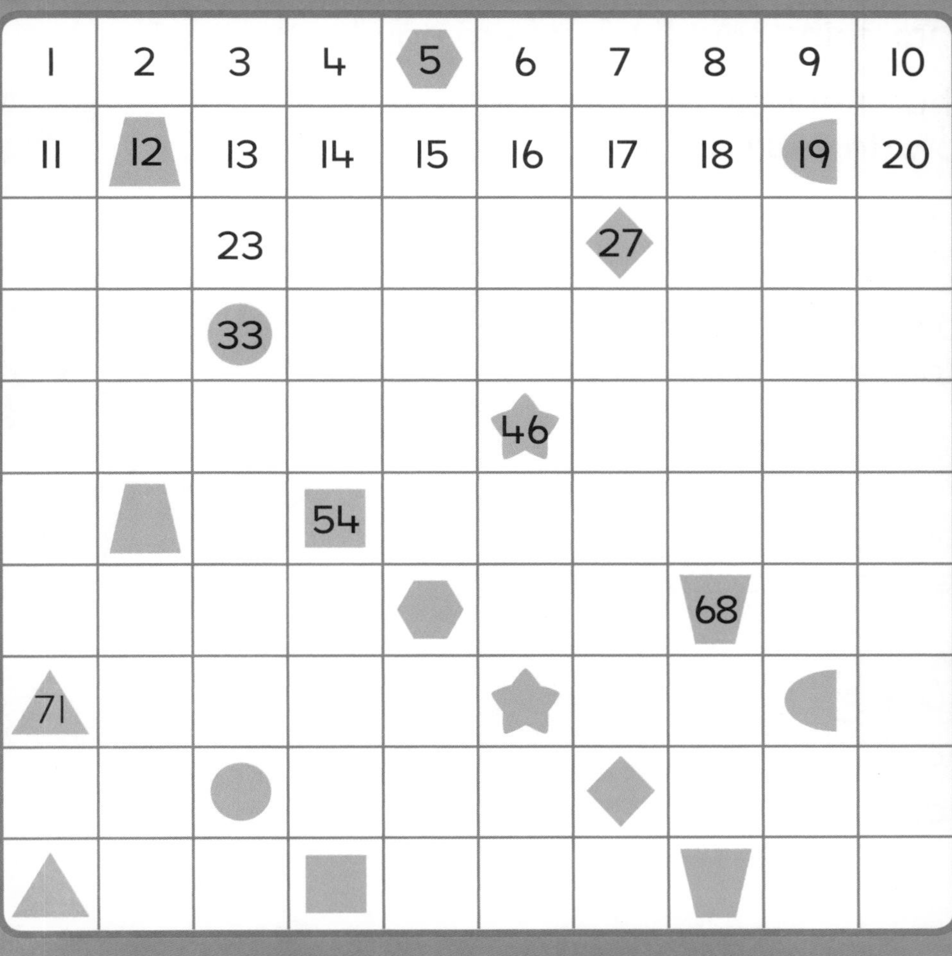

Step Ahead These are pieces of a hundred chart.
Write the missing numerals.

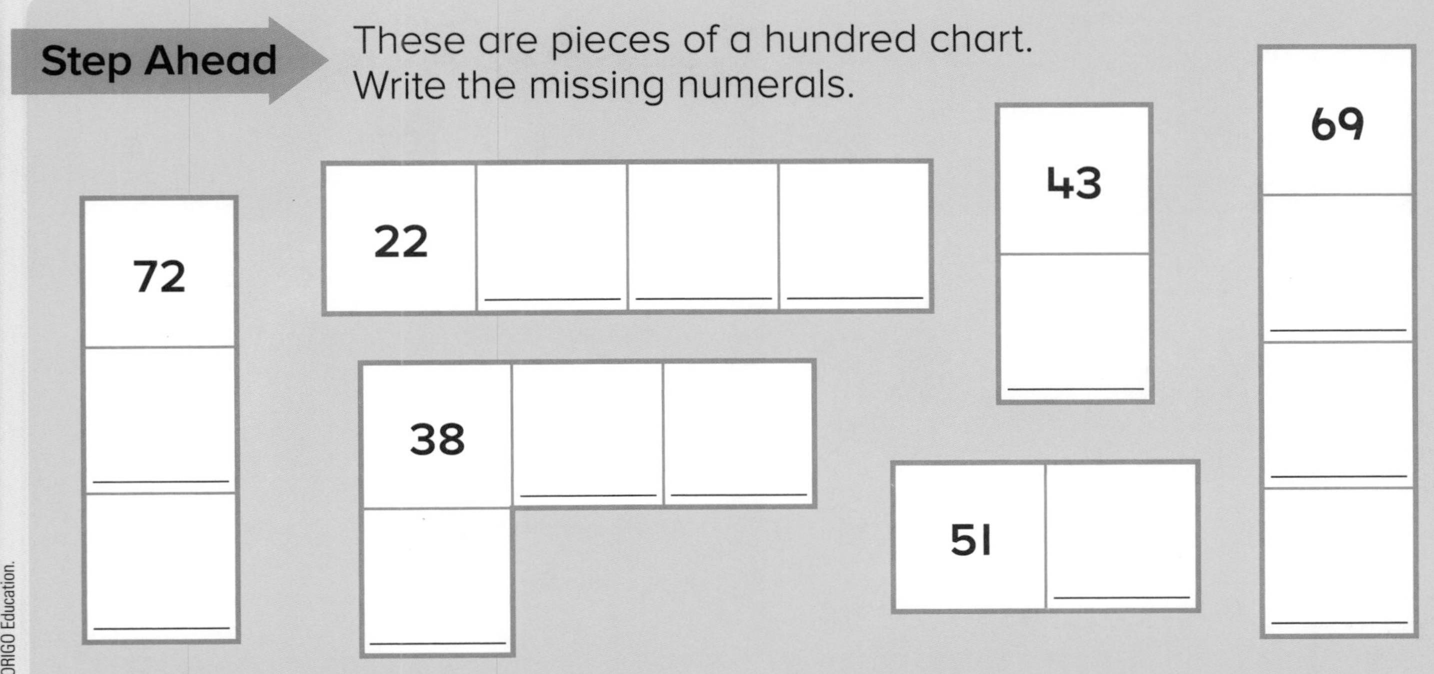

10.4 Adding Multiples of 10 Cents

What coins could you use to pay for this toy?

What other coins could you use?
How do you know?

How could you figure out the total cost of these two toys?

How could you figure out the total cost of all three toys?

Step Up

1. Write the amount in the purse.
Write the amount being added. Then write the total.

a.

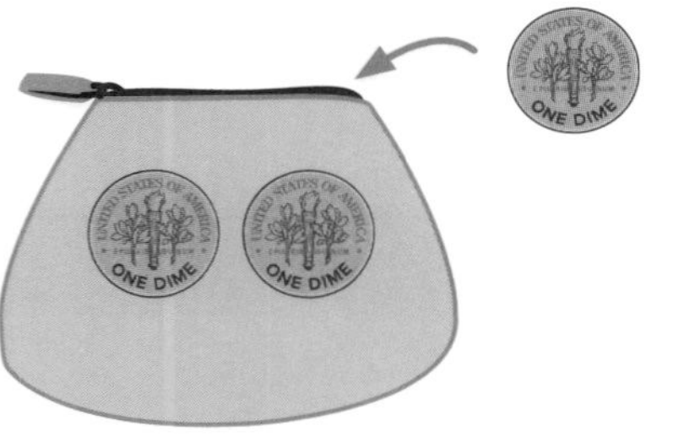

20 ¢ + ____ ¢ = ____ ¢

b.

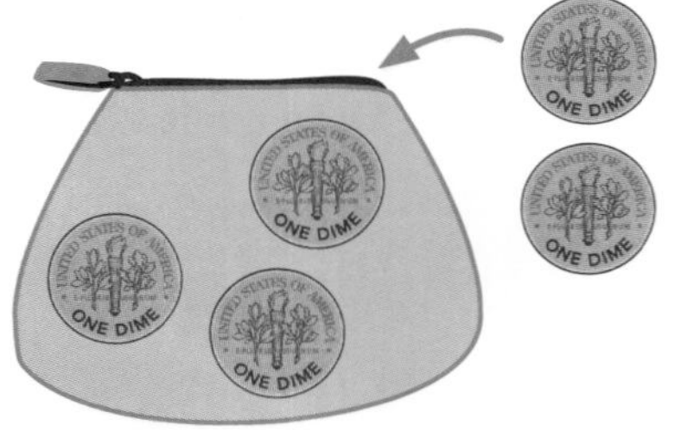

30 ¢ + ____ ¢ = ____ ¢

c.

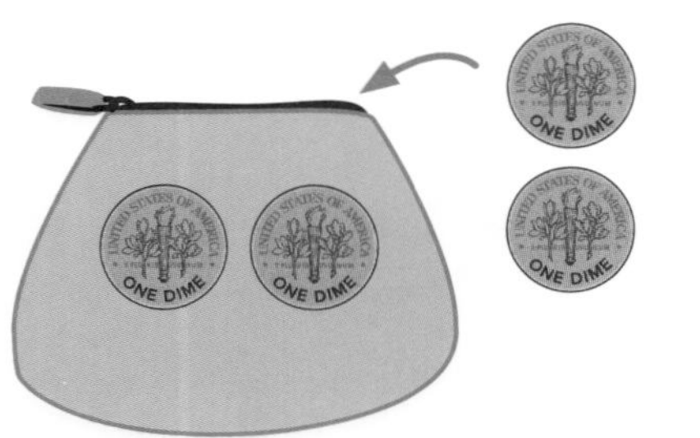

____ ¢ + ____ ¢ = ____ ¢

d.

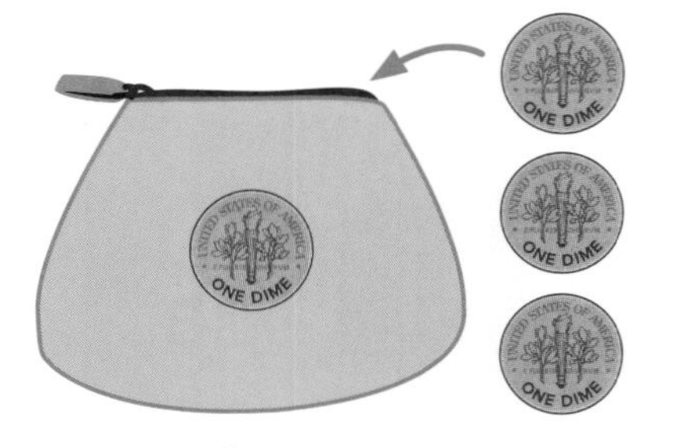

____ ¢ + ____ ¢ = ____ ¢

2. Write the amount in the wallet.
Write the amount being added. Then write the total.

a.

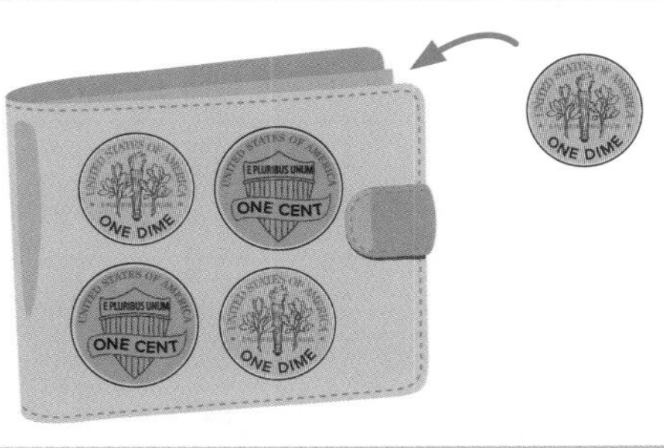

______ ¢ + ______ ¢ = ______ ¢

b.

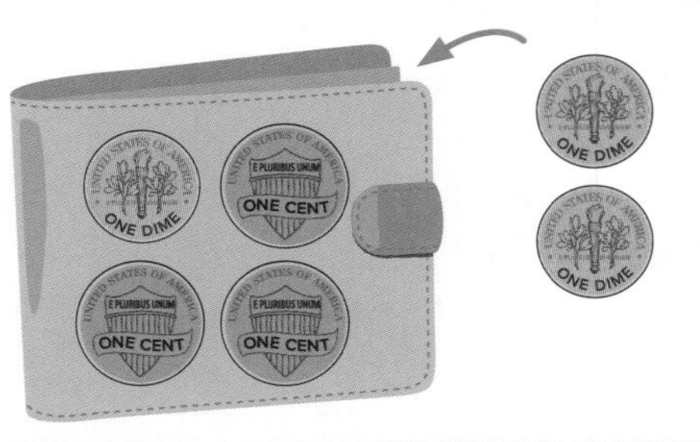

______ ¢ + ______ ¢ = ______ ¢

c.

______ ¢ + ______ ¢ = ______ ¢

d.

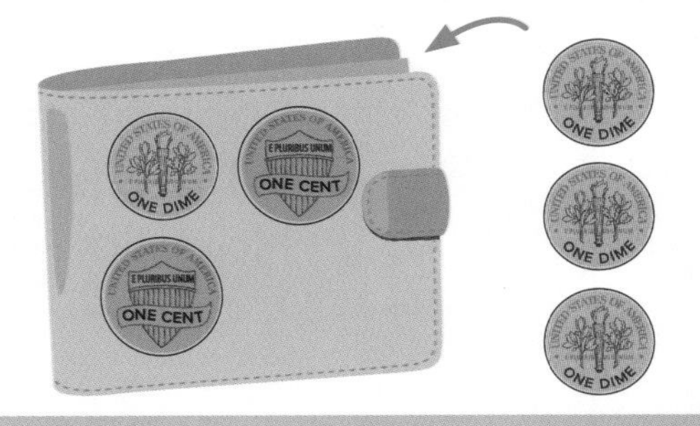

______ ¢ + ______ ¢ = ______ ¢

3. Count on 10¢ or 20¢ to complete each sentence.

a. 20¢ + 46¢ = ______ ¢   b. 75¢ + 10¢ = ______ ¢   c. 10¢ + 83¢ = ______ ¢

Step Ahead

a. How many dimes would you need to pay for the cards? ______

b. How many pennies would you need to pay for the cards? ______

10.5 Using Place Value (Hundred Chart) to Add One- and Two-Digit Numbers

Look at this piece of hundred chart.

1	2	3	4	5	6	7	8	9	10
11	12	13	14	15	16	17	18	19	20

What happens to the numbers as you move from left to right?

What happens to the numbers as you move down the chart?

Look at this piece of the same hundred chart.
What numbers are missing? How do you know?

23		

Look at this piece of the hundred chart.
What numbers could you write in the white spaces? How do you know?

Step Up I. Write the totals. You can use the chart to help.

a. 63 + 1 = ______

b. 47 + 10 = ______

c. 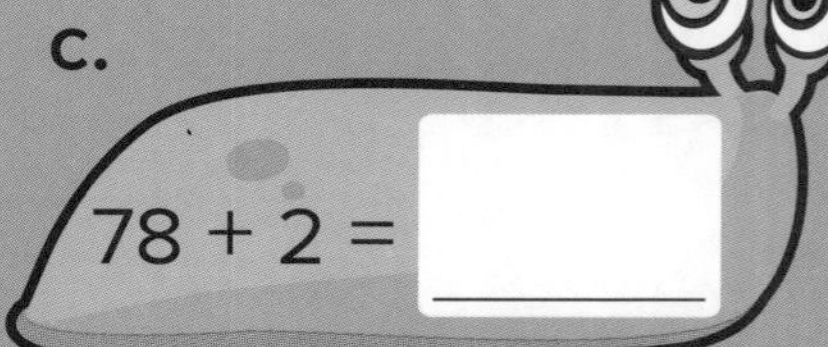
78 + 2 = ______

41	42	43	44	45	46	47	48	49	50
51	52	53	54	55	56	57	58	59	60
61	62	63	64	65	66	67	68	69	70
71	72	73	74	75	76	77	78	79	80
81	82	83	84	85	86	87	88	89	90

d. 52 + 20 = ______

e. 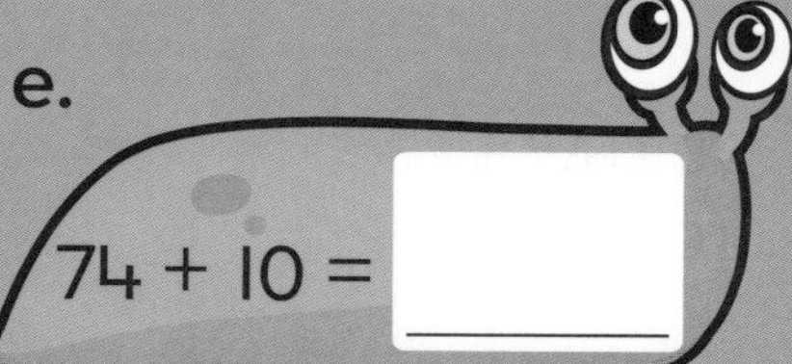
74 + 10 = ______

f. 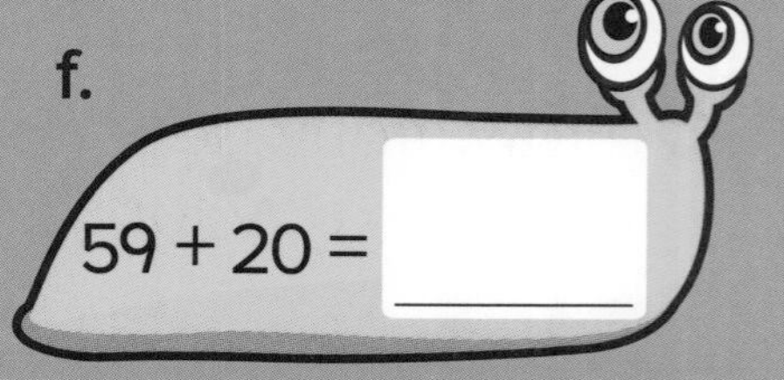
59 + 20 = ______

2. Figure out and write the totals.

a.
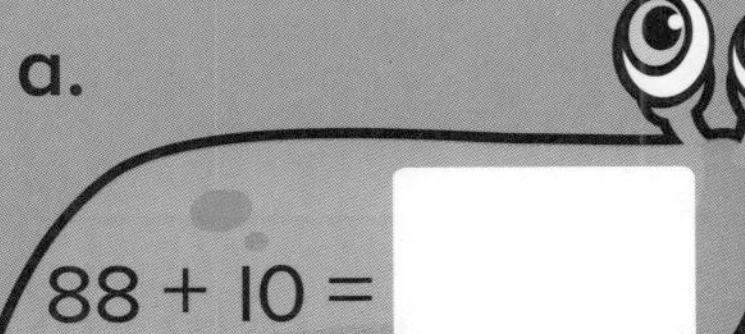
88 + 10 = ____

b.
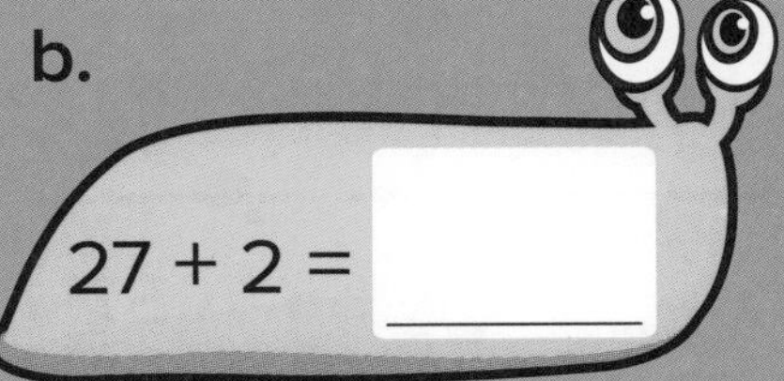
27 + 2 = ____

c.

31 + 20 = ____

d.
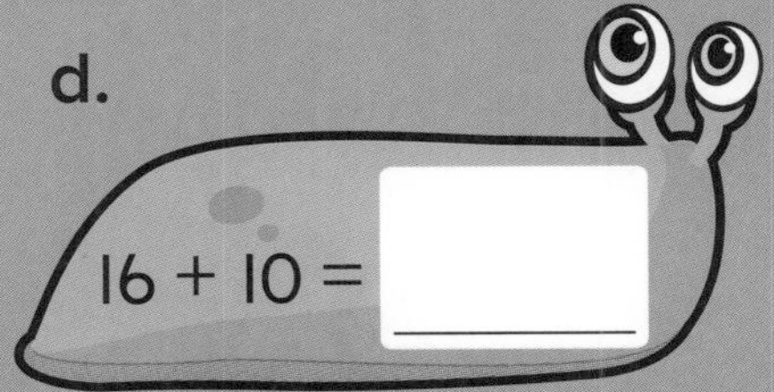
16 + 10 = ____

e. 36 + 2 = ____

f.
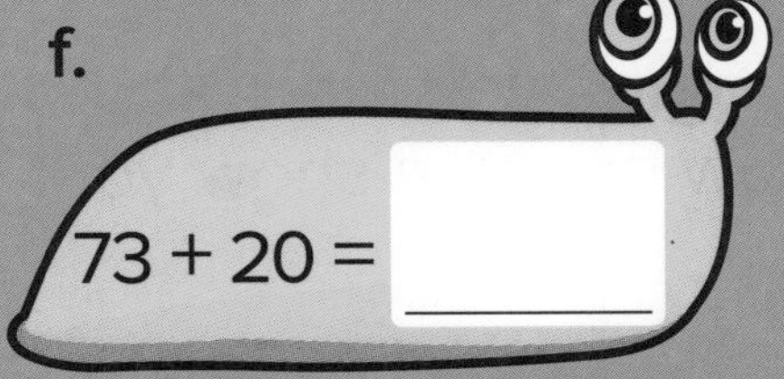
73 + 20 = ____

g.
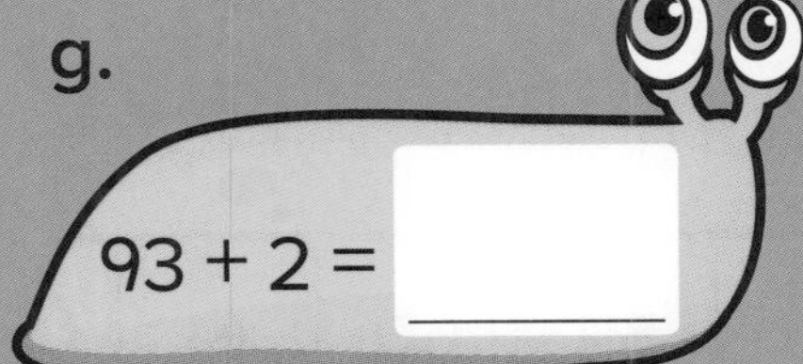
93 + 2 = ____

h. 42 + 30 = ____

i.
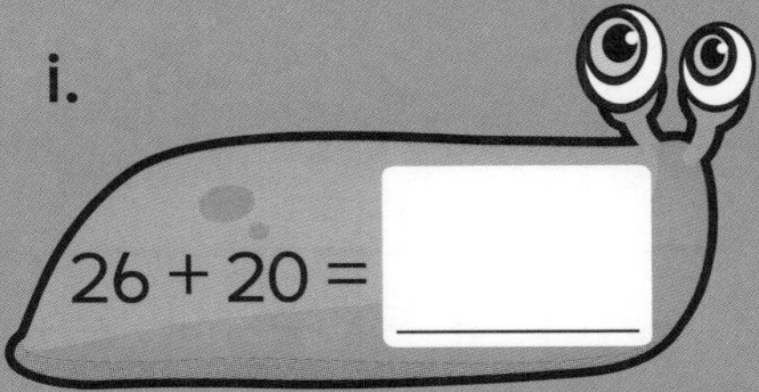
26 + 20 = ____

j.
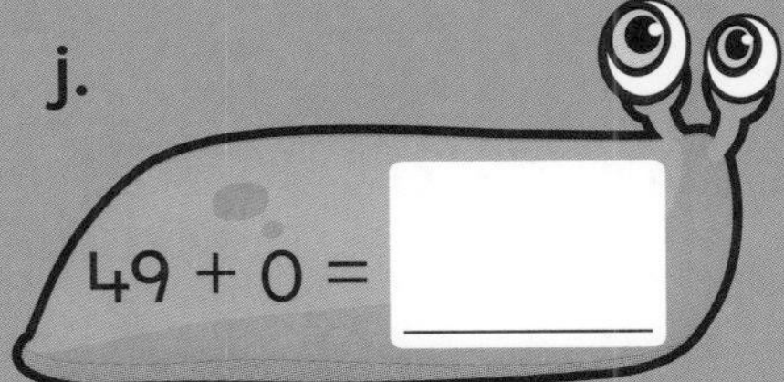
49 + 0 = ____

k. 10 + 56 = ____

l.
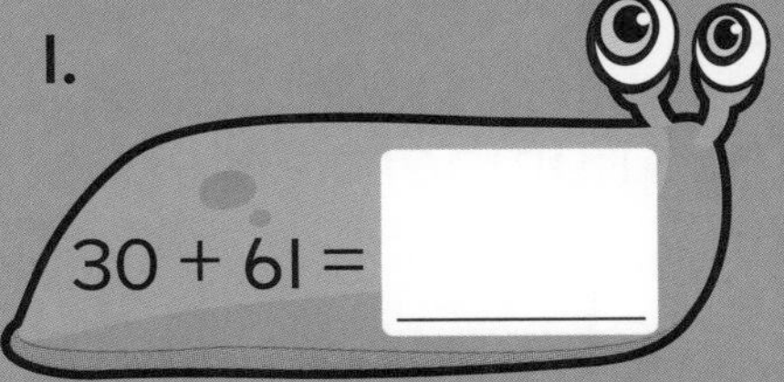
30 + 61 = ____

Step Ahead Write the missing numbers along the trail.

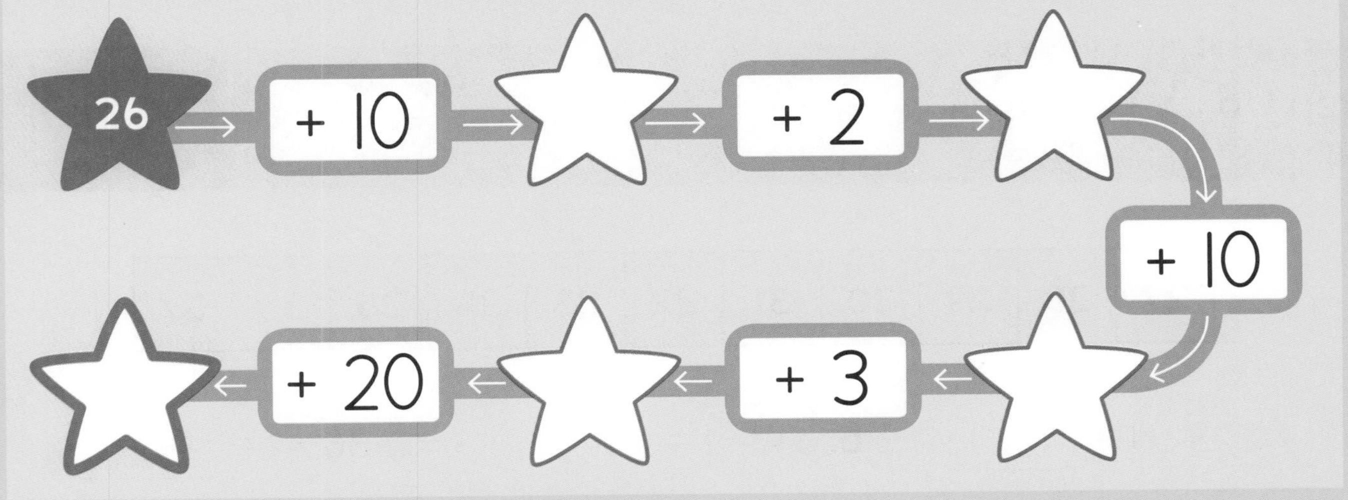

10.6 Extending the Count-Back Strategy Beyond the Facts

Look at this piece of a number track.

50	51	52	53	54	55	56	57	58	59	60	61

Imagine you were standing on 58 and made one jump back to 56.
How can you show your jump on the number track?

You could draw an arrow like this.

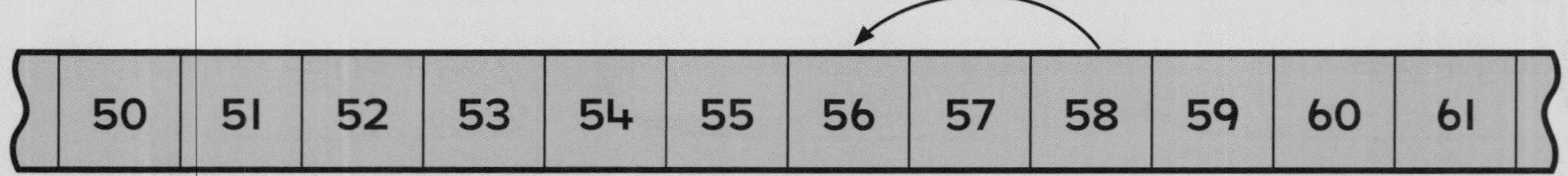

What number sentence could you write to show what you did?

____ − ____ = ____

What other jumps could you make on this piece of number track?
What number sentences could you write to show what you did?

Step Up 1. Write the answers.

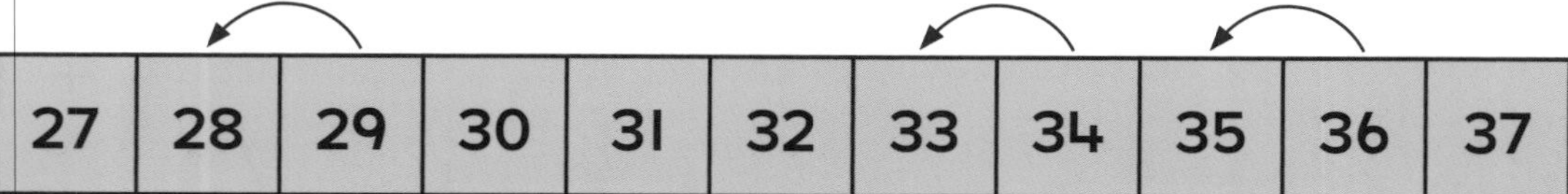

a. 29 − 1 = ____ **b.** 34 − 1 = ____ **c.** 36 − 1 = ____

2. Write the answers. Draw jumps on the number track to help you.

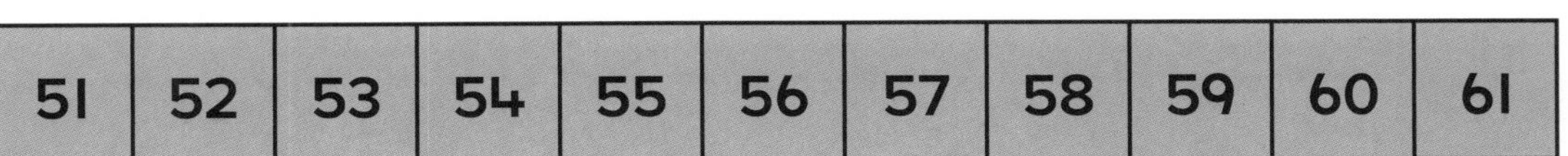

51	52	53	54	55	56	57	58	59	60	61

a. 54 − 2 = ______ **b.** 57 − 2 = ______ **c.** 61 − 3 = ______

74	75	76	77	78	79	80	81	82	83	84

d. 75 − 1 = ______ **e.** 78 − 2 = ______ **f.** 82 − 3 = ______

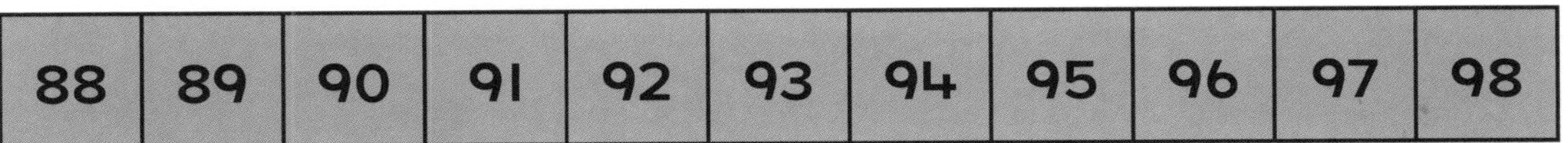

88	89	90	91	92	93	94	95	96	97	98

g. 91 − 3 = ______ **h.** 95 − 3 = ______ **i.** 98 − 2 = ______

3. Write the missing numbers.

a. ______ − 2 = 65 **b.** ______ − 1 = 47 **c.** ______ − 3 = 71

Step Ahead Use a number track above to help you figure out the answer.

Isabella has 95 cents.
Miguel has 2 cents less than Isabella.
Lily has 3 cents less than Miguel.
Gemma has 1 cent more than Lily.

How much money does Gemma have? ______ ¢

10.7 Exploring Subtraction Patterns

Look at these numbers.

1	2	3	4	5	6	7	8	9	10
11	12	13	14	15	16	17	18	19	20
21	22	23	24	25	26	27	28	29	30
31	32	33	34	35	36	37	38	39	40
41	42	43	44	45	46	47	48	49	50

What number is 2 less than 45? How do you know?

What number is 1 less than 38? How do you know?

What is different about all the numbers that have 4 in the ones place?

Step Up 1. Write the missing numbers.

a.

5 − 1 = ____

15 − 1 = ____

25 − 1 = ____

35 − 1 = ____

45 − 1 = ____

95 − 1 = ____

b.

18 − 2 = ____

28 − 2 = ____

38 − 2 = ____

48 − 2 = ____

78 − 2 = ____

88 − 2 = ____

c.

4 − 3 = ____

14 − 3 = ____

24 − 3 = ____

34 − 3 = ____

64 − 3 = ____

84 − 3 = ____

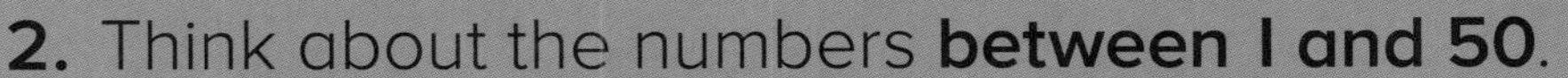

2. Think about the numbers **between 1 and 50**.

   a. Write all the numbers that have 6 in the ones place.

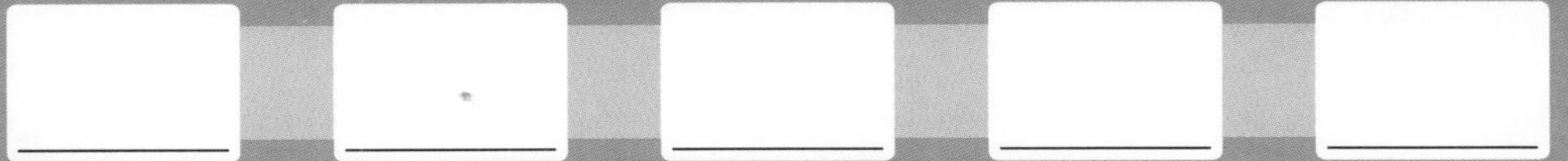

   b. Write the numbers that are **2 less** than the numbers you wrote.

3. Think about the numbers **between 50 and 100**.

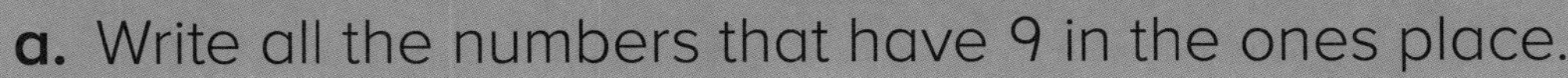

   a. Write all the numbers that have 9 in the ones place.

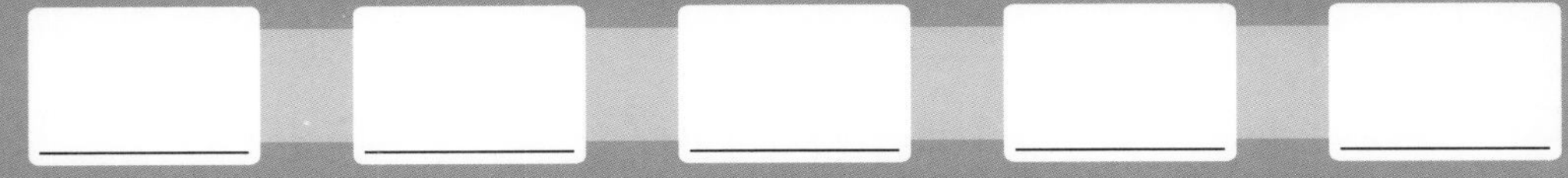

   b. Write the numbers that are **2 less** than the numbers you wrote.

4. Write numbers **between 11 and 50** to complete these to show different subtraction sentences.

a. ____ − 3 = ____	b. ____ − 2 = ____	c. ____ − 3 = ____
d. ____ − 2 = ____	e. ____ − 1 = ____	f. ____ − 2 = ____

Step Ahead

Grace had 65 cents. She spent 3 cents.
Andre had 66 cents. He lost 2 cents.
Caleb had 67 cents. He gave his little sister 3 cents.

a. Who had the least amount of money left over?

b. Write the subtraction sentences you used to help you.

10.8 Counting Back Multiples of 10 (Off the Decade)

Look at these numbers.

1	2	3	4	5	6	7	8	9	10
11	12	13	14	15	16	17	18	19	20
21	22	23	24	25	26	27	28	29	30
31	32	33	34	35	36	37	38	39	40
41	42	43	44	45	46	47	48	49	50

Start at 47 and count back in steps of 10. What do you notice?

Start at 32 and count back in steps of 10. What do you notice?

How could you use the chart to figure out 41 – 20?

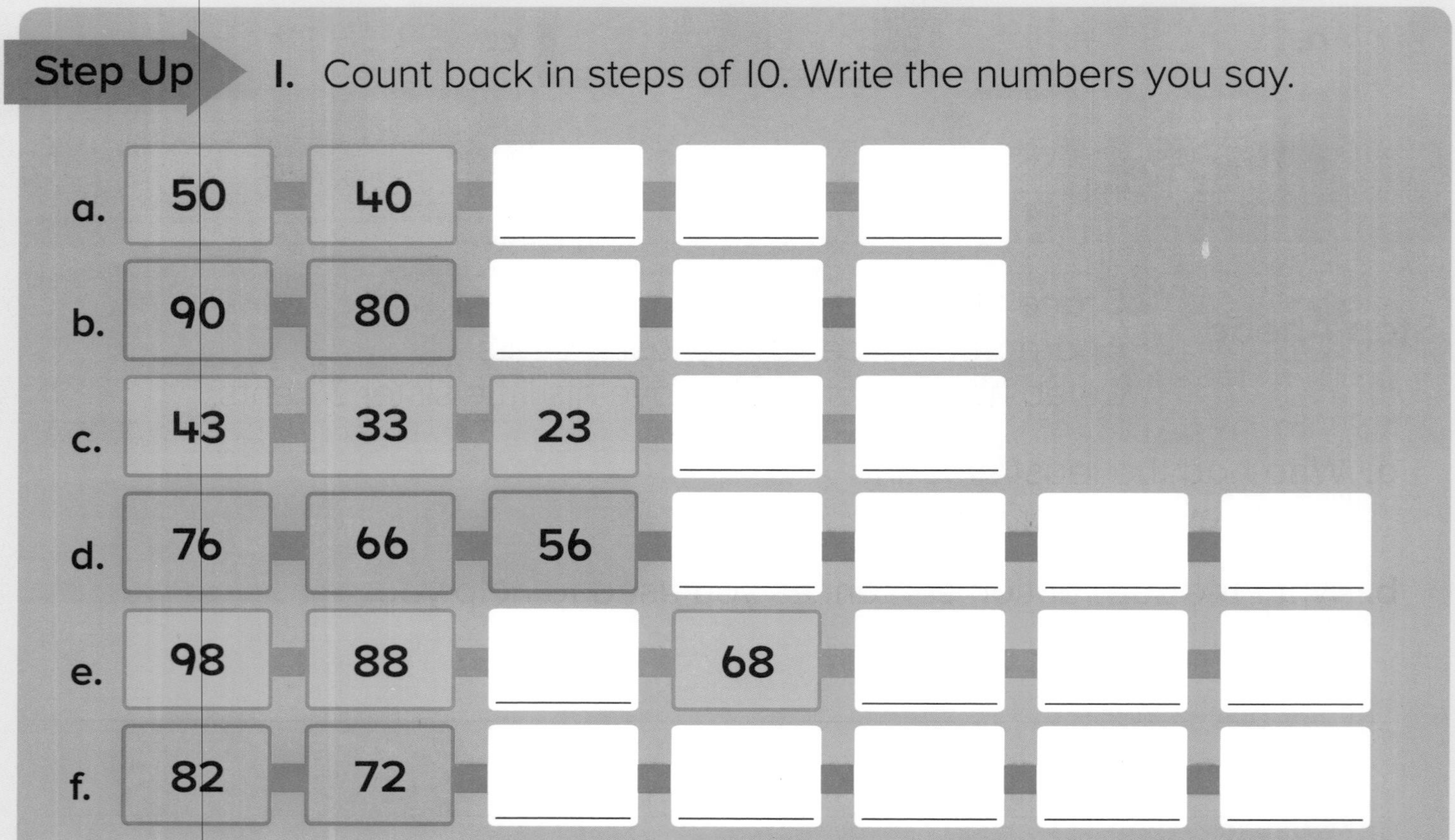

2. Find these numbers on the hundred chart.
Count back in steps of 10 to the matching shape. Write the numeral.

a. 96 ______

b. 70 ______

c. 74 ______

d. 57 ______

e. 61 ______

f. 83 ______

g. 92 ______

h. 89 ______

i. 48 ______

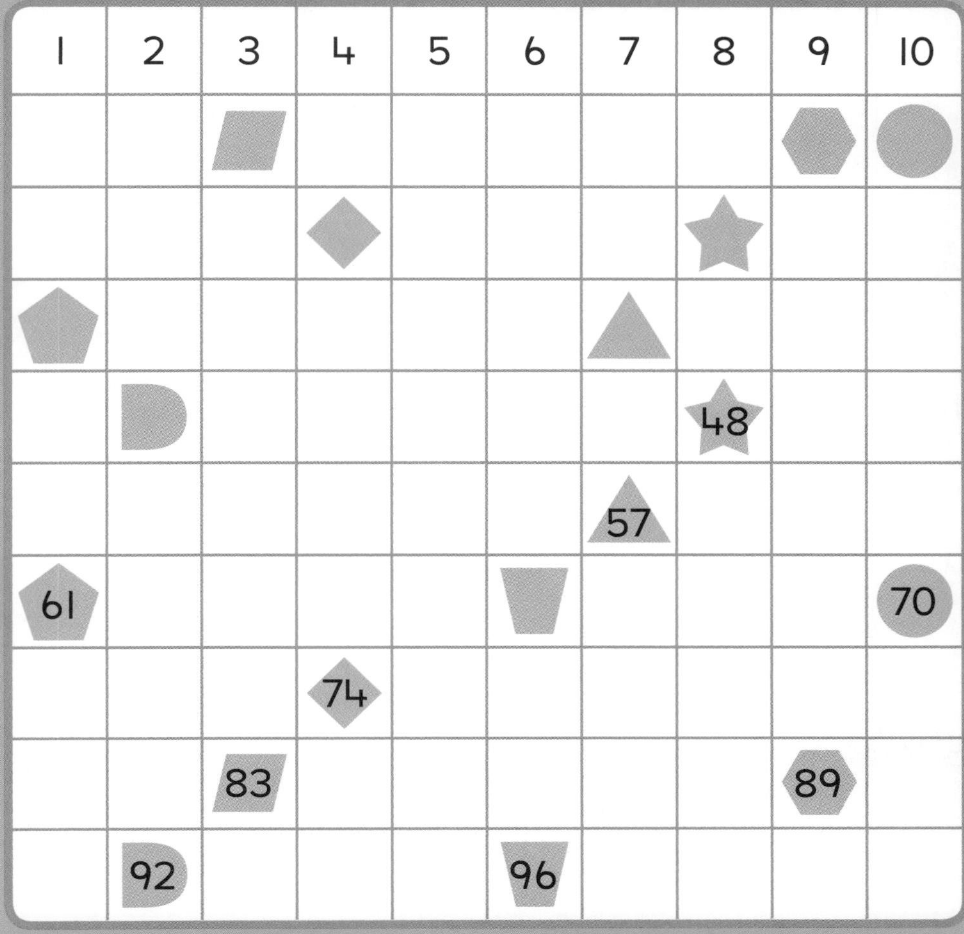

Step Ahead These are pieces of a hundred chart.
Write the missing numbers.

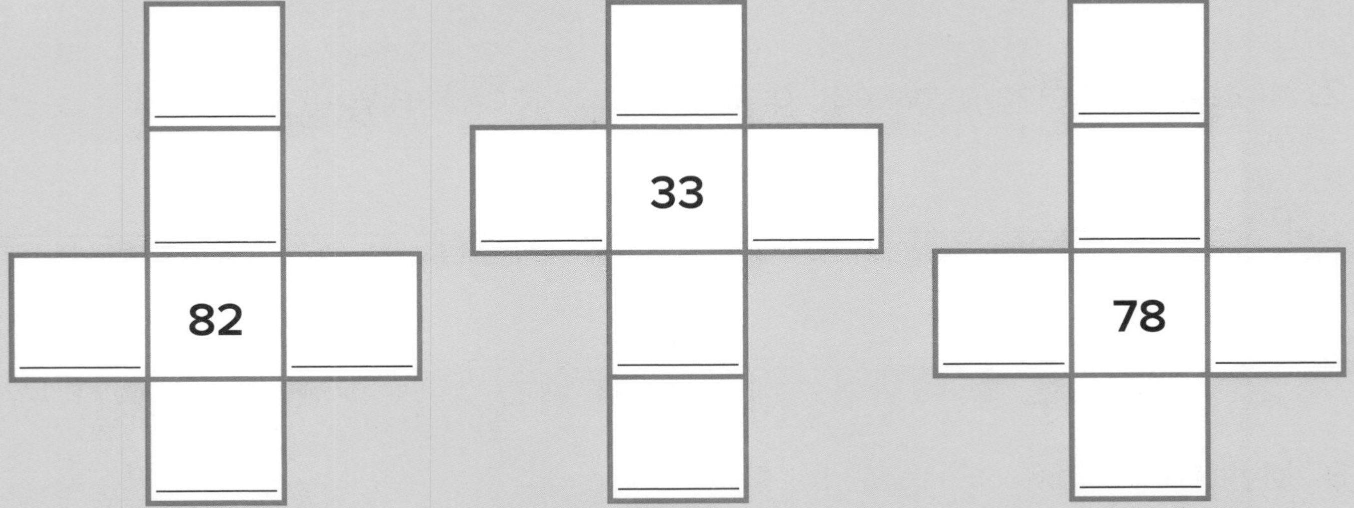

10.9 Identifying and Sorting 3D Objects

Look at these 3D objects.

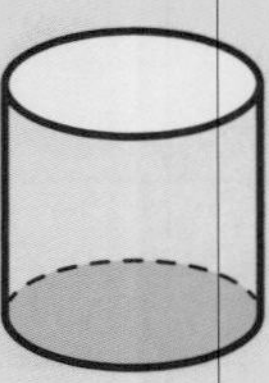
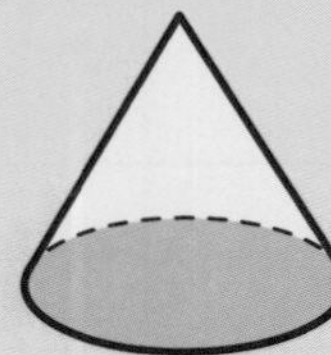
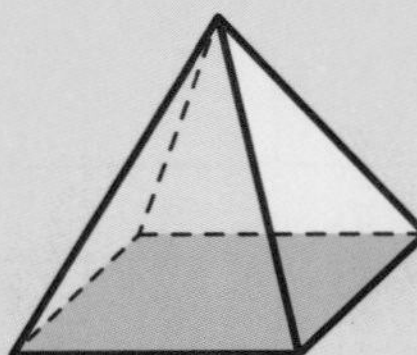
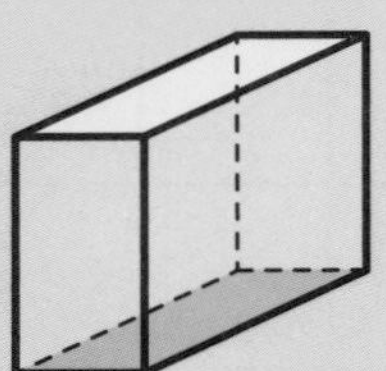
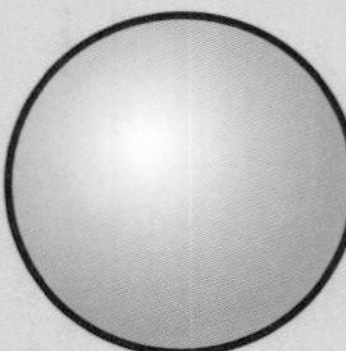
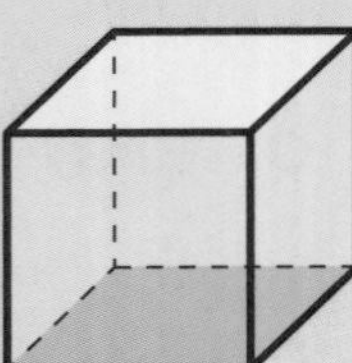

What 2D shapes were used to make these objects?

What other things do you know about these objects?

Step Up **1.** Your teacher will give you a 3D object. Draw your object.

2. Write the names of **two** other things that look like your object.

a. ____________________

b. ____________________

3. My object has ____ surfaces.

4. Draw a ✔ beside each statement that describes your object.

a.
- ◯ It can roll.
- ◯ It can stack.
- ◯ It cannot roll or stack.

b.
- ◯ It has all flat surfaces.
- ◯ It has no flat surfaces.
- ◯ It has some flat surfaces and some curved surfaces.

5. Draw each flat surface of your object.

Step Ahead Look at this 3D object.

a. How many surfaces does this object have? ____

b. What shape are the surfaces? ____________________

10.10 Analyzing 3D Objects

Look at these two objects.

What 2D shapes were used to make these objects?

What is the same about these two objects?

What is different about the two objects?

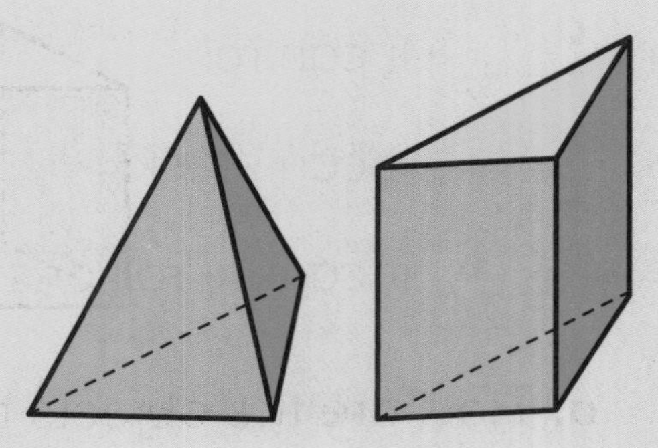

Both objects have only flat surfaces. One object was made with triangles and the other with triangles and non-square rectangles.

Step Up

1. Look at these pictures. Use real objects to help you answer the questions.

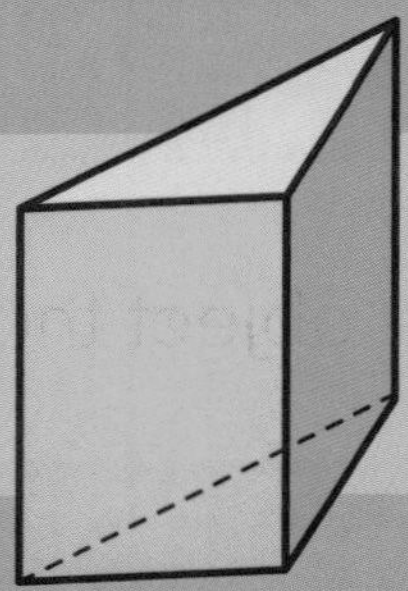

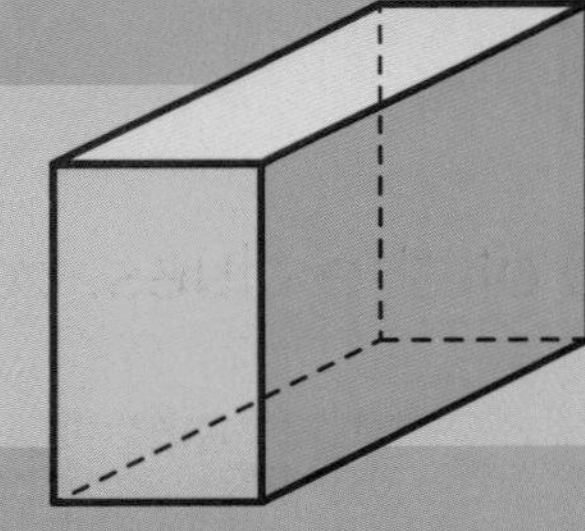

a. How are the objects the same?

b. How are the objects different?

2. Look at these pictures. Answer the questions.

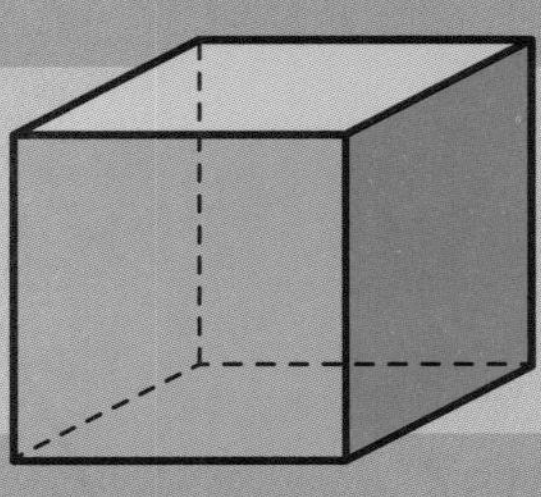

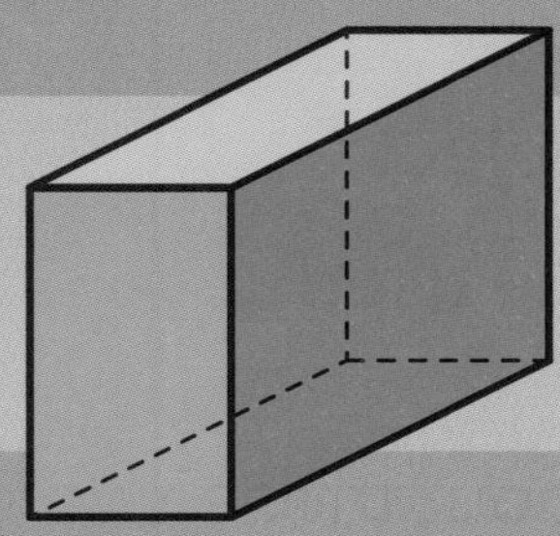

a. How are the objects the same?

b. How are the objects different?

Step Ahead Read all the clues. Loop the object that matches.

Clues

- I have 6 surfaces.
- I can be stacked.
- Only one of my surfaces is curved.

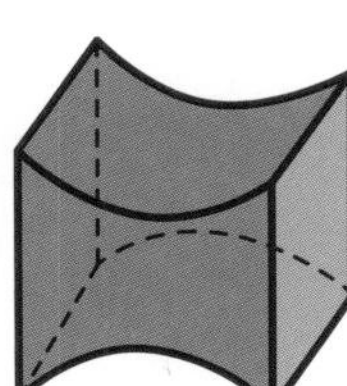

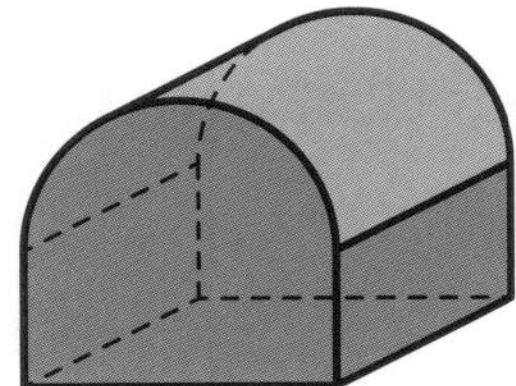

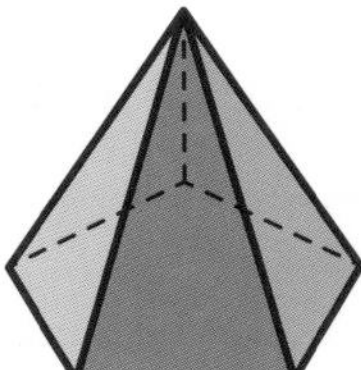

10.11 Making 3D Objects

Look at this building.
Which 3D objects can you see?

Think about the buildings in your neighborhood. Which 3D objects can you see in those buildings?

Think about blocks you have used at home or at school. Which blocks do you use the most? Why?

Step Up

1. Count how many of each object has been used to make each stack. The objects may be different sizes. Write the number of each object in the table.

a.

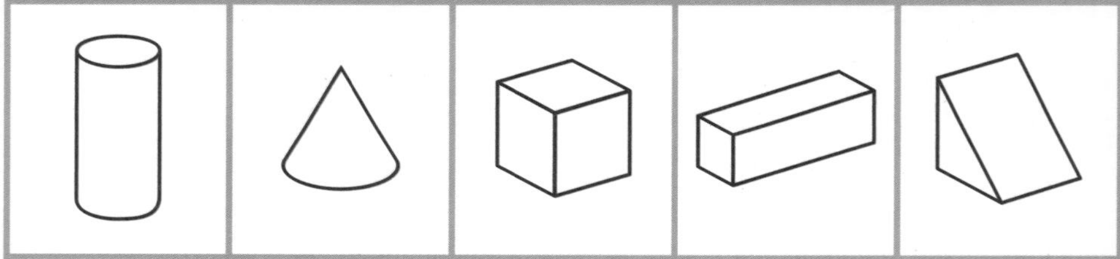

cylinder	cone	cube	rectangular prism	triangular prism
____	____	____	____	____

b.

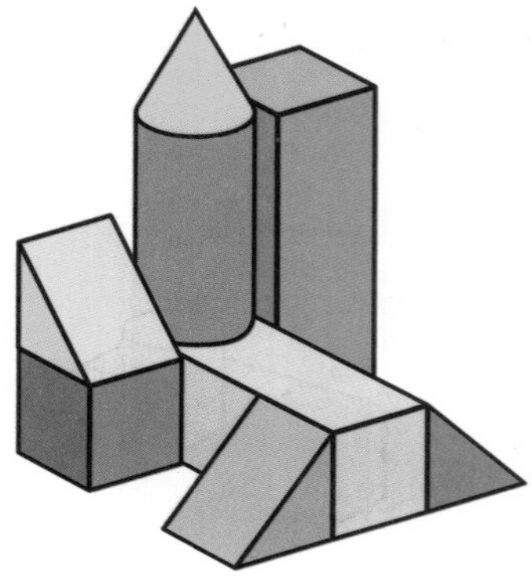

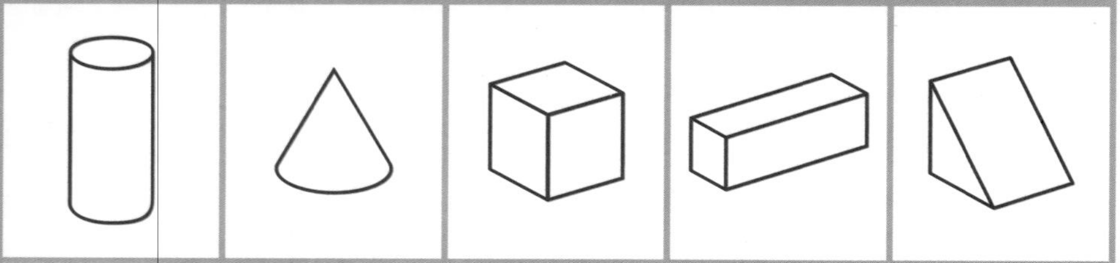

cylinder	cone	cube	rectangular prism	triangular prism
____	____	____	____	____

2. Loop the stacks below that can be made with these numbers of objects. The objects may be different sizes.

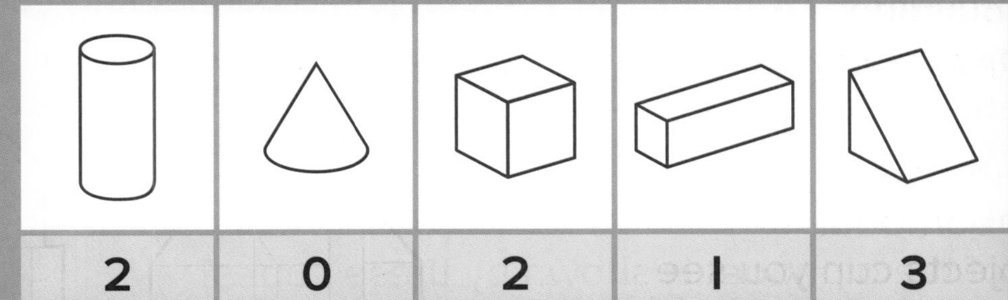

a.

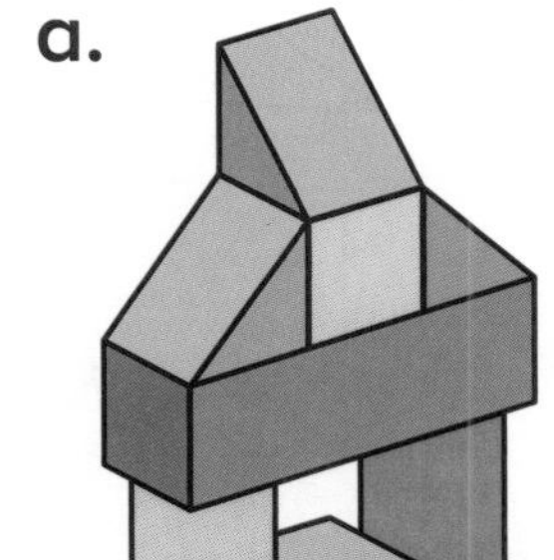

b.

c.

d.

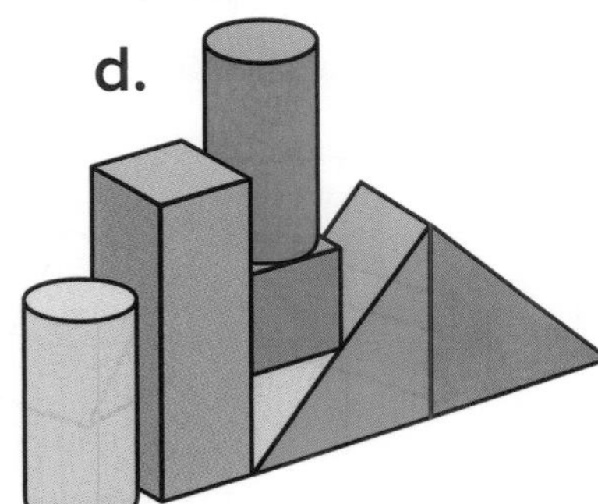

e.

f.

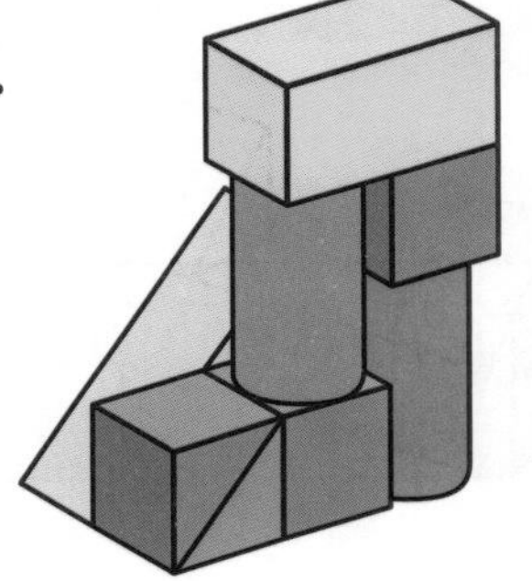

Step Ahead

Two of the stacks below match this stack.
One stack below does not match.
Loop the stack that does **not** match.

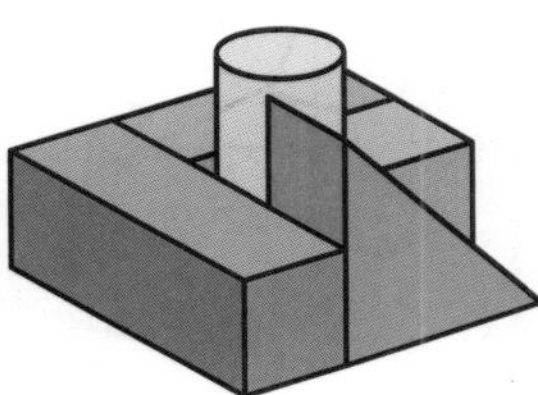

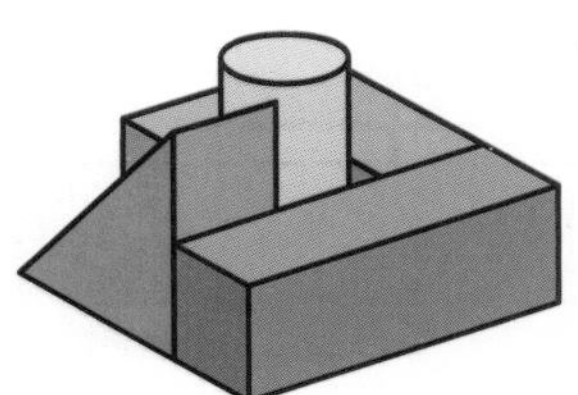

10.12 Joining 3D Objects

Think about the different ways that you can join 8 connecting cubes together.

What is the longest object you could make with all the cubes?
What is the shortest object you could make with all the cubes?

Which letter of the alphabet is shown by these cubes?
What other letters could you make using all 8 cubes?

What other objects could you make with all the cubes? Do you think your objects would stand up by themselves?

Step Up

1. Use connecting cubes to make each object. Ask another student to check your work after you make each object.

a. 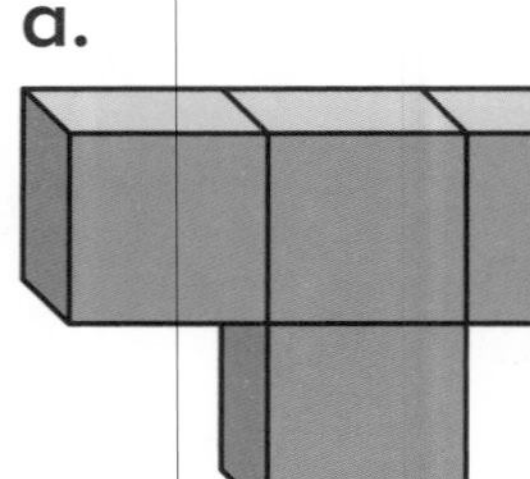

b. 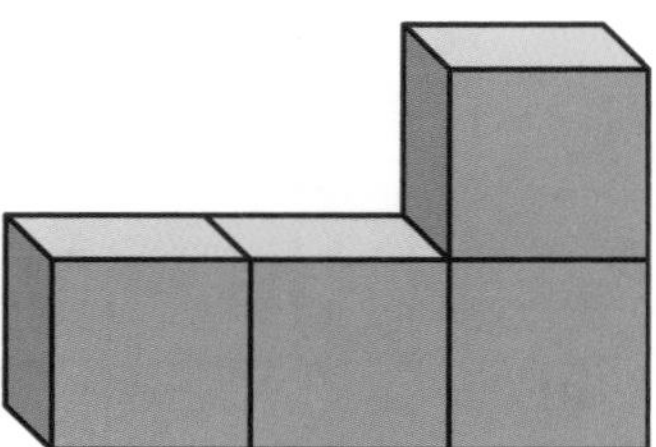

c. 

d. 

e. 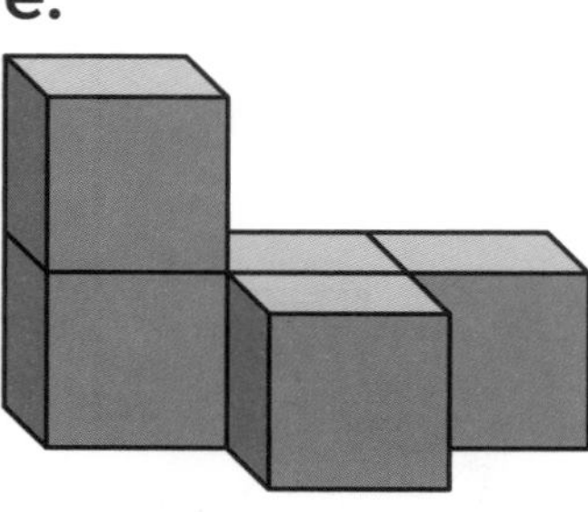

f. 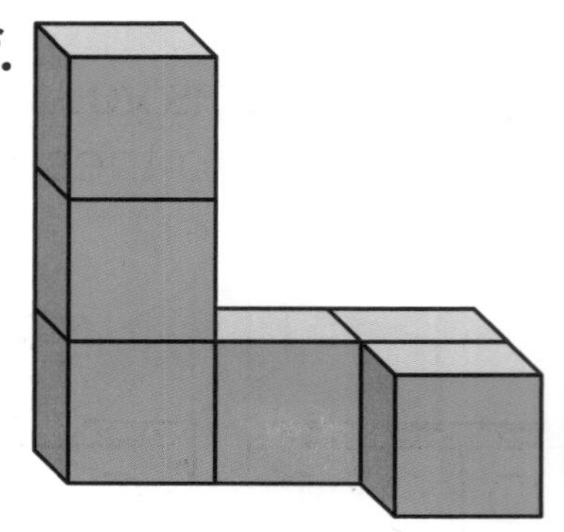

2. Look at each object. Shade the ⬭ that matches what you think will happen. Then check your thinking with real cubes and shade the ⬭ to match what happened.

a. **I think this object will**

⬭ stand up ⬭ fall over

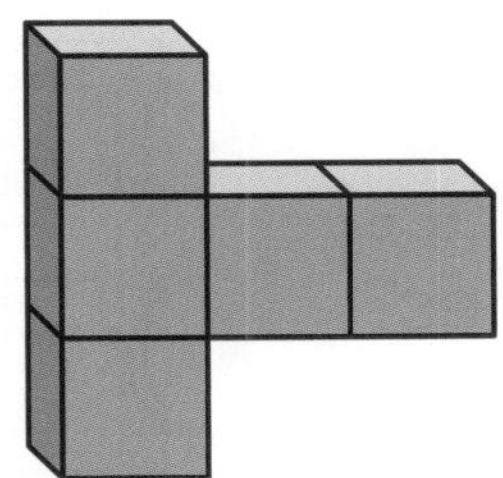

The real object did

⬭ stand up ⬭ fall over

b. **I think this object will**

⬭ stand up ⬭ fall over

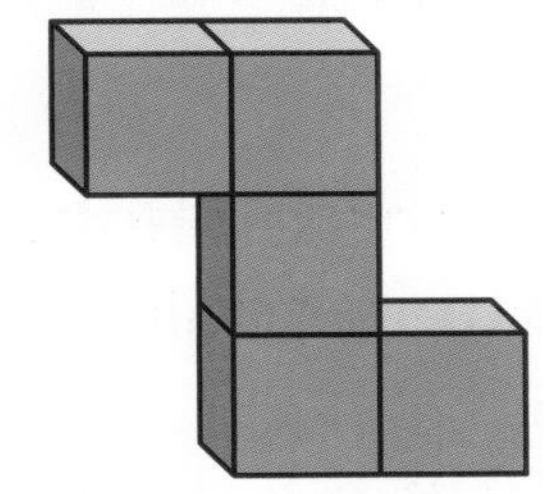

The real object did

⬭ stand up ⬭ fall over

c. **I think this object will**

⬭ stand up ⬭ fall over

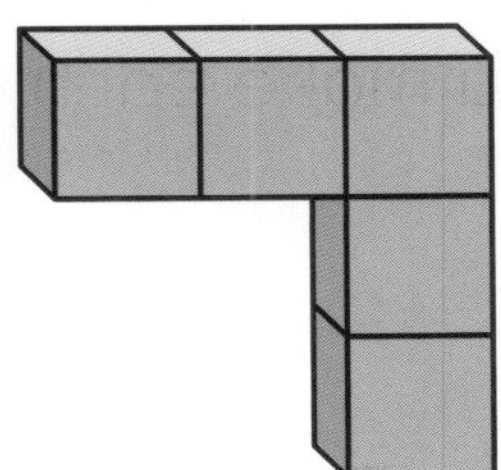

The real object did

⬭ stand up ⬭ fall over

d. **I think this object will**

⬭ stand up ⬭ fall over

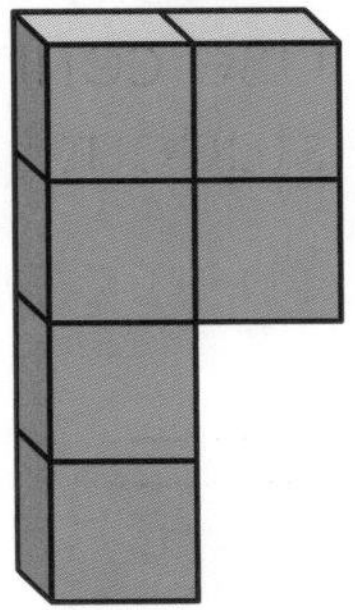

The real object did

⬭ stand up ⬭ fall over

Step Ahead

Loop the objects you could make by joining these two objects together.

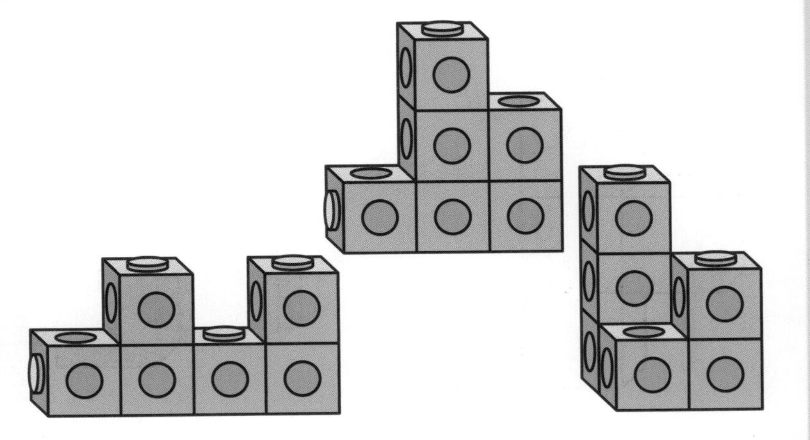

11.1 Adding Multiples of 10 (On the Decade)

How can you figure out the total cost of these two pieces of fruit?

Isabelle used this chart.

50 + 30 =

50 + 30 = 80

How do you think she figured out the total cost?

What does each block show? What do the blocks in each part of the chart show?

What other way could you add the prices to find the total?

Step Up

1. Draw tens blocks on the right to show the total. Then complete the sentence.

a. 40 + 30 =

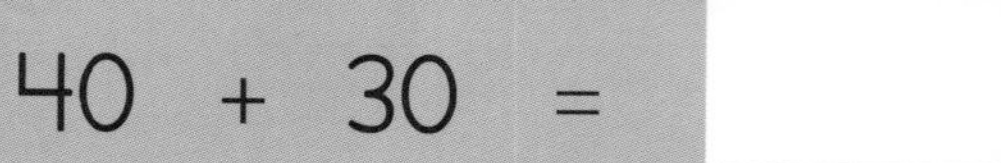

b. 30 + 60 =

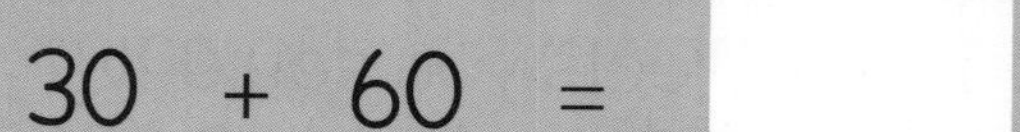

2. Add the two groups. Write the matching number sentence. You can use blocks to help you.

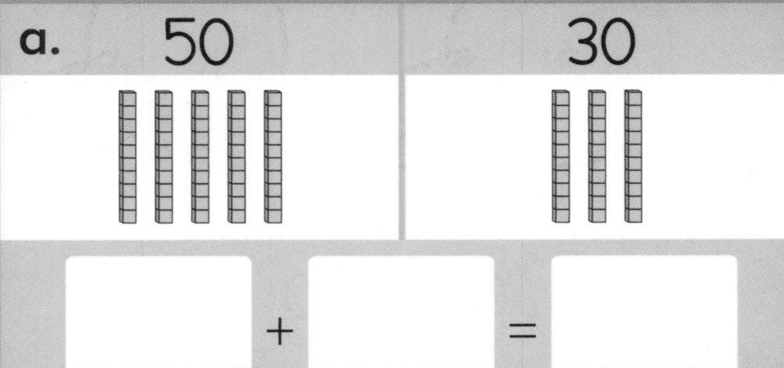

____ + ____ = ____

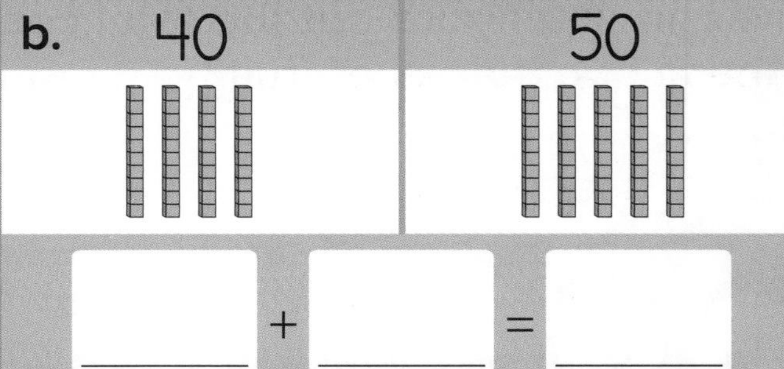

____ + ____ = ____

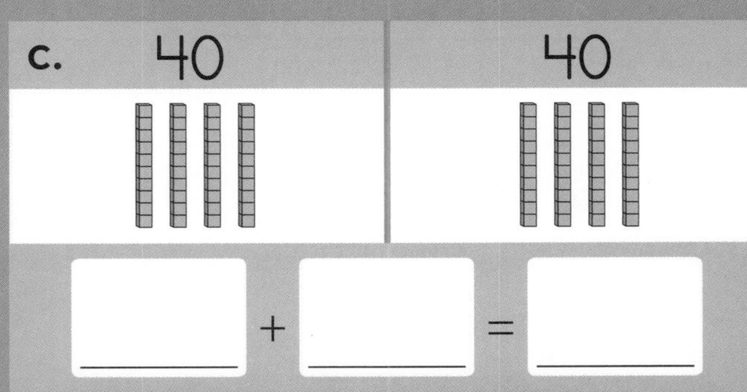

____ + ____ = ____

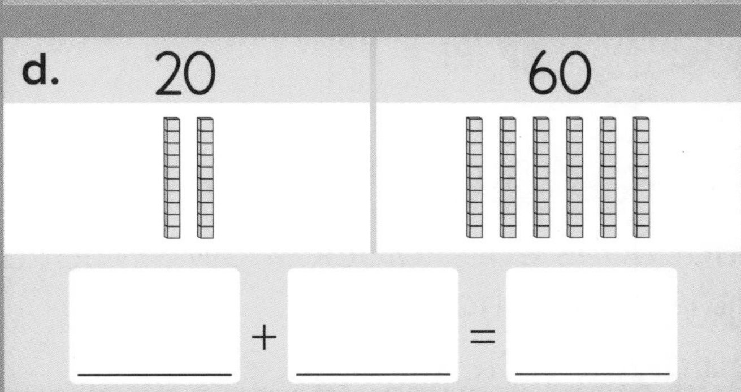

____ + ____ = ____

3. Write two parts that add to make each total. You can use blocks to help you.

a. ____ + ____ = 50

b. ____ + ____ = 70

c. ____ + ____ = 80

d. ____ + ____ = 60

Step Ahead

Write number sentences to show four different ways these coins could be split between two people.

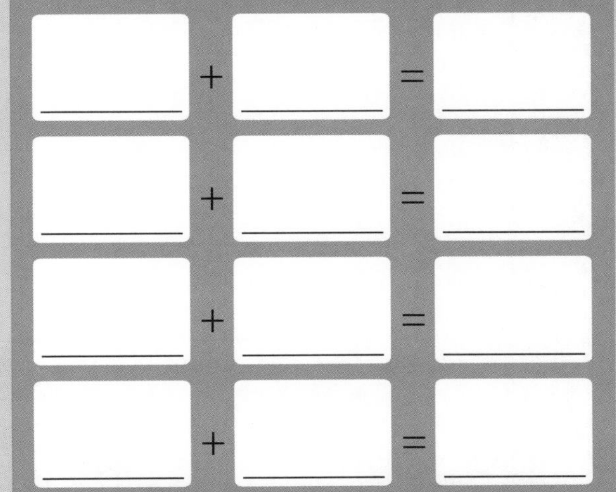

____ + ____ = ____

____ + ____ = ____

____ + ____ = ____

____ + ____ = ____

11.2 Adding Multiples of 10 (Off the Decade)

Look at this piece of hundred chart.

How can you figure out what number is behind the green tile?

I would start at 34 and count in steps of 10 to the green tile.

31	32	33	34	35
				45
	52			
			■	

How many steps of 10 is that?

What addition sentence could you write to match? ____ + ____ = ____

What other way could you add numbers like these?

Step Up

1. Write the totals. You can use this piece of hundred chart to help.

1	2	3	4	5	6	7	8	9	10
11	12	13	14	15	16	17	18	19	20
21	22	23	24	25	26	27	28	29	30
31	32	33	34	35	36	37	38	39	40
41	42	43	44	45	46	47	48	49	50
51	52	53	54	55	56	57	58	59	60

a. 29 + 20 = ____ **b.** 16 + 30 = ____ **c.** 14 + 40 = ____

2. Write the totals. You can use this piece of hundred chart to help.

41	42	43	44	45	46	47	48	49	50
51	52	53	54	55	56	57	58	59	60
61	62	63	64	65	66	67	68	69	70
71	72	73	74	75	76	77	78	79	80
81	82	83	84	85	86	87	88	89	90
91	92	93	94	95	96	97	98	99	100

a. 42 + 10 = ____ **b.** 54 + 40 = ____ **c.** 69 + 30 = ____

d. 49 + 20 = ____ **e.** 47 + 50 = ____ **f.** 55 + 40 = ____

3. Write these totals.

a. 33 + 50 = ____ **b.** 25 + 40 = ____ **c.** 38 + 60 = ____

d. 57 + 30 = ____ **e.** 15 + 70 = ____ **f.** 21 + 50 = ____

Step Ahead Alexis has 90¢. She wants to buy two pieces of fruit. Write number sentences to show all the possible combinations she can buy.

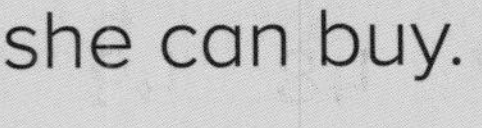

23¢ 37¢ 40¢ 60¢

____ + ____ = ____ ____ + ____ = ____

____ + ____ = ____ ____ + ____ = ____

11.3 Using Place Value (Hundred Chart) to Add Two-Digit Numbers

Look at this piece of hundred chart.

How would you move the counter to add 12 + 10?

How would you move the counter to add 12 + 2?

How would you move the counter to add 12 + 12?

1	2	3	4	5	6
11	12	13	14	15	16
21	22	23	24	25	26
31	32	33	34	35	36
41	42	43	44	45	46

How would you use the hundred chart to figure out 23 + 21?

Step Up

1. Draw arrows on this hundred chart to show how you add each of these. Then write the totals.

a. 31 + 12 = 43

b. 52 + 21 = ______

c. 28 + 32 = ______

d. 45 + 11 = ______

e. 64 + 23 = ______

f. 88 + 11 = ______

g. 57 + 21 = ______

h. 83 + 13 = ______

i. 69 + 21 = ______

1	2	3	4	5	6	7	8	9	10
11	12	13	14	15	16	17	18	19	20
21	22	23	24	25	26	27	28	29	30
31	32	33	34	35	36	37	38	39	40
41	42	43	44	45	46	47	48	49	50
51	52	53	54	55	56	57	58	59	60
61	62	63	64	65	66	67	68	69	70
71	72	73	74	75	76	77	78	79	80
81	82	83	84	85	86	87	88	89	90
91	92	93	94	95	96	97	98	99	100

2. Write the number at the end of each piece of hundred chart. Then complete the matching addition sentence.

a.

37 + 22 = ____

b.

71

____ + ____ = ____

c.

45

____ + ____ = ____

d.

52

____ + ____ = ____

Step Ahead

This is a piece of hundred chart. Write the numbers that should be shown in the white boxes.

						37			
	42								
51									
							68		
				75					

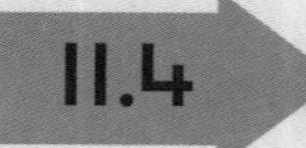

Using Place Value (Base-10 Blocks) to Add Two-Digit Numbers

Look at these scoreboards.

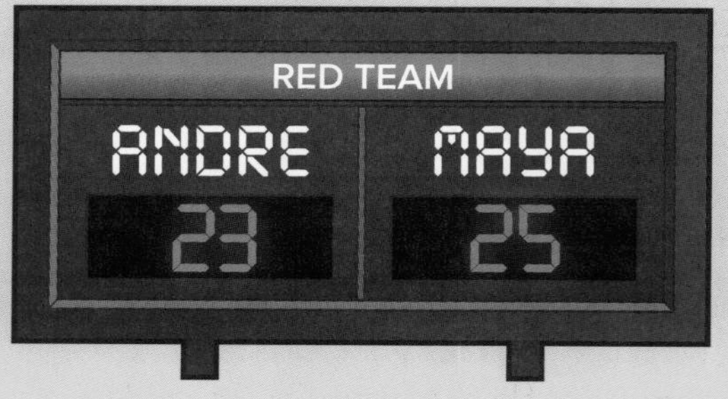

How can you figure out the total number of points scored by the Blue Team?

Chang used this chart.

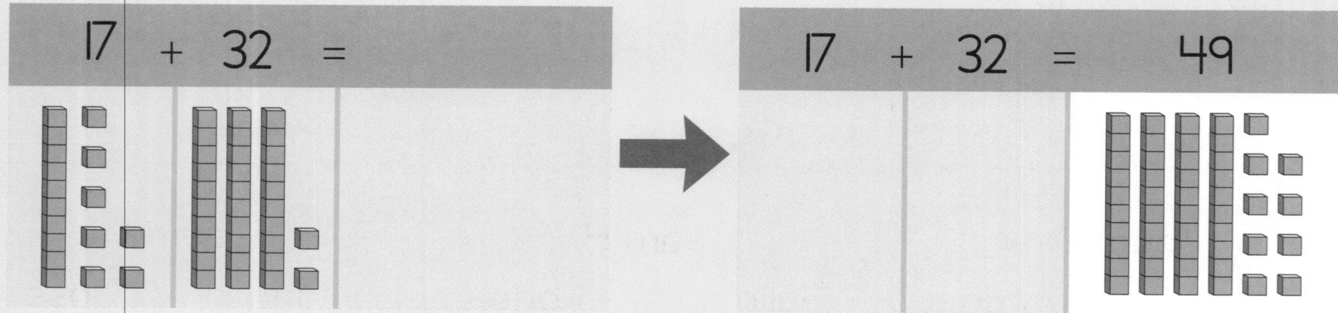

What steps do you think he used?

How could you figure out the total for the Red Team in your head?

I would start with 23 then add the tens and ones of the other number. 23 + 25 **is the same as** 23 + 20 + 5.

I would add the tens first then the ones. 23 + 25 **is the same as** 20 + 20 + 3 + 5.

What other way could you add to find out the total?

Step Up

1. Figure out the total for each team. You can use blocks to help. Then write a matching addition sentence.

Team A		Team B		Team C	
Chloe 51	Jacob 14	Jayden 45	Akari 34	Kay 26	Jackson 33
51 + 14 = ____		____ + ____ = ____		____ + ____ = ____	

2. Figure out the total for each team in your head. Write a number sentence to show your thinking.

Team D		Team E		Team F	
Morgan 43	Jamal 24	Jon 31	Lora 32	David 52	Audrey 17
____		____		____	

Team G		Team H		Team I	
Evan 23	Anna 22	Julia 26	Koda 12	Shona 16	Jose 11
____		____		____	

Step Ahead

Look at the total points scored by these teams. Write a pair of possible scores on each board. Then write the matching addition sentence.

Green Team Total Points – 84		Purple Team Total Points – 67		Orange Team Total Points – 76	
Gabriel ____	Lillian ____	Tyler ____	Kayla ____	Tisha ____	Isaac ____
____ + ____ = ____		____ + ____ = ____		____ + ____ = ____	

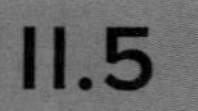

11.5 Using Place Value (Base-10 Blocks) to Add Two-Digit Numbers (with Bridging)

Look at these two groups of blocks.

How could you figure out the total?

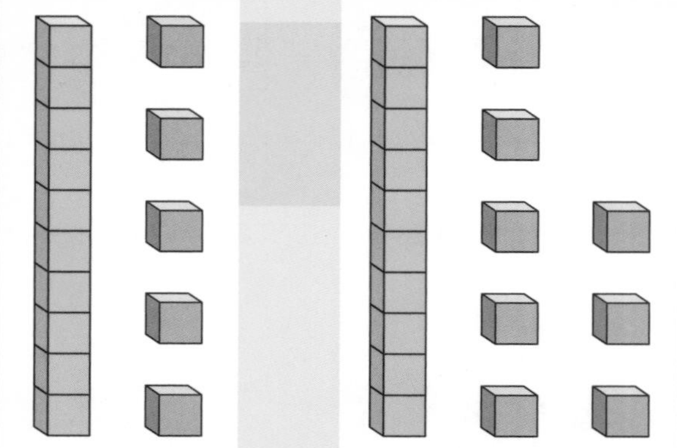

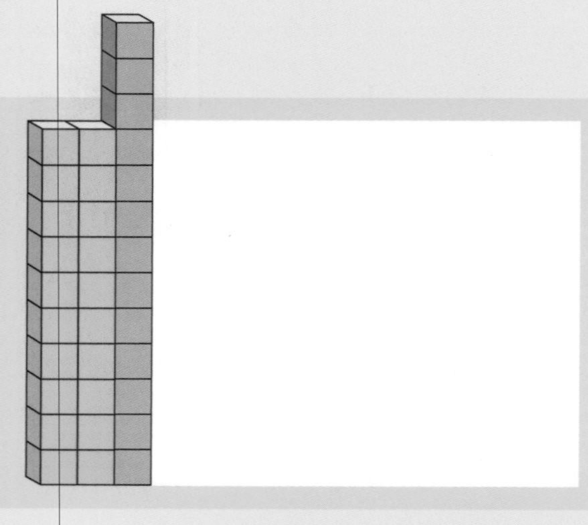

Amy arranged the blocks as shown on the left.

What do you notice about the total number of ones blocks?

What do you think Amy will do with the extra ones?

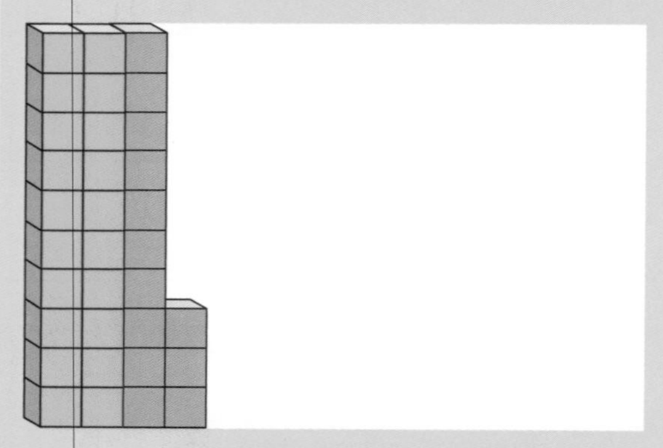

What is the total?

How could you figure out the total in your head?

I would add the tens then the ones.
15 + 18 **is the same as** 10 + 10 + 5 + 8.

What is another way you could figure out the total in your head?

Step Up

1. Draw blocks on the chart to show the total. Then complete the addition sentence.

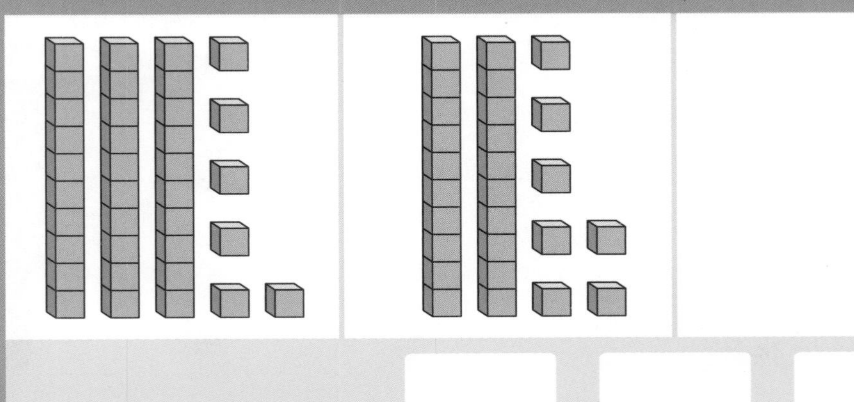

____ + ____ = ____

2. Use blocks to help you figure out these totals.

a. 22 + 18 = ____

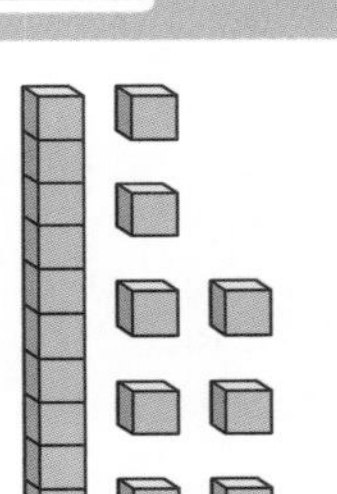

b. 46 + 26 = ____

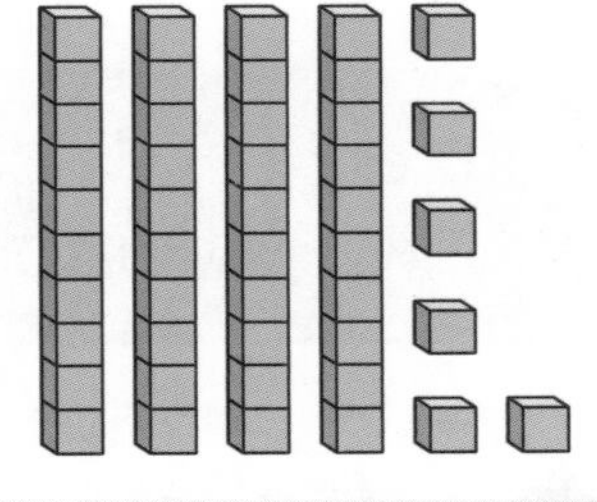

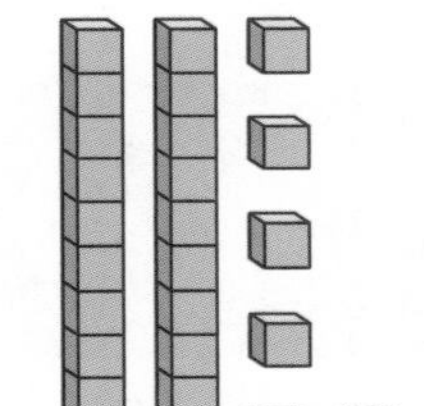

3. Figure out these totals in your head.

a. 53 + 28 = ____

b. 38 + 24 = ____

c. 17 + 25 = ____

Step Ahead

Each brick in this wall shows the total of the two numbers directly below. Write the missing numbers.

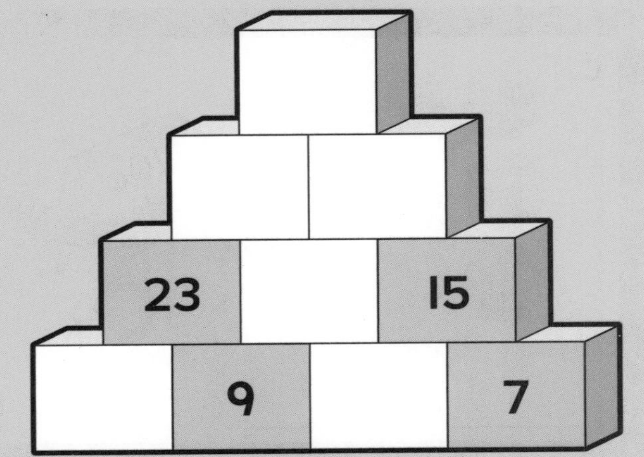

11.6 Subtracting Multiples of 10 (On the Decade)

Imagine you had these coins.

How much will you have left over if you buy the toy dinosaur?

How do you know?

What subtraction sentence could you write to show how much is left?

 –  = 

Imagine you had these coins.

How much would you have left after buying this toy dinosaur?

Step Up

1. Cross out coins you could use to buy the toy dinosaur. Then complete the subtraction sentence to show how much is left.

a.

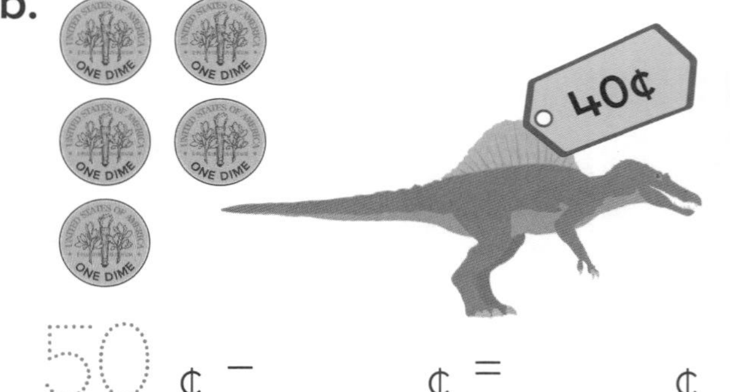

80 ¢ – 30 ¢ = 50 ¢

b.

50 ¢ – ____ ¢ = ____ ¢

c.

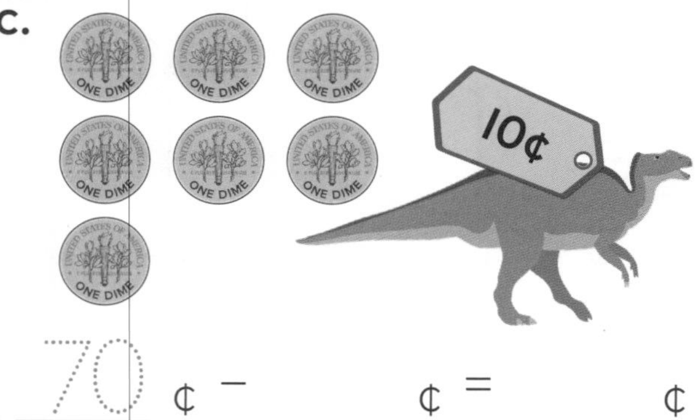

70 ¢ – ____ ¢ = ____ ¢

d.

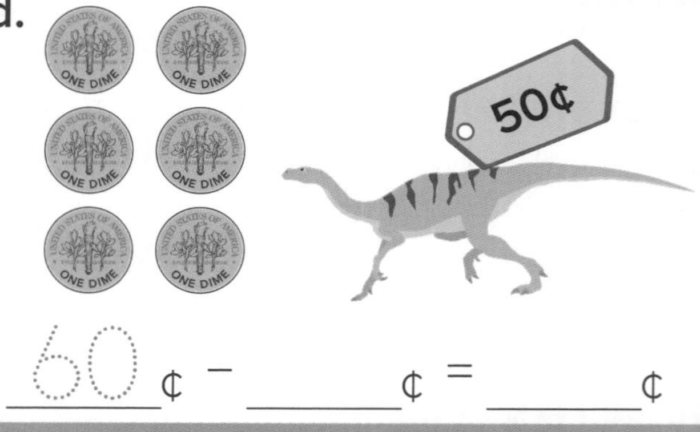

60 ¢ – ____ ¢ = ____ ¢

2. Cross out coins you could use to buy the toy dinosaur.
Then write the subtraction sentence to show how much is left.

a.

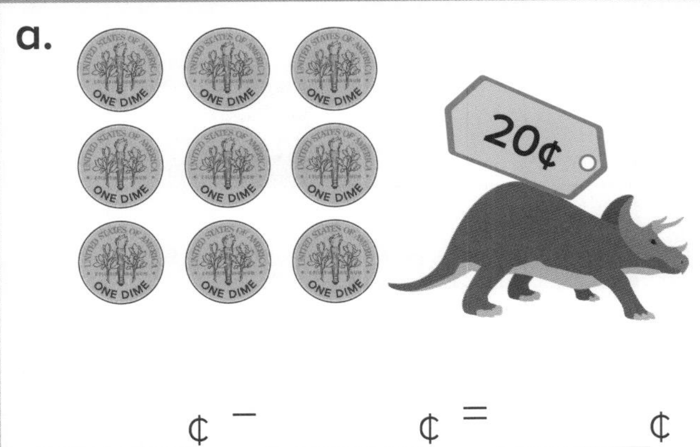

_______¢ − _______¢ = _______¢

b.

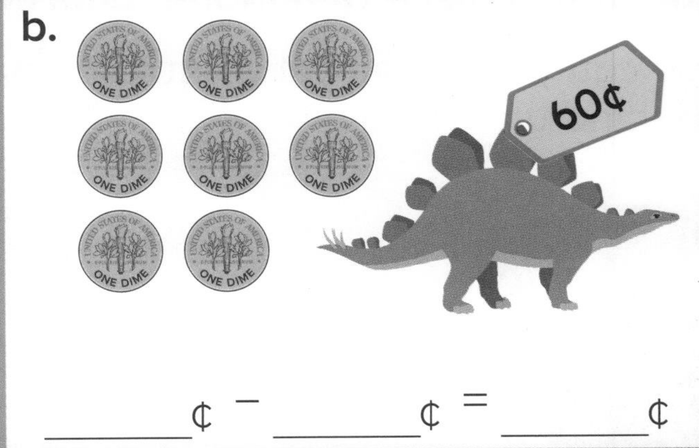

_______¢ − _______¢ = _______¢

c.

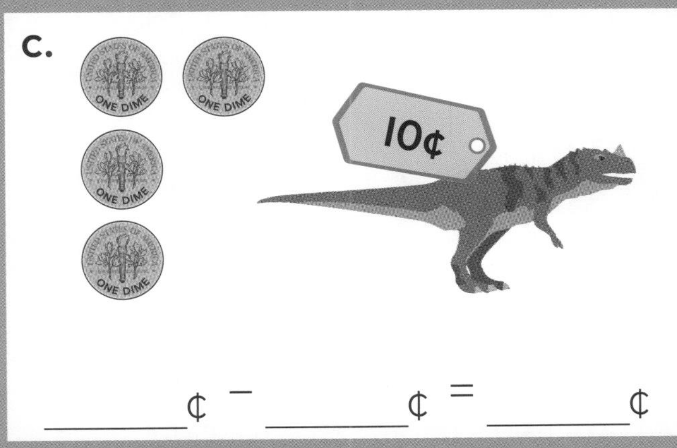

_______¢ − _______¢ = _______¢

d.

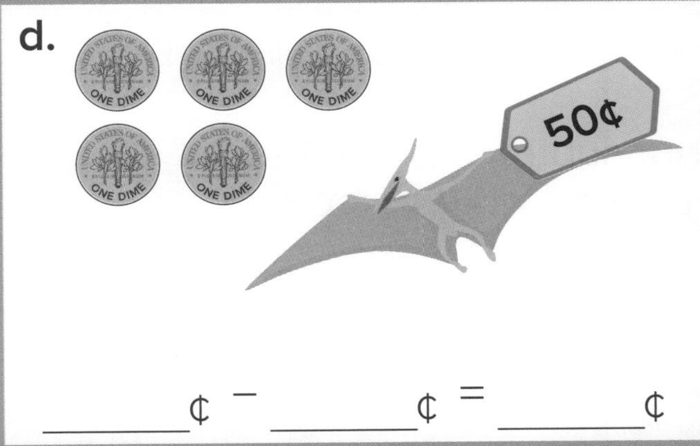

_______¢ − _______¢ = _______¢

Step Ahead

Imagine you had these coins and bought two of these toy dinosaurs.

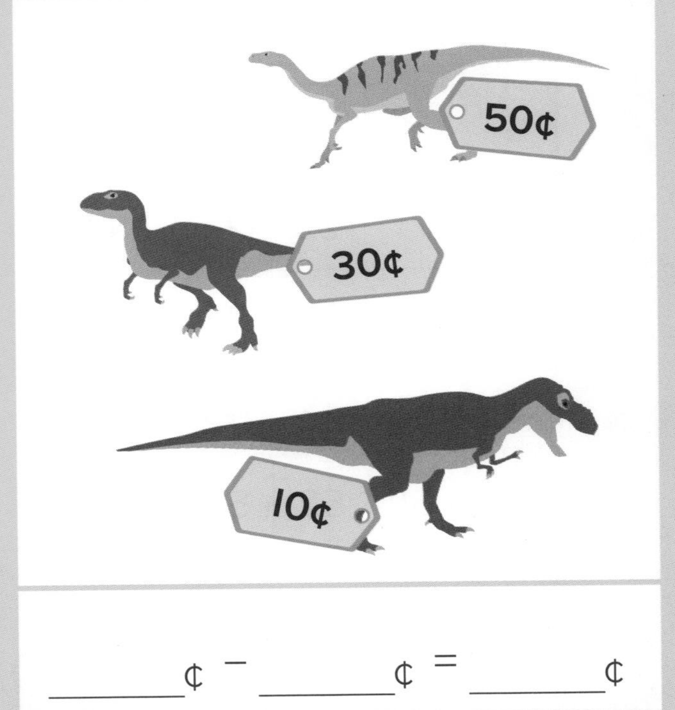

Loop the dinosaurs you would buy. Then write a number sentence to show how much money you would have left.

_______¢ − _______¢ = _______¢

11.7 Subtracting Multiples of 10 (Off the Decade)

Look at this piece of hundred chart.

How can you figure out what number is behind the red tile?

I would start at 44 and count back in steps of 10 to the red tile.

			■		
		33			
41	42	43	44	45	46

How many steps of 10 is that?

What subtraction sentence could you write to match?

____ – ____ = ____

What other way could you subtract numbers like these?

Step Up

1. Write the answers. You can draw arrows on this piece of hundred chart to help.

1	2	3	4	5	6	7	8	9	10
11	12	13	14	15	16	17	18	19	20
21	22	23	24	25	26	27	28	29	30
31	32	33	34	35	36	37	38	39	40
41	42	43	44	45	46	47	48	49	50
51	52	53	54	55	56	57	58	59	60

a. 34 – 10 = ____

b. 41 – 30 = ____

c. 59 – 50 = ____

2. Write the answers. You can use this piece of hundred chart to help.

41	42	43	44	45	46	47	48	49	50
51	52	53	54	55	56	57	58	59	60
61	62	63	64	65	66	67	68	69	70
71	72	73	74	75	76	77	78	79	80
81	82	83	84	85	86	87	88	89	90
91	92	93	94	95	96	97	98	99	100

a. 73 − 20 = ____
b. 96 − 40 = ____
c. 85 − 30 = ____
d. 94 − 10 = ____
e. 78 − 30 = ____
f. 61 − 20 = ____

3. Figure out and write each difference.

a. 52 − 50 = ____
b. 33 − 20 = ____
c. 88 − 30 = ____
d. 99 − 60 = ____
e. 67 − 30 = ____
f. 56 − 20 = ____

Step Ahead Write **+10**, **+20**, **−10**, or **−20** to make the number trails true.

a. 25 → ____ → 45 → ____ → 35 → ____ → 55

b. 74 → ____ → 64 → ____ → 74 → ____ → 54

11.8 Constructing and Interpreting a Tally Chart

What does this table show?

Where We Go at Lunch Break

Place	Tally	Total
Gym	卌 卌 卌 II	
Playground	卌 卌 III	
Library	卌	

What do the marks in the **Tally** column mean? How do you know?

How could you figure out what numbers to write in the **Total** column?

I counted by fives and then ones.
The total for the gym is 5, 10 , 15, 16, 17.

Where is the most popular place to go at lunch break?

Where is the least popular place to go?

How many more students go to the gym than the playground?
How do you know?

I compared the groups of tallies.
The gym has 4 more tallies so there were 4 more students in the gym.

How many students go inside? How do you know?

How many students were asked where they go at lunch break?

How do you know?

Step Up **a.** Write 3 places where your friends like to go at lunch break.

______ ______ ______

b. Write the place names you wrote in Question 1 in the chart below.

Place	Tally	Total

c. Ask some friends to tell you which place they like to go at lunch break. Draw tallies in the chart to show their answers.

d. Write the totals in the chart.

e. What was the most popular place? ______

f. What was the least popular place? ______

g. How many friends voted in total? ______

Step Ahead Look at this tally chart.
Find and correct the two mistakes that were made.

Where We Go at Lunch Break

Place	Tally	Total
Gym	|||/ ||||/ ||||/ ||||/ |||	23
Playground	||||/ ||||/ |||	13
Library	||||/	6

11.9 Constructing and Interpreting a Vertical Picture Graph

What does this picture graph show?

How many books did each student read?

Who read the most books? How do you know?

Who read the fewest books?

How many more books did Emilia read than Hunter and William together?

How did you figure it out?

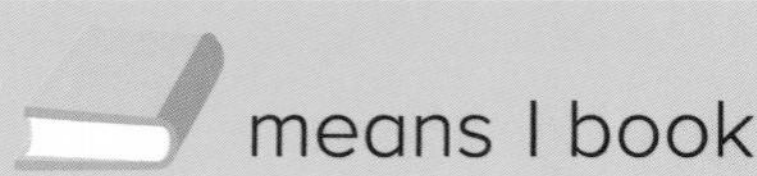

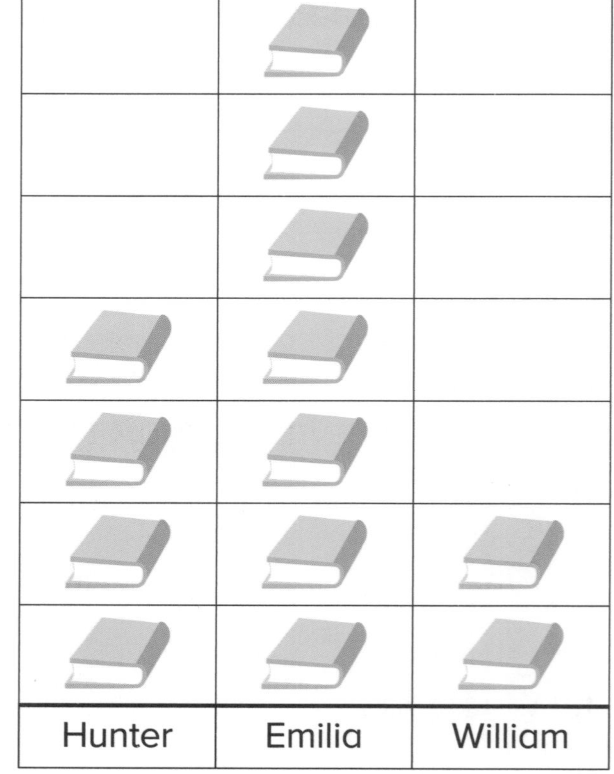

Step Up

1. Write the names of all the books you read last week. If you need more space, you can use a spare sheet of paper.

____

____

____

____

2. a. Write your initials and the initials of two other students in the graph below.

[ ] means 1 book

b. Draw [ ] to show how many books each student read.

Number of Books Read in One Week

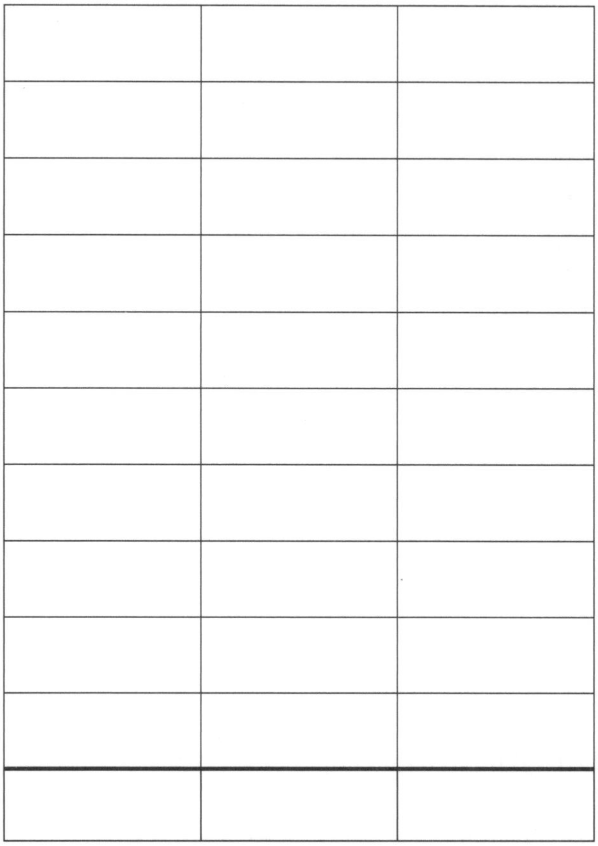

Students

3. How many books did each student read?

Name ____________

Number of books read ______

Name ____________

Number of books read ______

Name ____________

Number of books read ______

4. Write names to make a true sentence.

____________ read more books than ____________.

Step Ahead Jamar reads more than Maka but has read fewer books. How could this be?

____

____

11.10 Constructing and Interpreting a Horizontal Picture Graph

Some students recorded how many connecting cubes they could pick up with one hand.

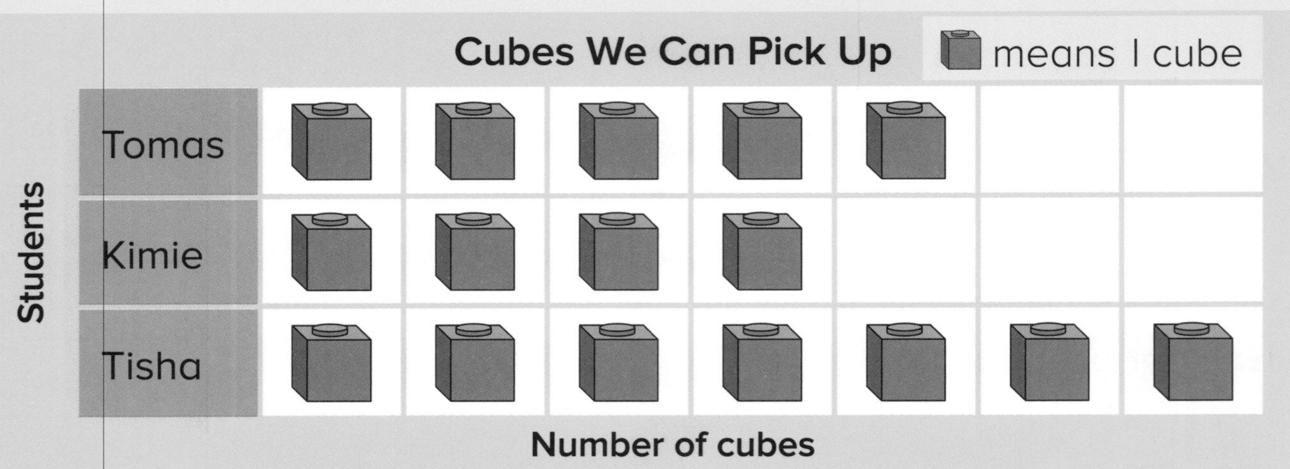

What does this picture graph show?

How many connecting cubes could each student pick up with one hand? How do you know?

Who could pick up the most cubes? How do you know?

Who could pick up the fewest cubes?

How many more cubes could Tisha pick up than Tomas? How did you figure out?

How many more cubes could Tomas pick up than Kimie?

Step Up

1. Write the number of connecting cubes that you think you could pick up in one hand.

2. a. Write your name and the names of two other students in the graph below.

Cubes We Can Pick Up

■ means 1 cube

Students										
______										
______										
______										

Number of cubes

b. Draw ■ in the graph to show how many cubes each person could pick up.

3. How many cubes could each person pick up?

Name ______ Number of cubes ______

Name ______ Number of cubes ______

Name ______ Number of cubes ______

4. a. Who picked up the most cubes? ______

b. Who picked up the fewest cubes? ______

Step Ahead Ask your teacher to pick up one handful of cubes. Write a subtraction sentence to show the difference between the number of cubes you can pick up and the number of cubes your teacher can pick up.

______

11.11 Constructing and Interpreting a Horizontal Bar Graph

Look at this bar graph.

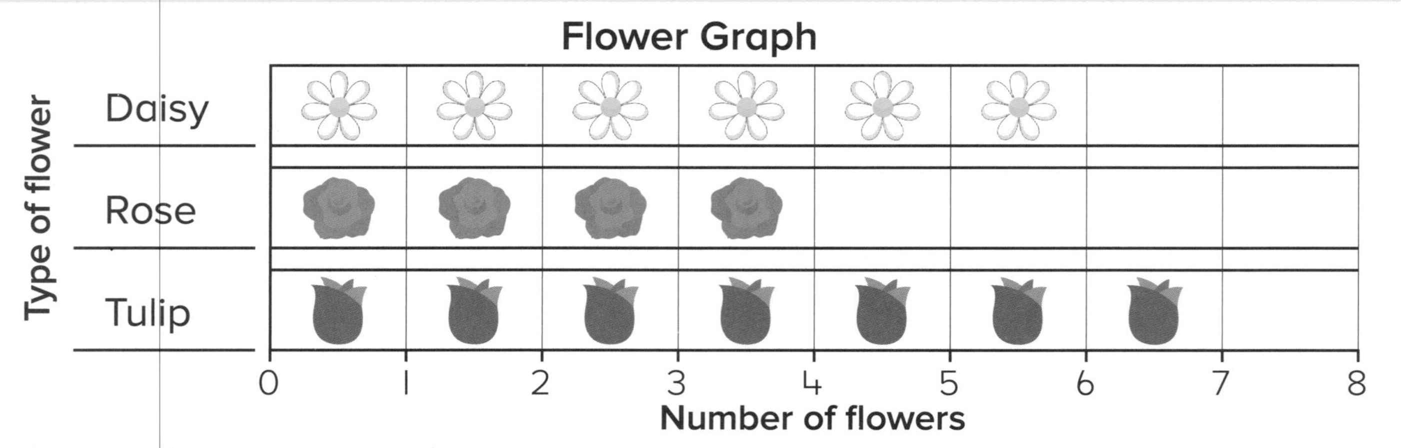

How many different flowers are there?

How can you figure out the total number of each type of flower without counting each one?

How could you make it easier to record the number of flowers?

You don't need to draw flowers. You could just color spaces beside each flower name.

How many more daisies are there than roses? How do you know?
How many fewer roses are there than tulips?

Step Up

1. Use colors to show flowers that are the same.

2. Color this graph to show the number of each type of flower in Question 1.

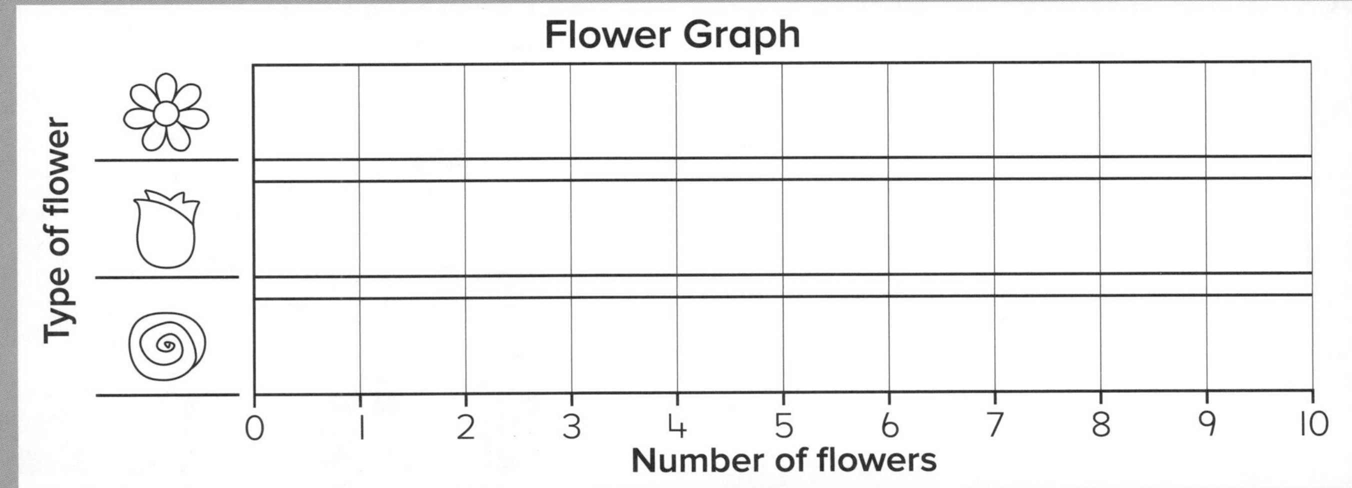

3. Write **more** or **fewer** to make true sentences.

a. There are ______________ than .

b. There are ______________ than .

4. Write numbers to make true sentences.

a. There are ____ more than .

b. There are ____ and together.

Step Ahead Loop the mistake in this bar graph.

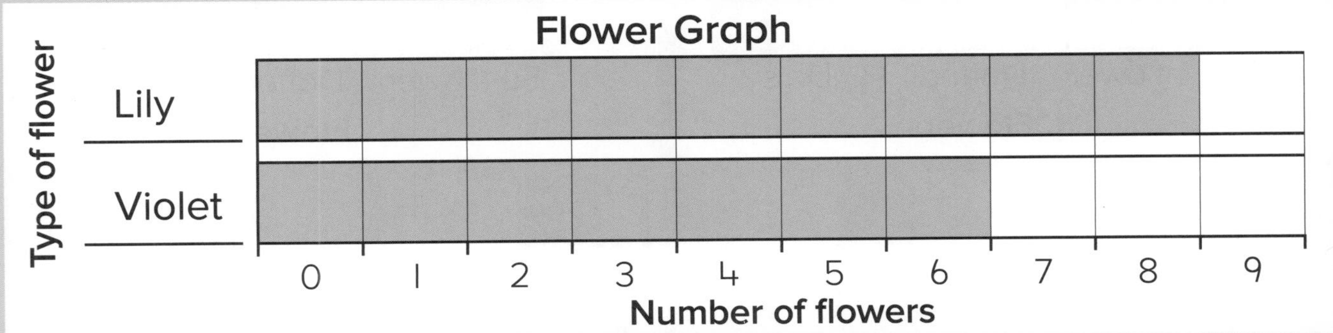

11.12 Constructing and Interpreting a Vertical Bar Graph

Look at these flowering plants.

How would you describe the height of each plant?

What type of graph could you use to compare the heights?

Why did you choose that type of graph?

Where would you write the numbers that show the height of each plant?

How will this bar graph be different to the flower graph we looked at in the previous lesson?

Step Up 1. Write the height of each plant.

a.

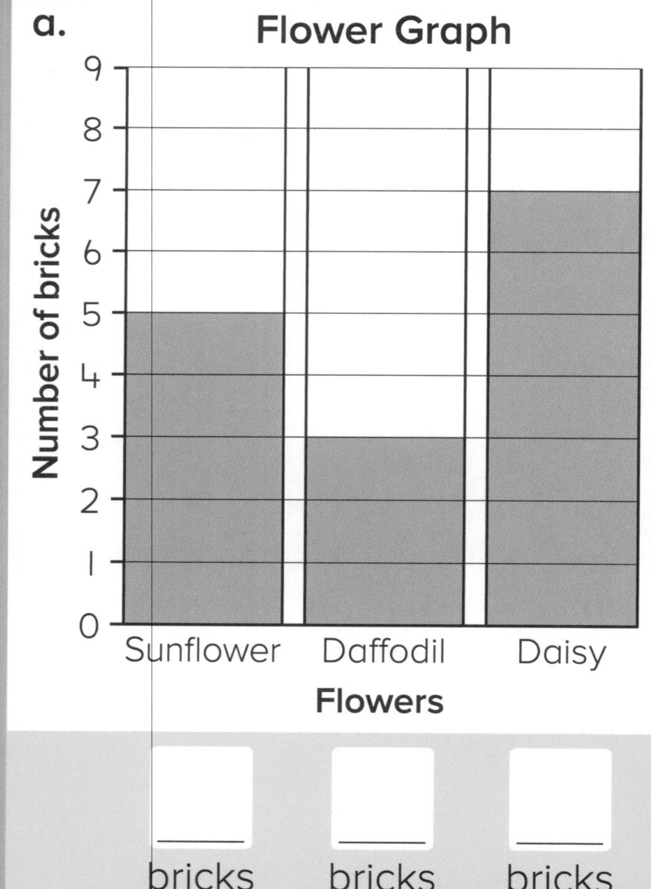

____ bricks ____ bricks ____ bricks

b.

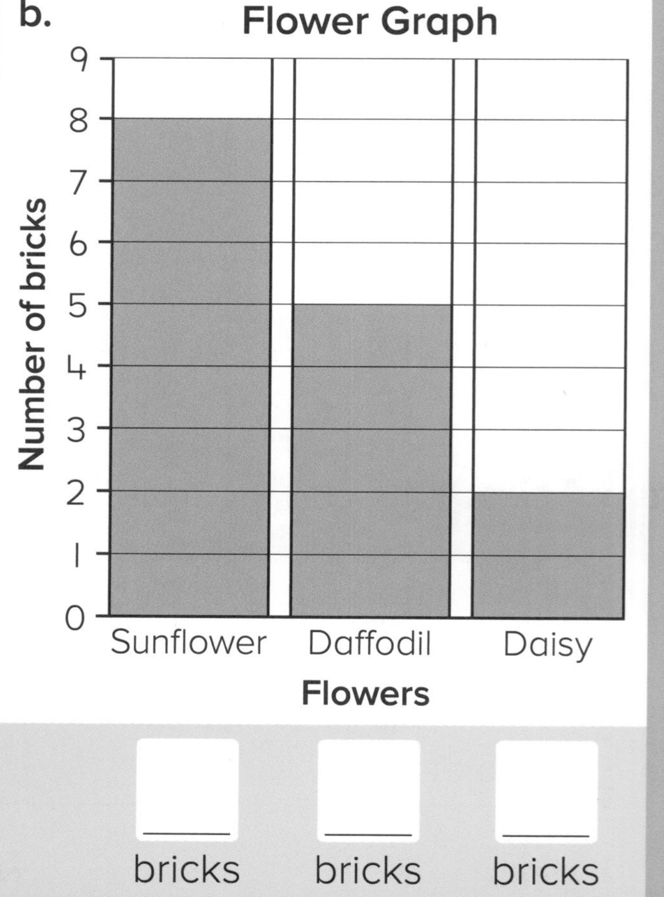

____ bricks ____ bricks ____ bricks

2. Color the bar graph to match the plant heights.

a.

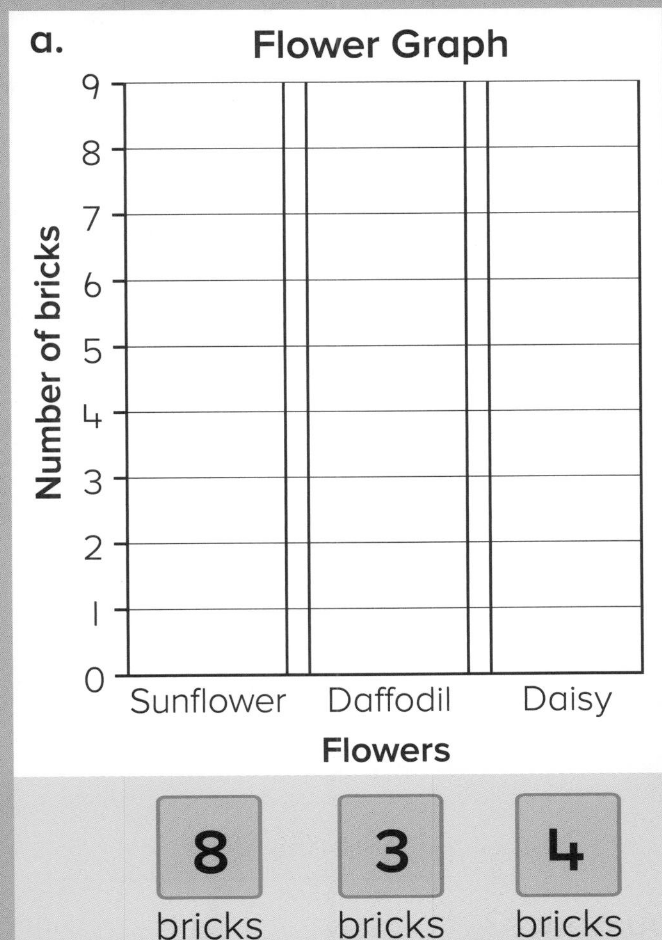

b.

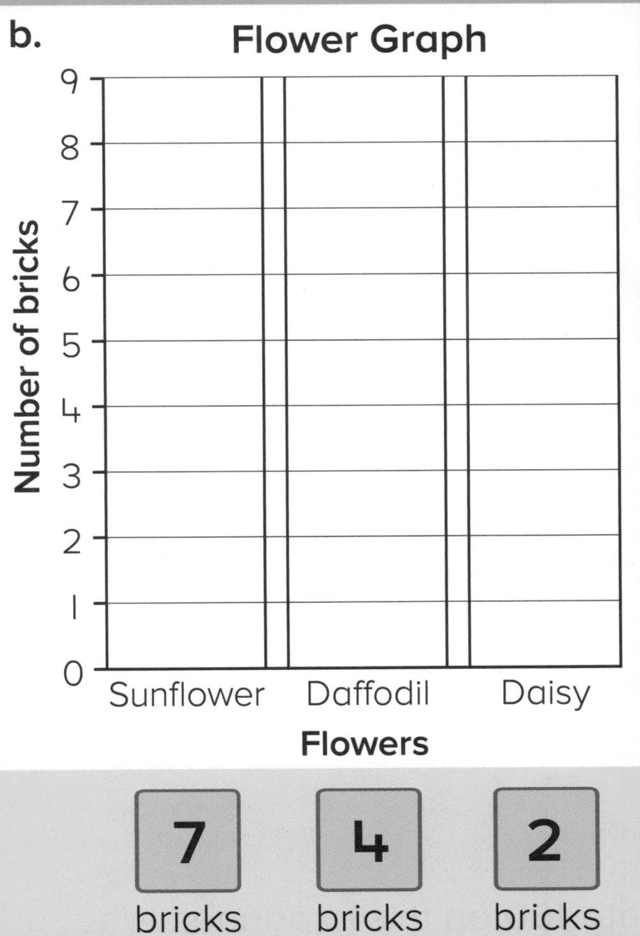

Step Ahead

Color this bar graph to match the clue. Then write the numbers.

Clue

The marigold is shorter than the rose but taller than the violet.

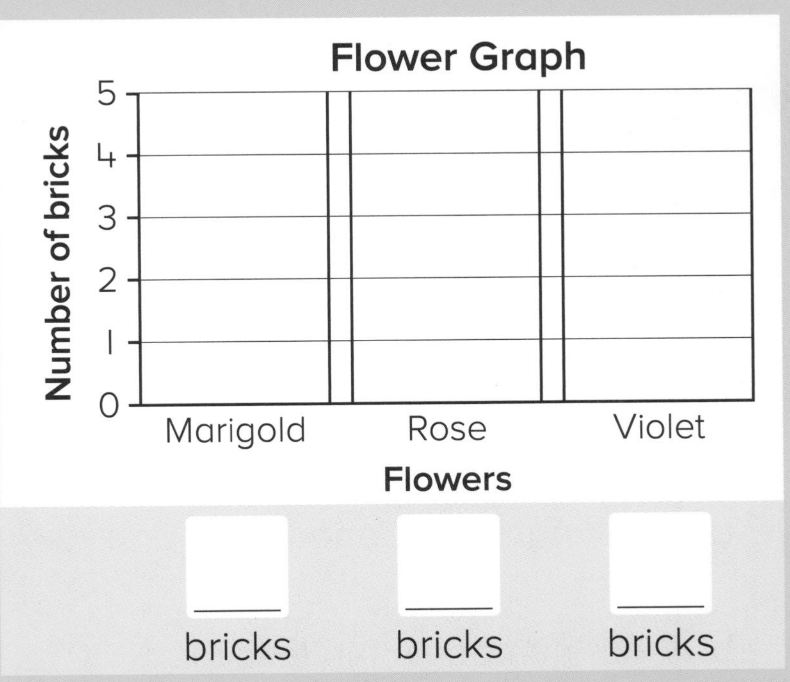

12.1 Analyzing 100

What do you know about one hundred?

There are 100 cents in one dollar.

I have seen 100 miles on signs.

Where have you seen **100** written?

How would you write 100 on this expander? [ ] hundreds [ ] [ ]

Write **100** on this expander. What do you notice? [ ] [ ] tens [ ]

Write **100** on this expander. What do you notice? [ ] [ ] [ ] ones

Step Up

1. Use the number chart to help you answer the questions.

61	62	63	64	65	66	67	68	69	70
71	72	73	74	75	76	77	78	79	80
81	82	83	84	85	86	87	88	89	90
91	92	93	94	95	96	97	98	99	100

a. What number is **one less** than 100? 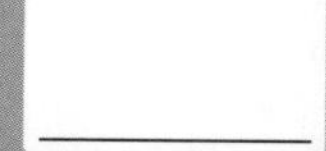

b. What number is **ten less** than 100? ______

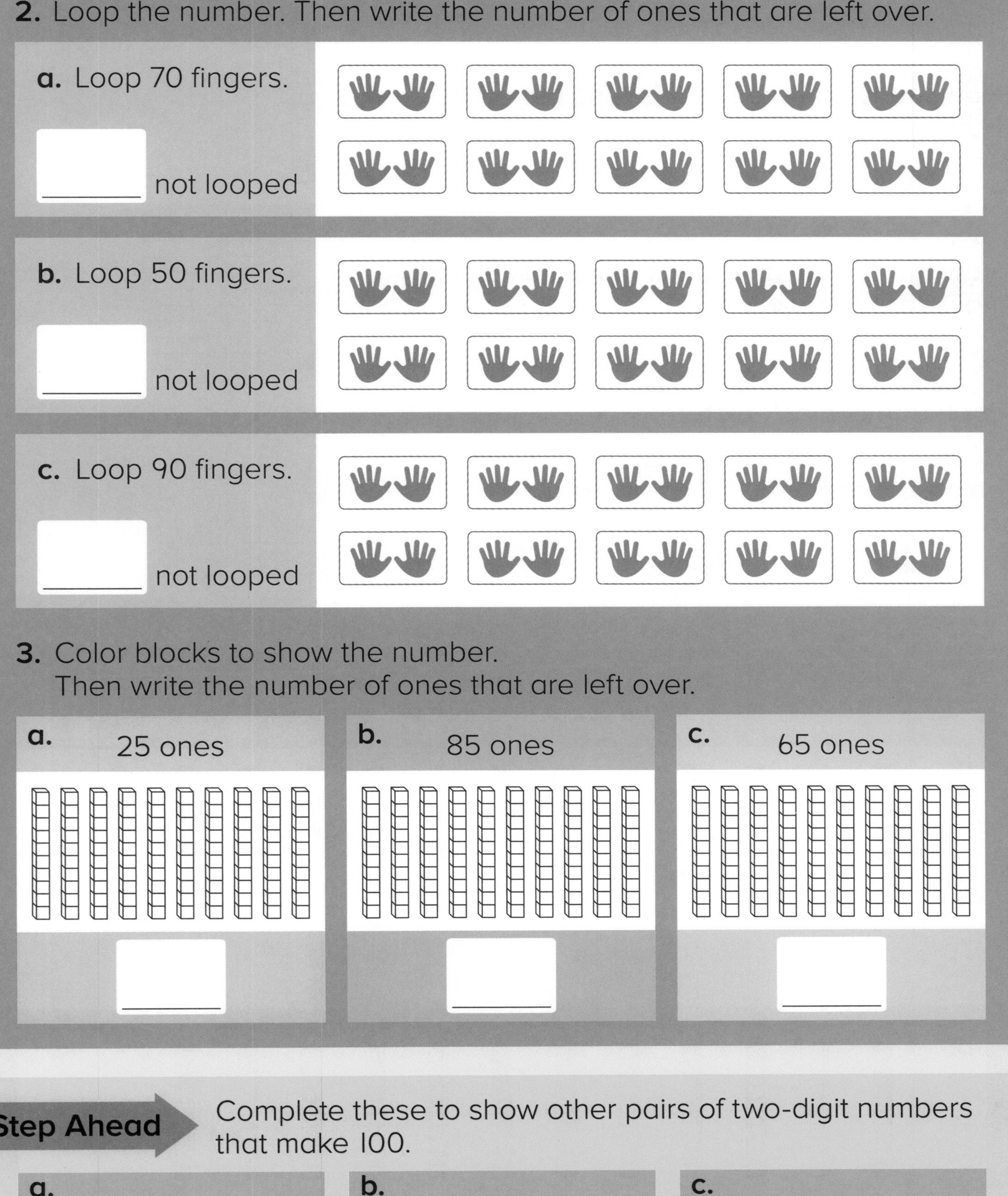

2. Loop the number. Then write the number of ones that are left over.

a. Loop 70 fingers.

_____ not looped

b. Loop 50 fingers.

_____ not looped

c. Loop 90 fingers.

_____ not looped

3. Color blocks to show the number.
Then write the number of ones that are left over.

a. 25 ones

_____

b. 85 ones

_____

c. 65 ones

_____

Step Ahead Complete these to show other pairs of two-digit numbers that make 100.

a. [ ][0] and [ ][0]

b. [ ][5] and [ ][5]

c. [ ][5] and [ ][5]

12.2 Writing Three-Digit Numbers to 130 (without Internal Zeros or Teens)

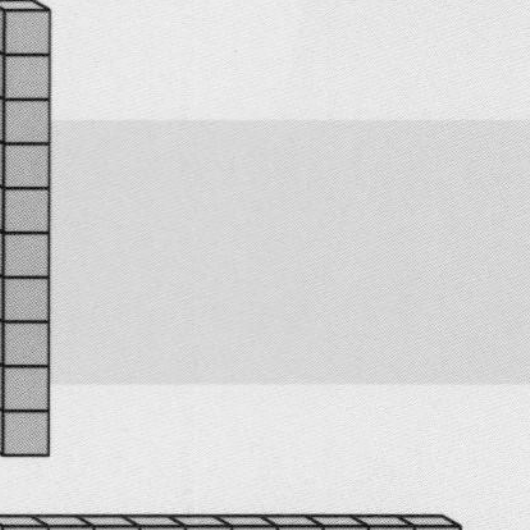

How many ones are in this tens block?
How do you know?

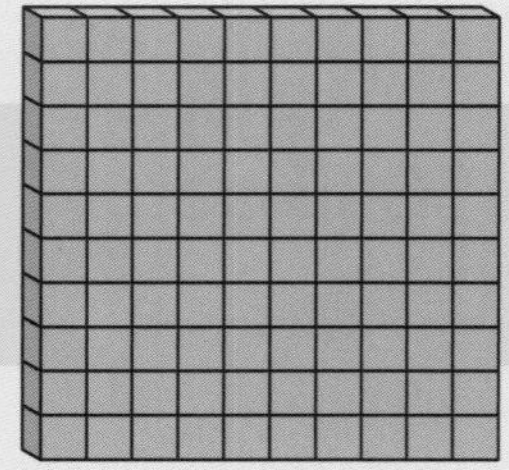

How many tens are in this hundreds block?
How do you know?

Look at this block picture.

How would you write this number on an expander? How do you know?

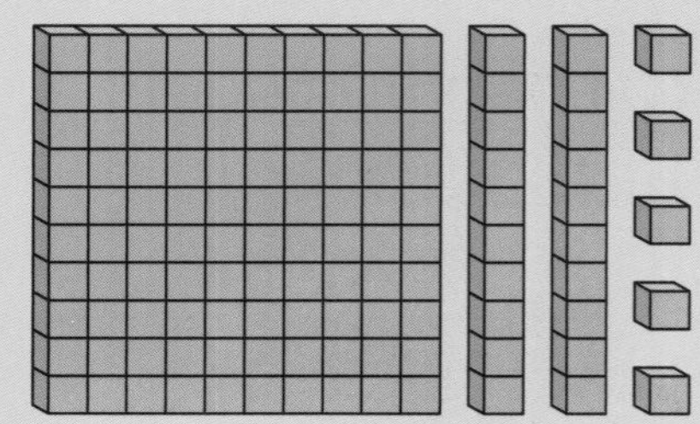

Step Up

1. Loop groups of 10 tens blocks. Write the number of **hundreds**. Then write the number of **tens** and **ones** left over.

a.

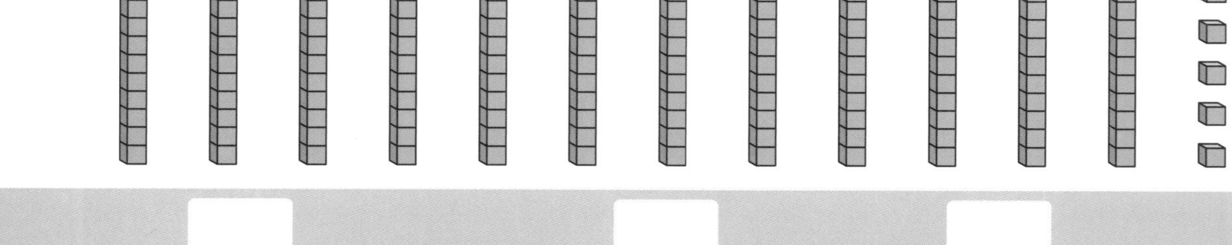

_____ hundreds _____ tens _____ ones

b.

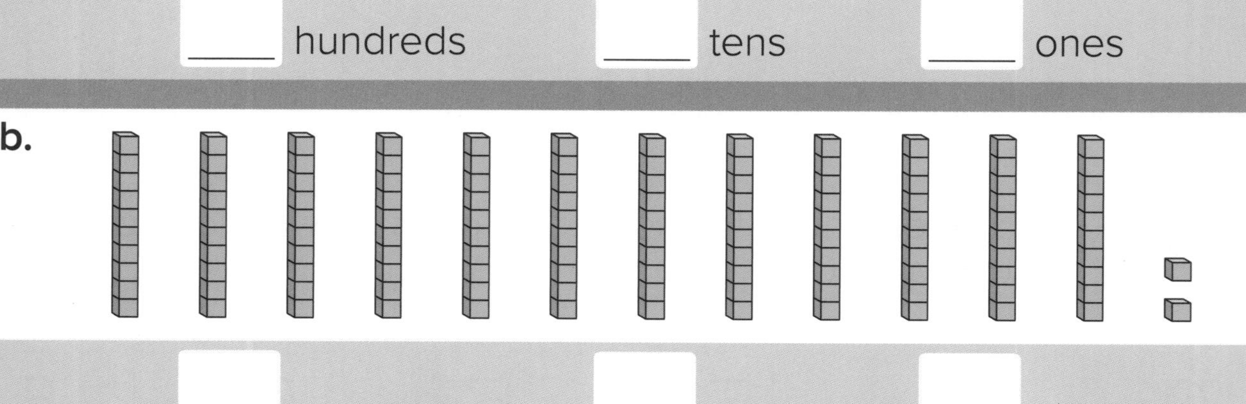

_____ hundreds _____ tens _____ ones

2. Look at the blocks. Write the number on the expanders to match.

a.

hundreds tens ones

hundreds

b.

hundreds tens ones

hundreds

c.

hundreds tens ones

hundreds

d.

hundreds tens ones

hundreds

Step Ahead Write the matching number on the expander. Remember that only one digit is written in each space on the expander.

a. 126 ones — hundreds tens ones

b. 1 hundred and 22 ones — hundreds tens ones

c. 12 tens and 8 ones — hundreds tens ones

12.3 Writing Three-Digit Numbers to 130 (without Teens)

What number does this block picture show?

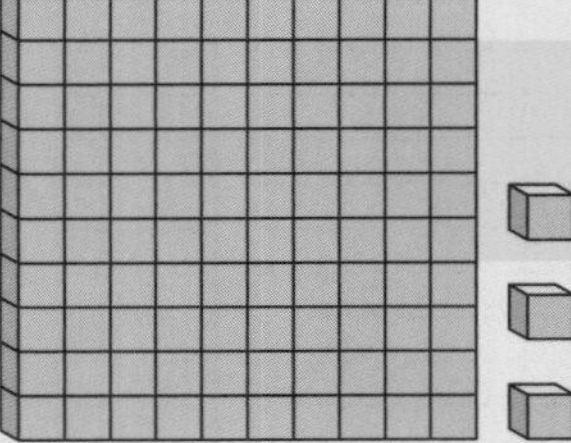

How would you write this number on an expander? How do you know?

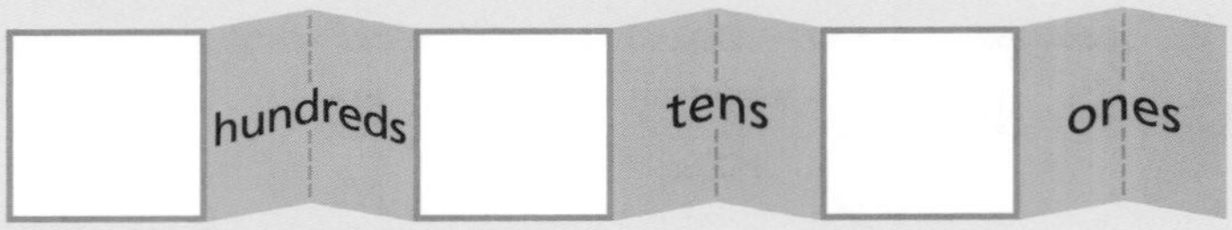

	hundreds		tens		ones

Look at the number on this expander. What does each digit mean?

1	hundreds	3	tens	0	ones

How is that number different from the number on the expander above?

Step Up

1. Look at the blocks. Write the number on the expanders to match.

a.

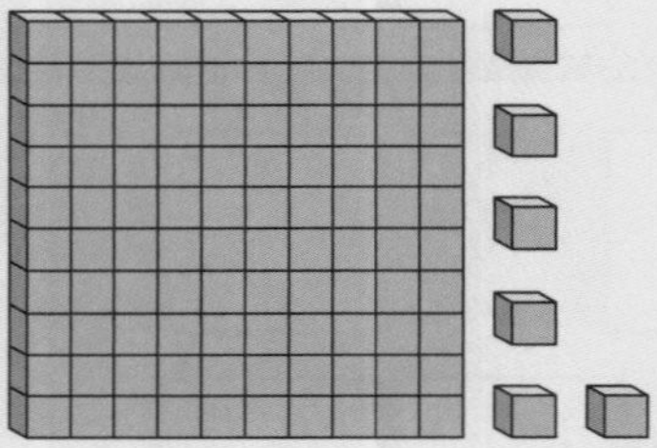

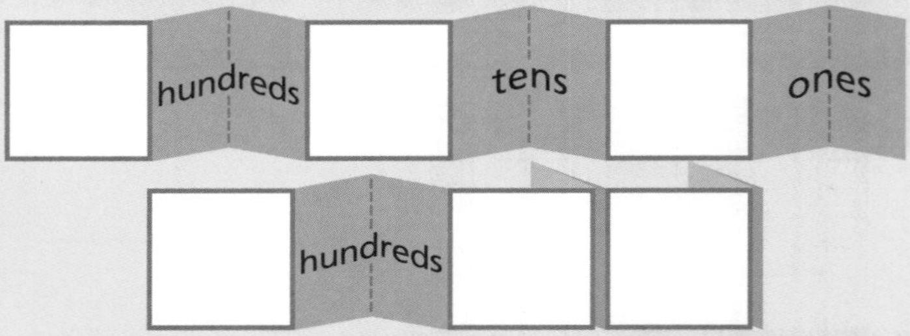

	hundreds		tens		ones

	hundreds		

b.

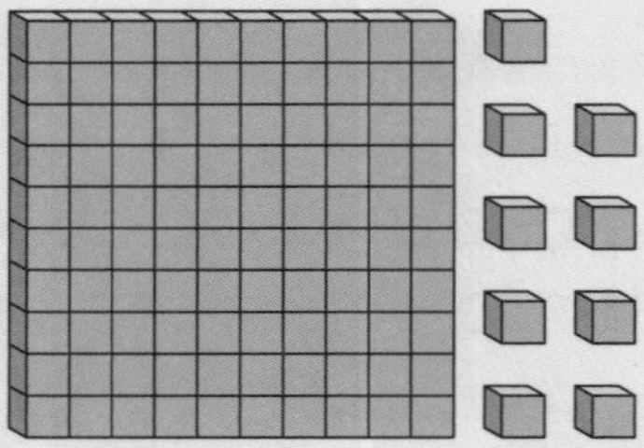

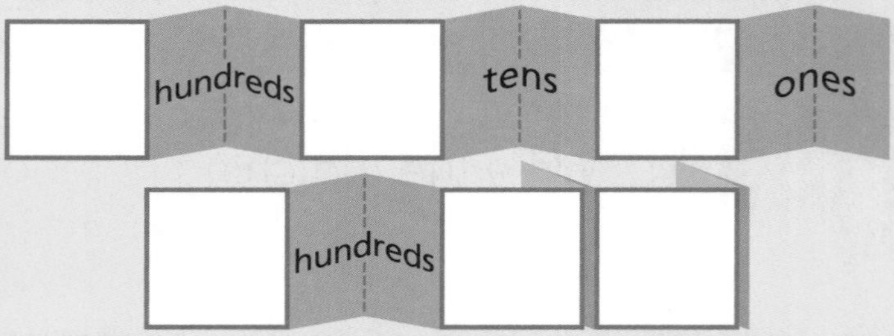

	hundreds		tens		ones

	hundreds		

c.

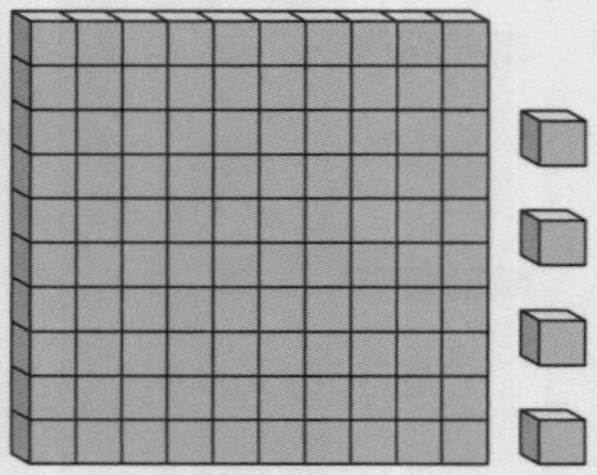

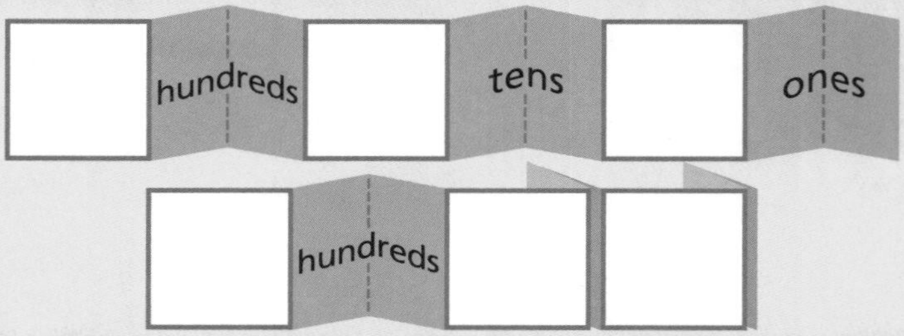

	hundreds		tens		ones

	hundreds		

2. Color the blocks to match the number shown on each expander.

a.

1	hundreds	2	3

b.

1	hundreds	0	2

c.

1	hundreds	0	8

d.

1	hundreds	1	0

Step Ahead This block picture has been mixed around. Figure out the number it shows. Then write the number on the expander.

	hundreds		

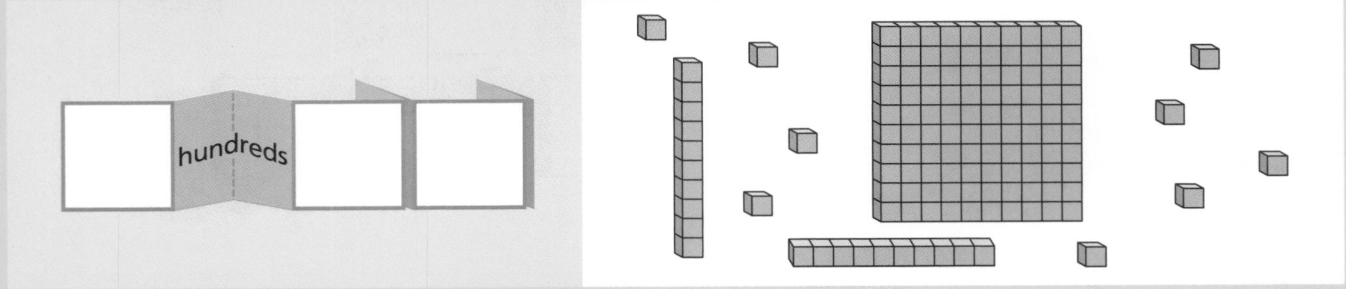

12.4 Writing Numerals and Number Names to 130 (without Teens)

How would you read and say the number on this expander?

When you read and say three-digit numbers, you say the value of the tens and ones together.

How would you write the number in words?

____

How would you read and say these numbers?

What do you notice about the zero in each number? What does the zero do?

Step Up

1. Look at each block picture. Write the number on the expanders. Then write the matching number name.

a.

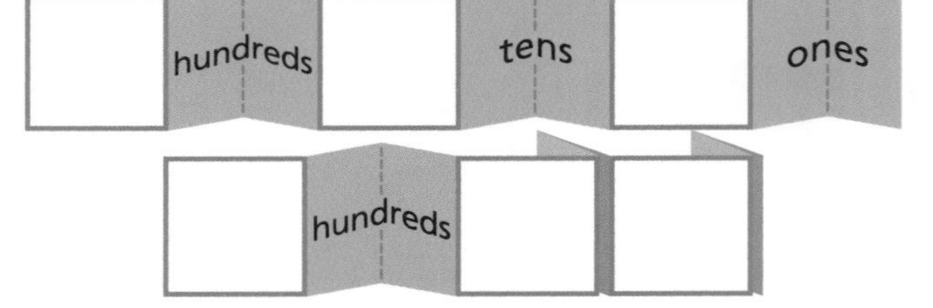

__________ hundred __________________________

b.

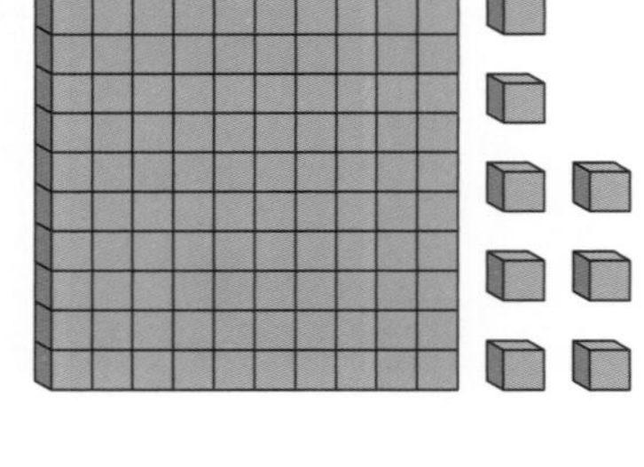

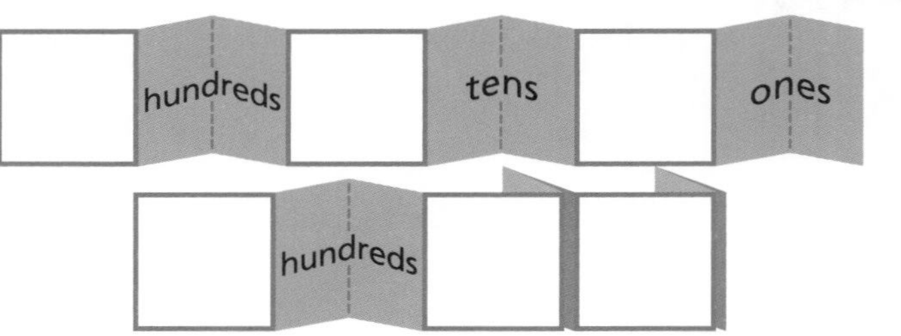

__________ hundred __________________________

2. Read the number name. Write the matching number on the expander.

a. one hundred twenty-six

hundreds

b. one hundred seven

hundreds

c. one hundred twenty-two

hundreds

d. one hundred one

hundreds

e. one hundred nine

hundreds

f. one hundred twenty-three

hundreds

g. one hundred twenty-one

hundreds

h. one hundred six

hundreds

Step Ahead

a. Write a different three-digit number on this expander.

hundreds

b. Color blocks to show your number.

c. Write the number in words.

12.5 Writing Three-Digit Numbers to 130 (with Teens)

Look at this block picture.

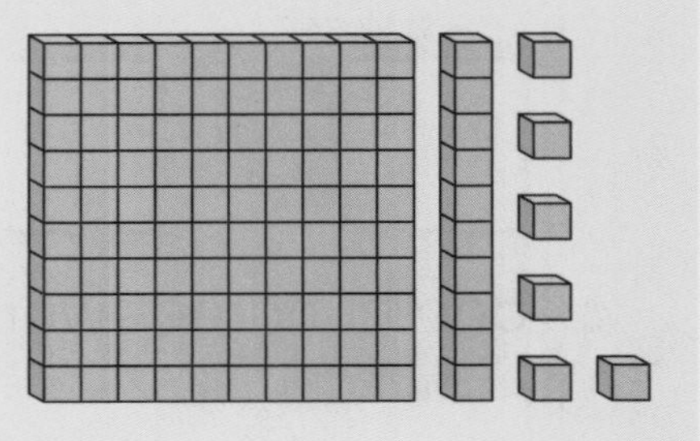

What number does it show?
How would you write the number on an expander?

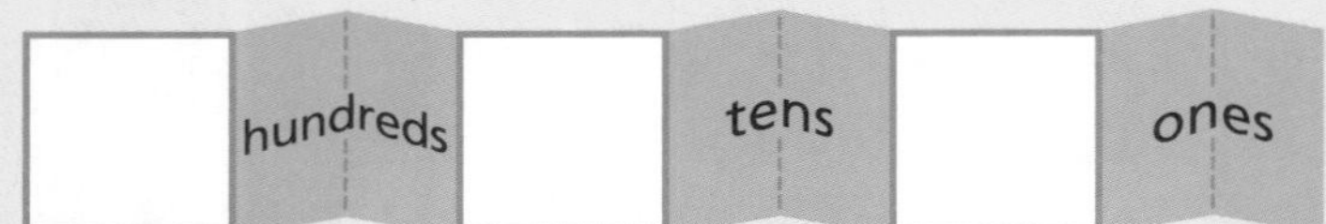

How did you know where to write the digits? What does each digit mean?

How would you read and say the number?

When you read and say three-digit numbers, you say the value of the tens and ones together. You can close the expander like this to help you.

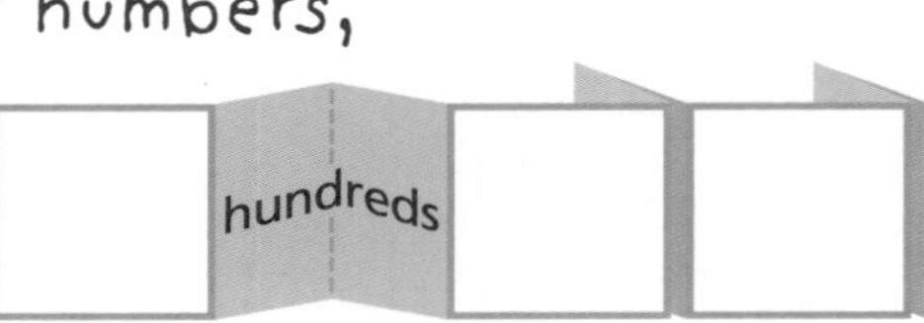

Step Up

1. Look at the blocks. Write the number on the open and closed expanders.

a.

hundreds tens ones

hundreds

b.

hundreds tens ones

hundreds

c.

hundreds tens ones

hundreds

2. Draw lines to join each block picture to a matching expander. Cross out the expander that does not have a match.

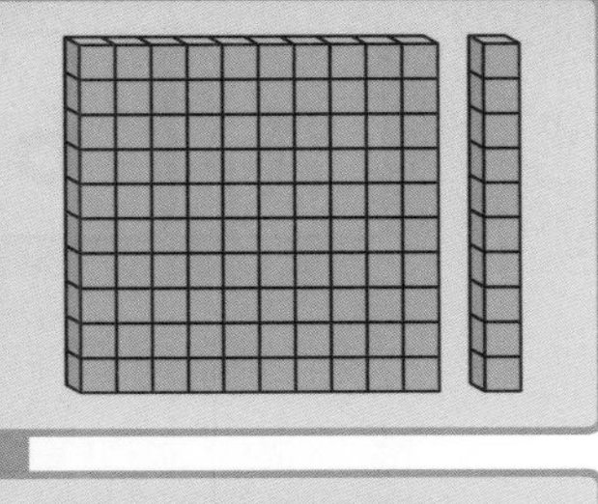

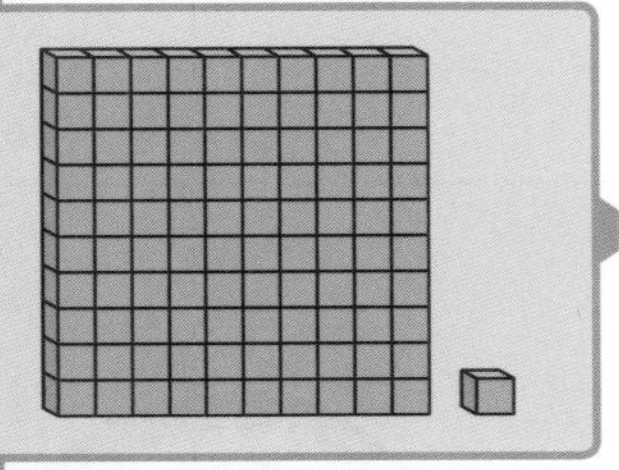

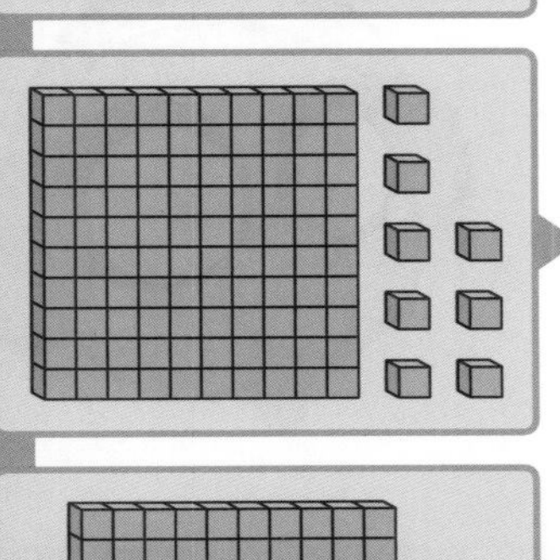

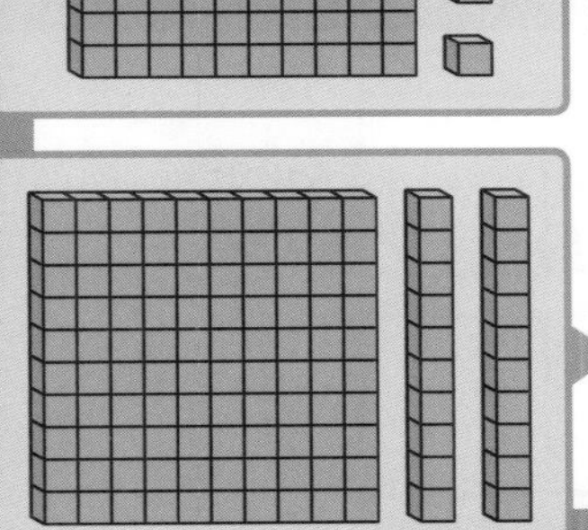

1	hundreds	0	8
1	hundreds	0	2
1	hundreds	1	8
1	hundreds	0	1
1	hundreds	2	0
1	hundreds	1	0

Step Ahead Complete these sentences.

a. 113 **is the same as** ____ tens and ____ ones

b. 104 **is the same as** ____ tens and ____ ones

12.6 Writing Numerals and Number Names to 130 (with Teens)

How would you read and say the number on this expander?

How would you write the number in words?

____

How would you read and say these two numbers?

What is the same about these numbers?
What is different?

Step Up

1. Look at each block picture. Write the number on the expanders. Then write the matching number name.

a.

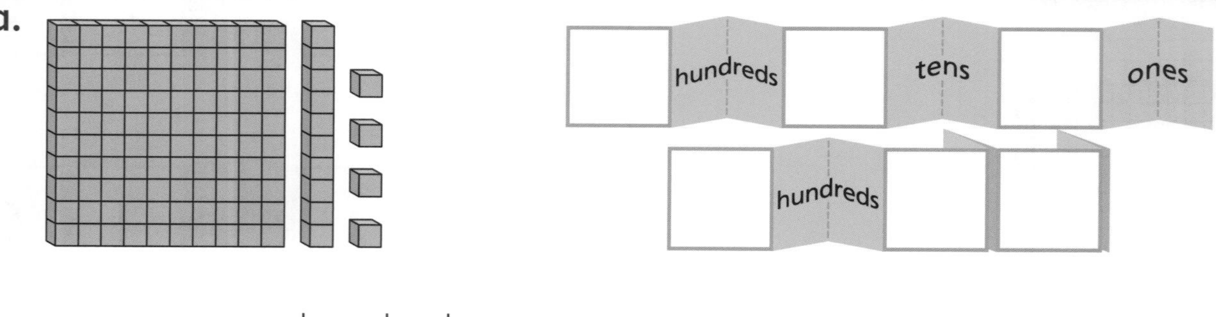

__________ hundred ______________________________

b.

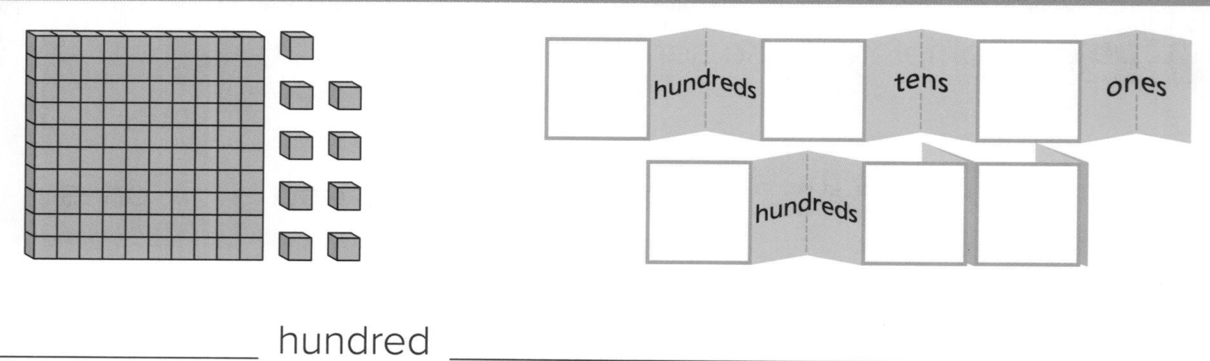

__________ hundred ______________________________

2. Read the number name. Write the matching number on the expander.

a. one hundred thirteen

hundreds

b. one hundred eight

hundreds

c. one hundred eleven

hundreds

d. one hundred thirty

hundreds

e. one hundred seventeen

hundreds

f. one hundred seven

hundreds

g. one hundred twenty

hundreds

h. one hundred twelve

hundreds

Step Ahead

a. Write a different three-digit number on this expander.

hundreds

b. Color blocks to show your number.

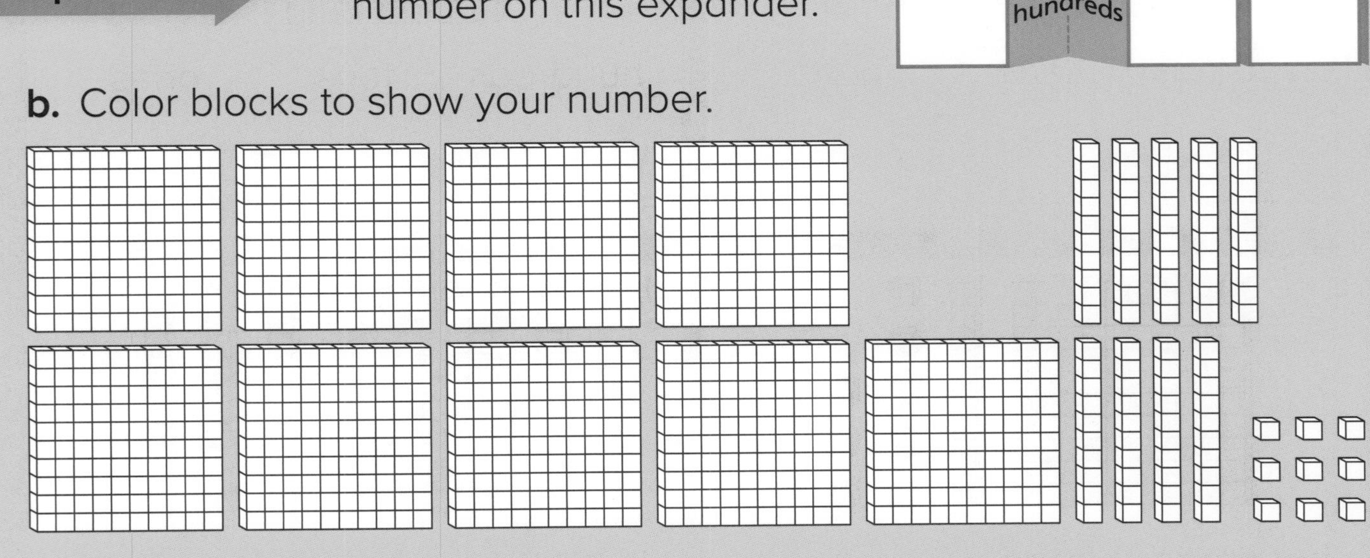

c. Write the number in words.

12.7 Writing Three-Digit Numbers to 130

How do you read and say the number on this expander?

1	hundreds	0	tens	7	ones

What blocks would you use to show the number?

How could you use this place-value chart to show the number?

hundreds	tens	ones

How would you write the numeral without using an expander or a place-value chart?

Step Up 1. Look at the picture of blocks.
Write the number of hundreds, tens, and ones.

a.

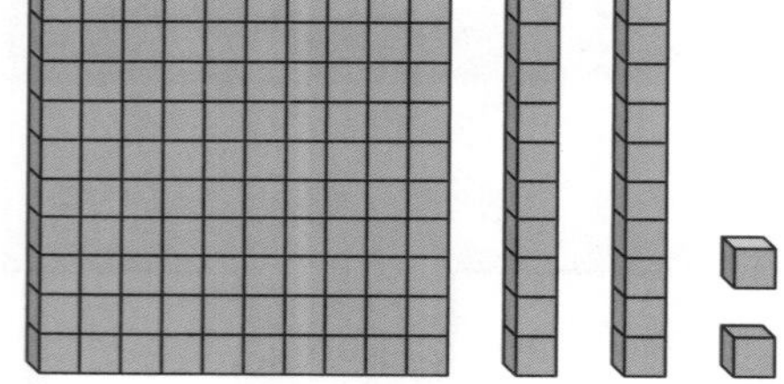

hundreds	tens	ones

b.

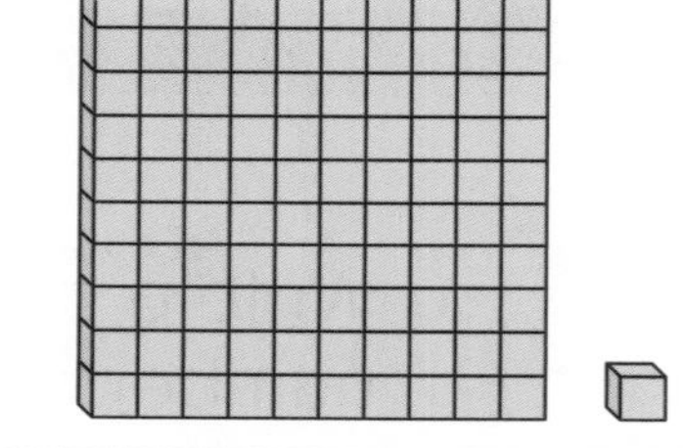

hundreds	tens	ones

c.

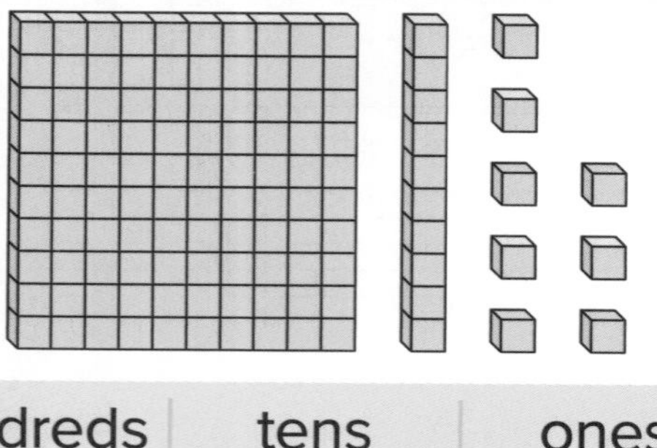

hundreds	tens	ones

d.

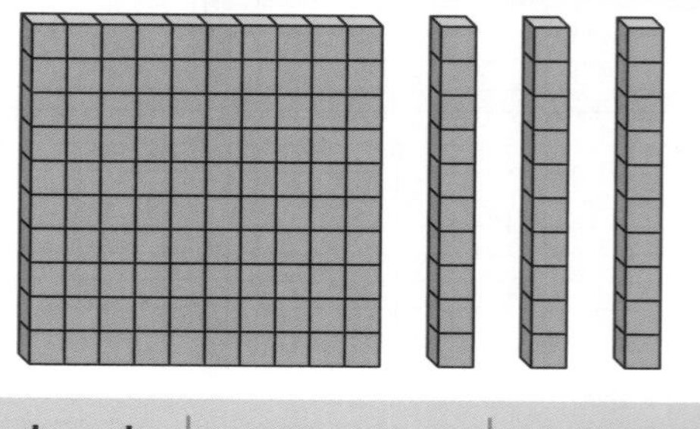

hundreds	tens	ones

2. Look at the picture of blocks. Write the matching number in the place-value chart. Then write the numeral without the chart.

a.

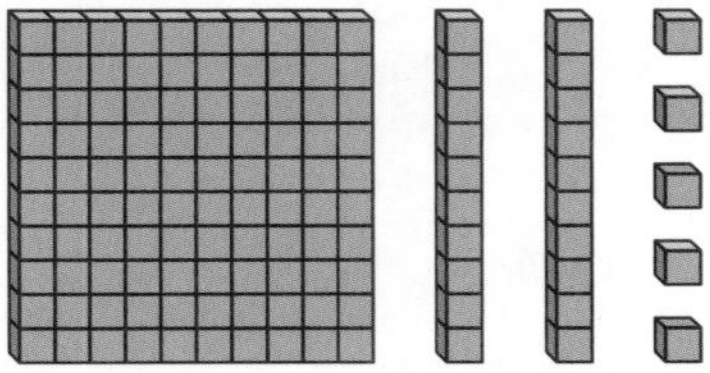

hundreds	tens	ones

b.

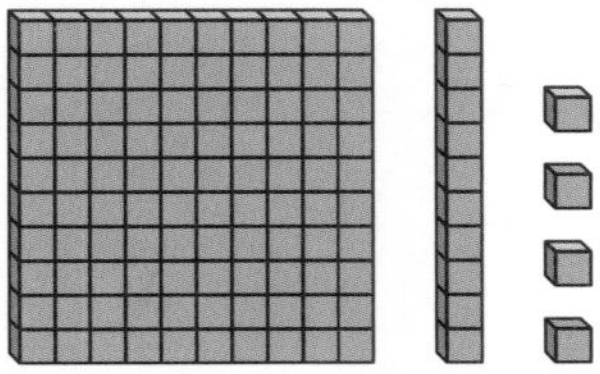

hundreds	tens	ones

c.

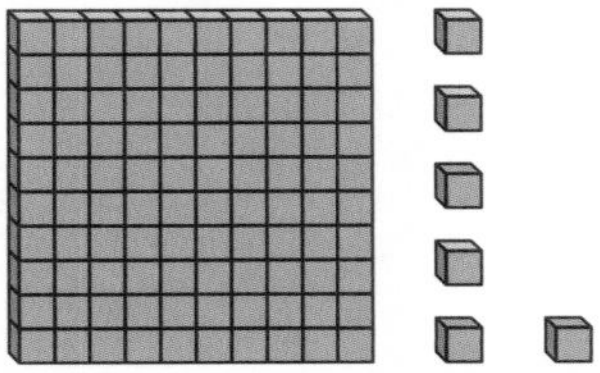

hundreds	tens	ones

d.

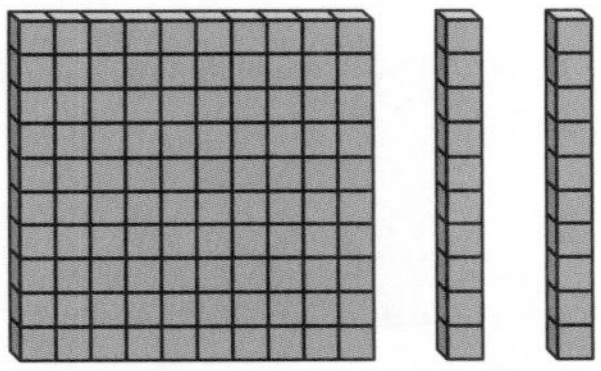

hundreds	tens	ones

e.

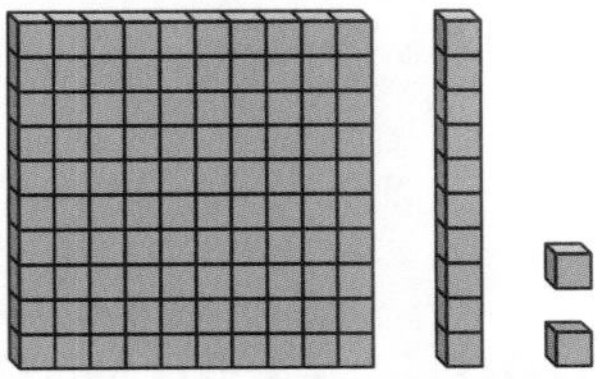

hundreds	tens	ones

Step Ahead Draw **another tens block and a ones block** in each picture. Write the new numeral.

a.

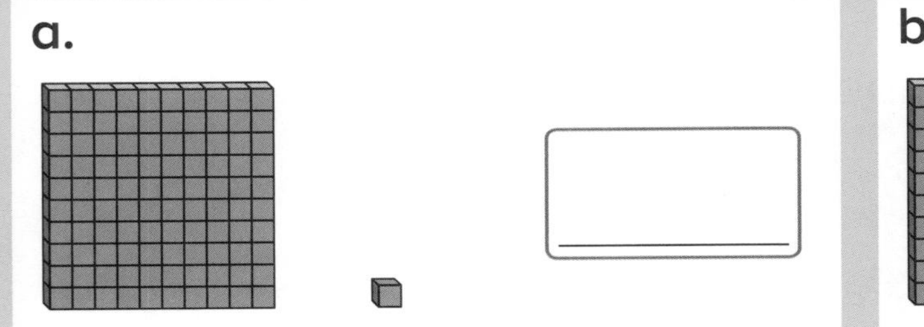

b.

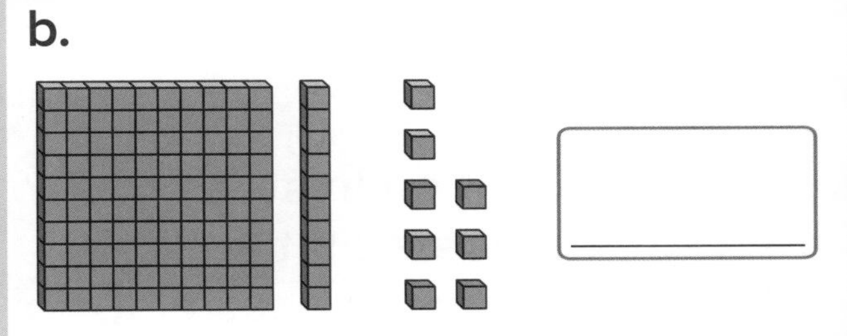

12.8 Exploring the Counting Sequence to 130

Look at this number chart.

61	62	63	64	65	66	67	68	69	70

Start at 70. Count on in steps of 10. What numbers do you say?
Where will you write these numbers on the chart?
How do you know?

Think about the numbers that come just before the numbers you wrote.
What digit will be in the ones place of each number? How do you know?
Write these numbers on the chart.

Start at 70. Count on in steps of 5.
Write these numbers on the chart.
What digit will be in the ones place of each number **just after**?
How do you know? Write these numbers on the chart.

Start at 70. Count on in steps of 2.
Write these numbers on the chart.
What digit will be in the ones place of each number **just before**?
How do you know?

Step Up 1. Complete the chart on page 286.

2. Write the number that comes **just before** each of these.

a. ______ 120 b. ______ 125 c. ______ 119

3. Write the number that comes **just after** each of these.

a. 129 ______ b. 110 ______ c. 108 ______

4. Write the numbers missing from these number chart pieces.

a.

____	____	105	____

b.

____	114	____	____

c.

121	____	____	____

d.

____	128	____	____

e.

112	____	____	____	116	____	____	____	____

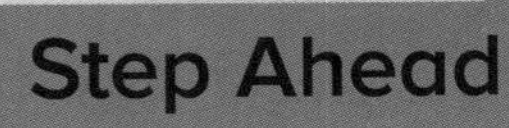

Step Ahead

a. Loop in blue the numbers you say when you start at 100 and count on in steps of 5.

b. Loop in red the numbers you say when you start at 100 and count on in steps of 2.

102 110 122 120 115 125

c. Write what you notice.

____

____

____

12.9 Comparing Quantities Greater Than 100

Look at these pictures of blocks. What number does each picture show?

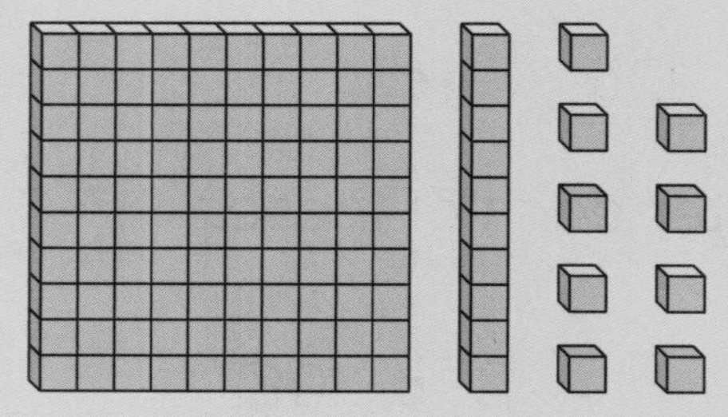
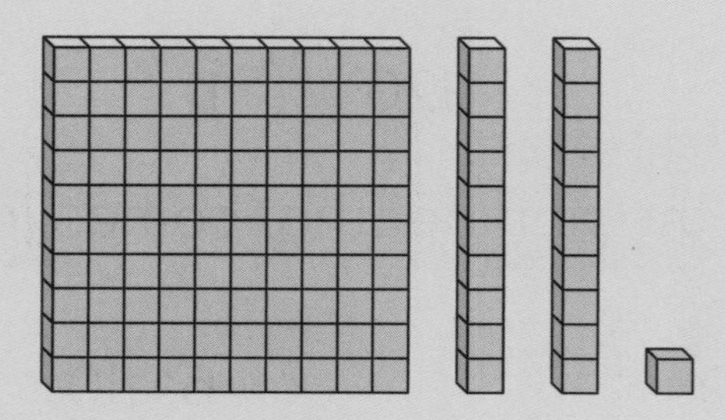

How could you figure out which number is greater?

Complete this sentence to describe the two numbers.

 **is greater than** 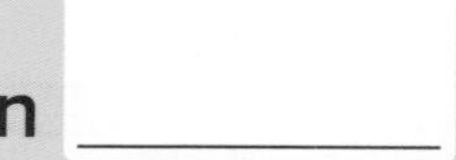

What other sentences could you write to describe the two numbers?

119 is less than 121.

121 > 119

Step Up

1. Color blocks to match each number name.
   Then write the numerals to complete the sentence.

one hundred twenty-three	one hundred twenty-eight
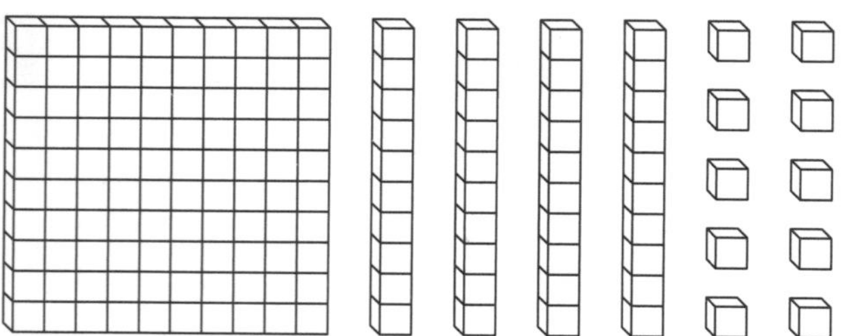	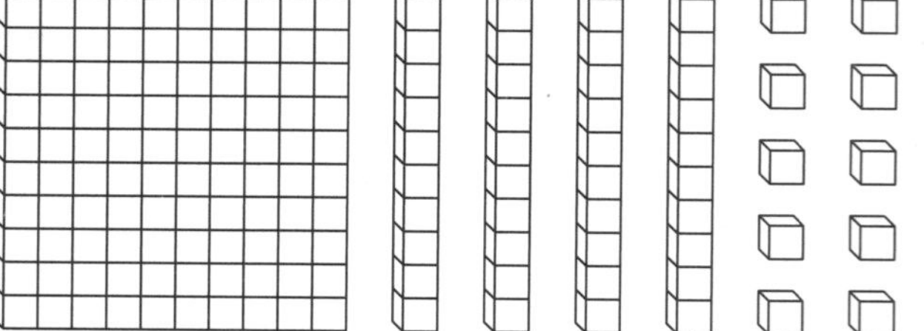

________ is less than ________

2. Color blocks to match each number name.
Then write the numerals to complete the sentence.

a. **one hundred fifteen**

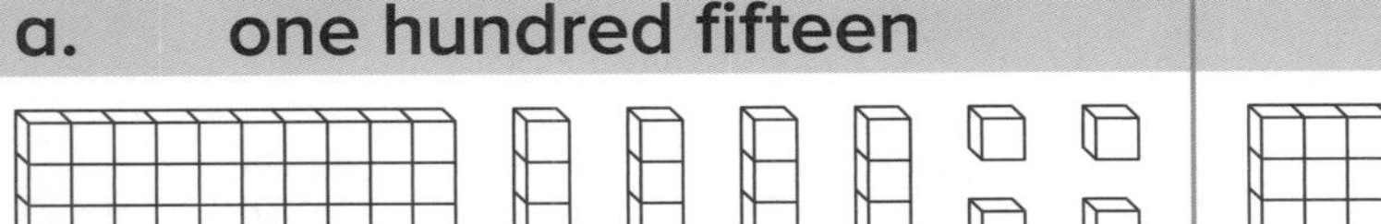

one hundred ten

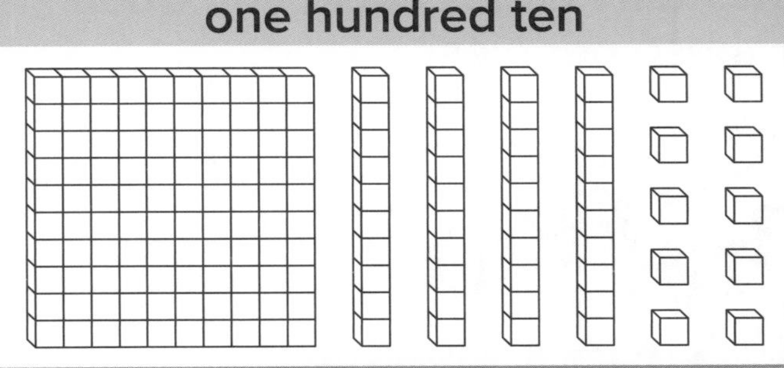

_____ < _____

b. 

one hundred sixteen

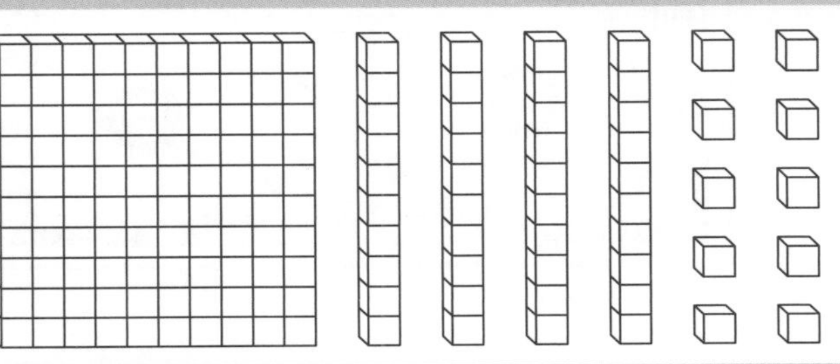

one hundred six

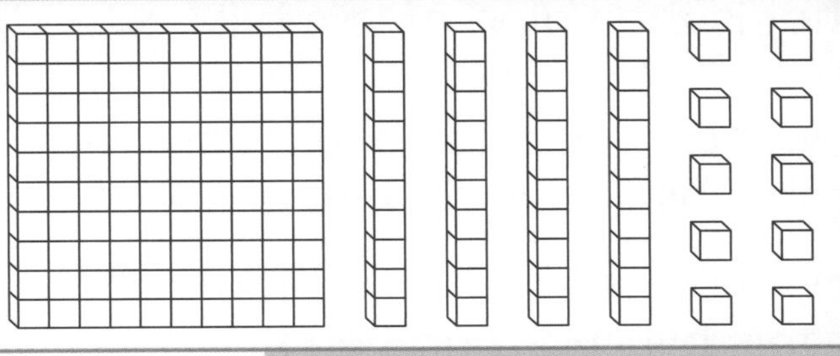

_____ > _____

c. **one hundred two**

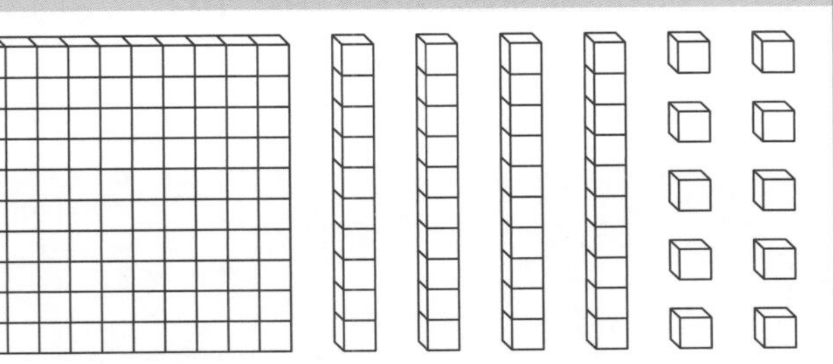

one hundred twenty

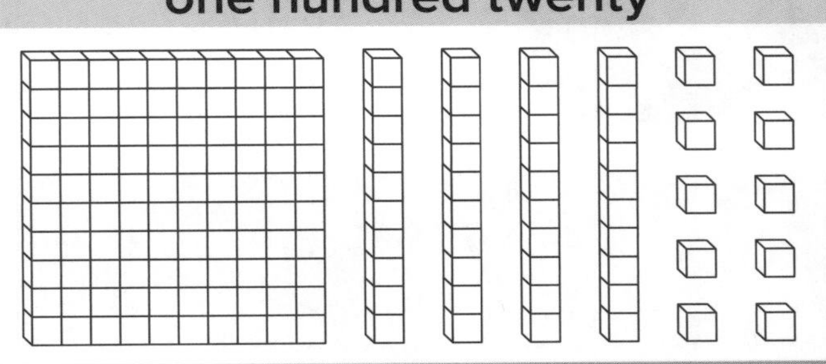

_____ > _____

Step Ahead Write a numeral to make a true statement.

_____ **is less than** 120 **but greater than** 112.

12.10 Relating Dollars, Dimes, and Pennies

How many dimes could you trade for these pennies?

I can trade 10 pennies for one dime.

What is the name of this **bill**?
What is the value of this **bill**?

How many pennies could you trade for this bill? How do you know?

How many dimes could you trade for this bill? How do you know?

100 pennies can be traded for one dollar so 10 dimes can be traded for one dollar.

Step Up

1. Loop together the dimes you could trade for one dollar. Then write the total amount.

a.

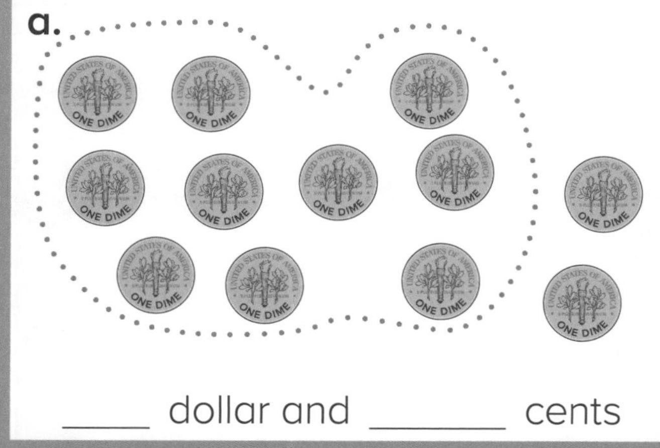

_____ dollar and _______ cents

b.

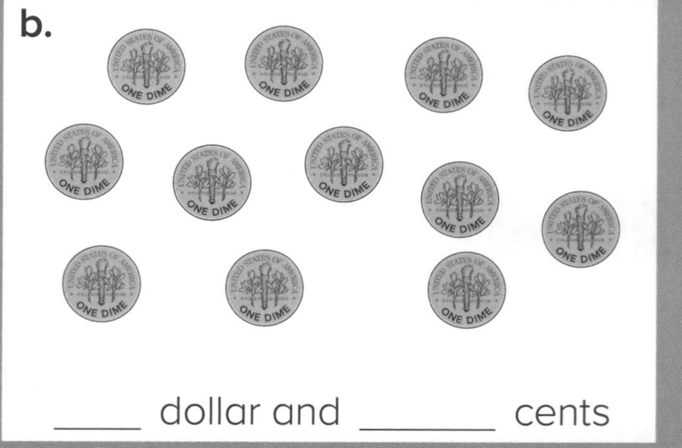

_____ dollar and _______ cents

2. Loop together the coins you could trade for one dollar. Then write the total amount.

a.

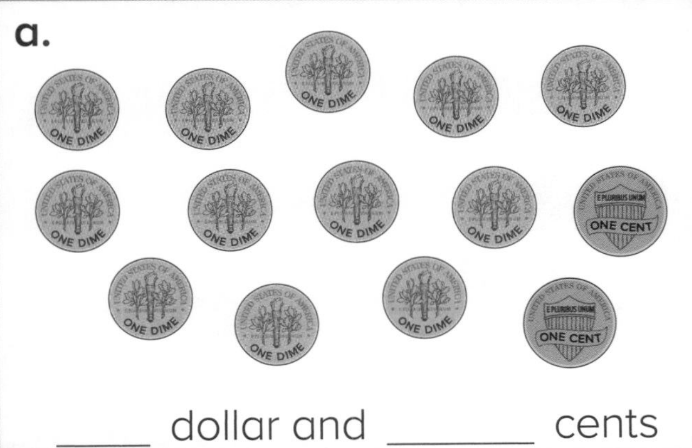

_____ dollar and _______ cents

b.

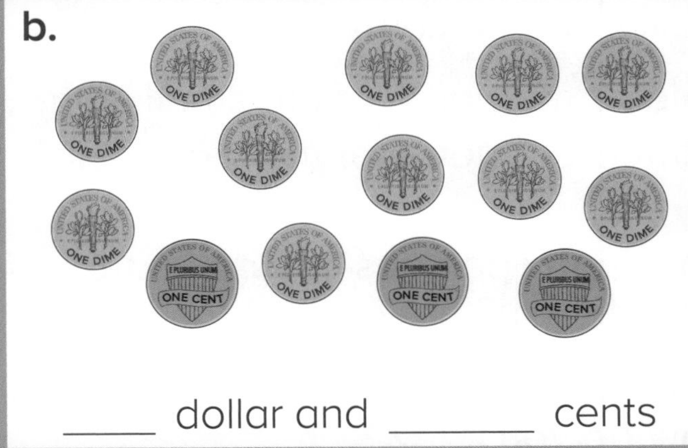

_____ dollar and _______ cents

c.

_____ dollar and _______ cents

d.

_____ dollar and _______ cents

3. Write these amounts as dollars and cents.

a. 126 cents is the same as _____ dollar and _______ cents.

b. 105 cents is the same as _____ dollar and _______ cents.

Step Ahead Draw more coins to pay the exact amount for the toy. No change will be given.

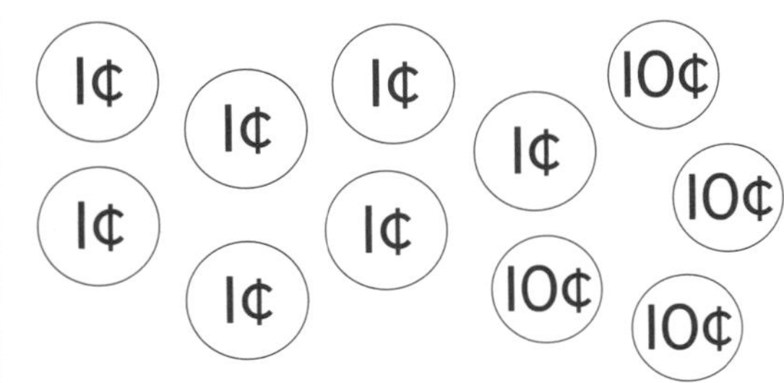

12.11 Relating Dollars, Quarters, and Nickels

Look at these coins

What is the name of the small coin?
What is the name of the large coin?

How many pennies could you trade for one nickel? How do you know?

How many pennies could you trade for one quarter? How do you know?

One quarter is the same as one-fourth of one dollar, so thats 25¢ or 25 pennies.

How many quarters could you trade for one dollar? How do you know?

How many nickels could you trade for one quarter? How do you know?

How can you figure out the number of nickels you could trade for one dollar?

Step Up

1. Loop together the coins you could trade for one dollar. Then write the total amount.

a.

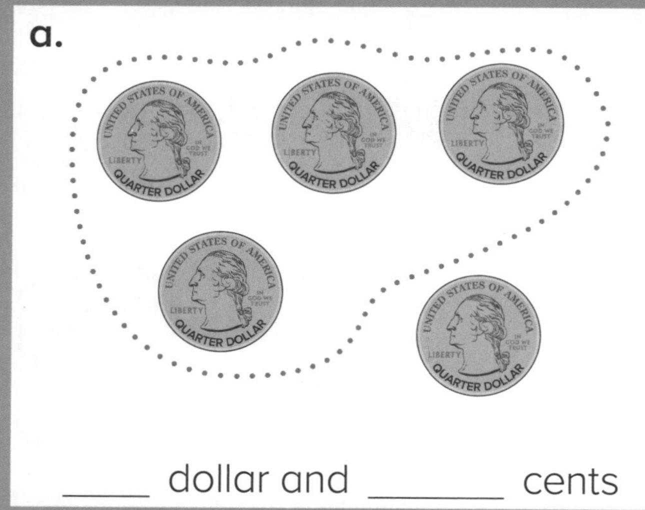

_____ dollar and _______ cents

b.

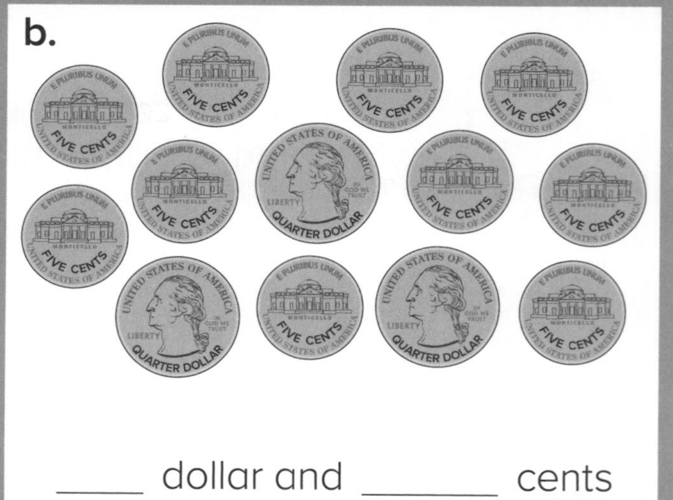

_____ dollar and _______ cents

2. Draw lines to join matching amounts.

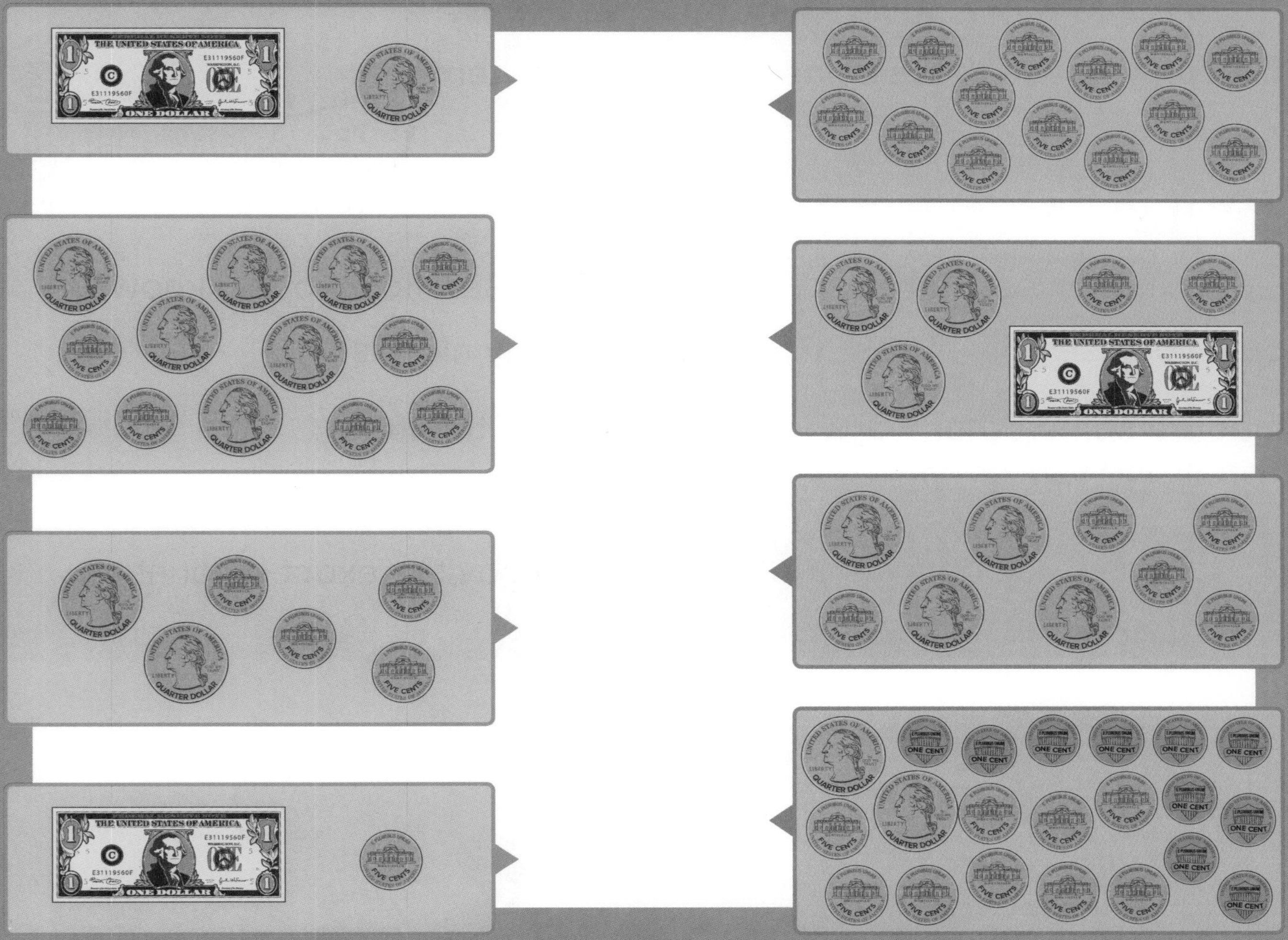

Step Ahead Color coins to show 50¢ in **two** different ways.

12.12 Paying with Coins

How can you use these coins to pay for this item?

What is the fewest number of coins you can use? How do you know?

Could you use only dimes? Could you use only nickels?

What are some other ways you could pay for the item?

Step Up

1. Color coins you would use to pay the **exact** amount for each item.

a.

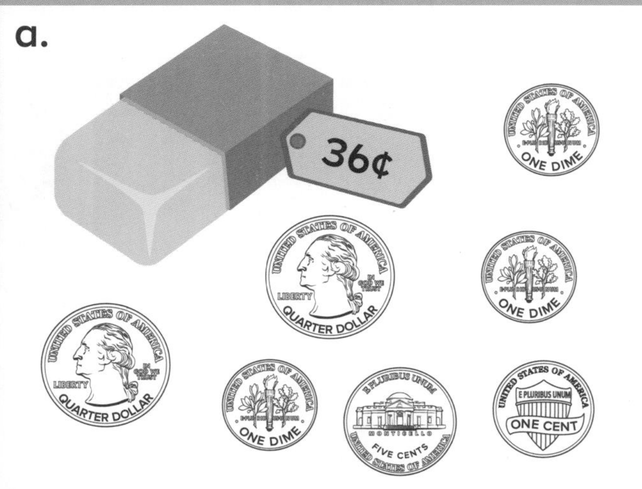

b.

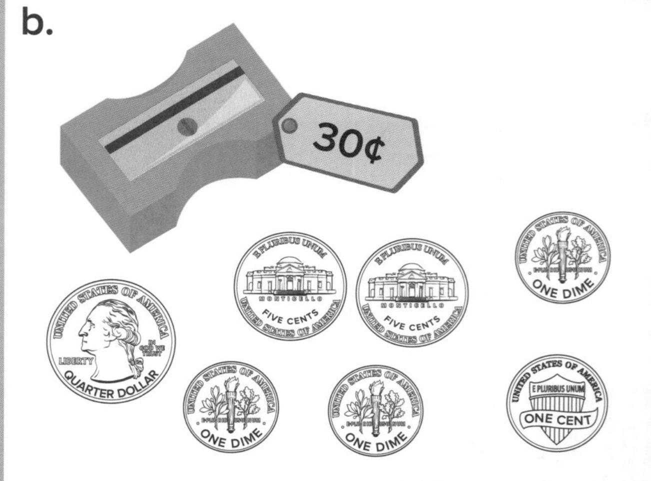

c.

d.

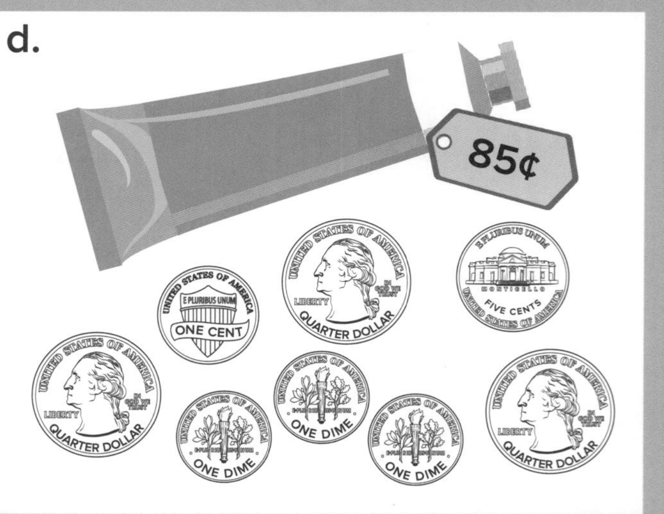

2. Color coins you would use to pay the **exact** amount for each item. Then write the amount left over.

a.

Amount left over _______ ¢

b.

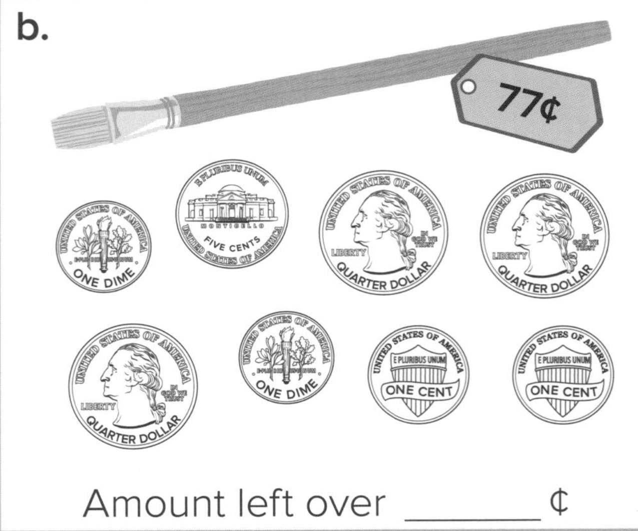

Amount left over _______ ¢

c.

Amount left over _______ ¢

d.

Amount left over _______ ¢

Step Ahead

Maya used **five** coins to pay for this card. No change was given. Draw the coins she used.